ONLY
SECONDS
TO LIVE

By the same author:

Barracuda Pilot
Air Medical Notes For Hang Glider Pilots

ONLY SECONDS TO LIVE

Pilots' Tales of the Stall and the Spin

DUNSTAN HADLEY

Airlife
England

First published in the UK in 1997
by Airlife Publishing Ltd

British Library Cataloguing-in-Publication Data
A catalogue record for this book
is available from the British Library

ISBN 1 85310 877 4

Typeset by Phoenix Typesetting, Ikley, West Yorkshire.
Printed and bound in Great Britain by Biddles Ltd, Guildford and King's Lynn

Airlife Publishing Ltd
101 Longden Road, Shrewsbury, SY3 9EB, England.

Acknowledgements

The good thing about an anthology is that you can just dip into it anywhere and read a little bit. Each piece is complete and they can be read in any order. Because of this there is some overlap and repetition of events and opinions; but this only emphasises the important points.

An anthology is the words of many authors. Some I have been unable to contact, but I have included their articles nevertheless, with gratitude to them for writing them, as I am sure that they will save somebody's life. Both I and the publishers are grateful for permission to include the following copyright material in this volume.

'Aerodynamicist'. Article published in *Flight International*, March 1972. Reprinted by kind permission of *Flight International*.

Wing Commander Roland Beamont RAF, DSO, DFC, CBE. Article 'Spinning the P 1A' *Aeroplane Monthly*, January 1992. Reprinted by kind permission of Wing Commander Beamont and *Aeroplane Monthly*.

A.E. Berriman, Technical Editor of *Flight*. Article 'Parke's Dive' from *Flight*, 31 August 1912. Reprinted by kind permission of *Flight International*.

L.K. Blackmore. Extract from *Hawker*, published by Airlife, 1990. Reprinted by kind permission of Mrs Patricia Blackmore and Airlife.

Maurie Bradney. Article from *Basic Gliding Knowledge*, 1986. Reprinted by kind permission of Maurie Bradney.

Charles Bremner. Report 'Fatal Nosedive of Flight 585 Baffles Experts' from *The Times*, 4 March 1992. Reprinted by kind permission of Charles Bremner.

Captain Eric Brown RN, CBE, DSC, AFC, MA, FRAeS. Extracts from *Wings On My Sleeve* 1961 and *Wings of the Weird and Wonderful* Vol. 1 1983, published by Airlife. Reprinted by kind permission of Captain Brown and Airlife.

Flight Lieutenant Catherine Coton RAF. Letter, March 1994. Crown copyright. Reprinted by kind permission of Flight Lieutenant Coton and the Controller of Her Majesty's Stationery Office.

Frank T. Courtney. Article 'Spins and Things' from *Aeronautics*, November 1961. Reprinted with gratitude.

Mike Cuming. Article 'Don't Pull the Stick, Push It' from *Sailplane and Gliding*, April/May 1991. Reprinted by kind permission of Mike Cuming and *Sailplane and Gliding*.

Sir Geoffrey de Havilland, OBE. Extract from *Sky Fever*, published by Airlife, 1979. Reprinted by kind permission of Anne and Peter de Havilland and Airlife.

Richard Dennis. Extract from Article 'Farnborough Caterpillars' from *Aeroplane Monthly*, January 1994. Reprinted by kind permission of Richard Dennis and *Aeroplane Monthly*.

Ray di Mascio. Letter to *Flight International* September 1978. Reprinted by kind permission of *Flight International*.

Major C. Draper. Article 'The Flat Spin' from *Aeronautics*, March 1962. Reprinted with gratitude.

Lou Frank. Article 'To Spin or Not to Spin' from *Sailplane and Gliding Yearbook 1993*. Reprinted by kind permission of Lou Frank and *Sailplane and Gliding*.

General Aviation Safety Committee. Article 'To Spin or Not to Spin' in *General Aviation Safety Committee Bulletin*, Spring 1982 (1/82). Reprinted by kind permission of the General Aviation Safety Committee and John Stewart-Smith.

Richard P. Hallion. Three extracts 'A Study of Spinning by NACA', 'The Chance Vaught Corsair X F4U' and 'The Götterdammerung of the Bell X 2' from *Test Pilots. The Frontiersmen of Flight*, published by the Smithsonian Institution, 1989. Reprinted by kind permission of Richard P. Hallion.

N. Roy Harben, DFC. Extract from *The Complete Flying Course*, published by C. Arthur Pearson about 1940. Reprinted with gratitude.

Harry W. Hawthorne. Letter to *Flight International*, September 1978. Reprinted by kind permission of *Flight International*.

Squadron Leader R. Irving RAF. Letter, November 1994. Crown copyright. Reproduced by kind permission of Squadron Leader Irving and the Controller of Her Majesty's Stationery Office.

A.C. Kermode. Extract from *The Mechanics of Flight* ninth edition, revised and edited by R.H. Barnard and D.R. Philpott, published by Addison Wesley Longman. Reprinted by kind permission of Addison Wesley Longman.

Lord John Kilbracken, DSC. Four extracts from *Bring Back My Stringbag*, published by Peter Davies in 1979 and republished by Leo Cooper in 1996. Reproduced by kind permission of Lord Kilbracken.

Frederick Lindemann (Lord Cherwell). Extract from *Fifty Years at Farnborough*, Crown copyright. Reprinted by kind permission of the Controller of Her Majesty's Stationery Office.

Alec Lumsden, FRAeS. Extract from articles 'Gloster Gamecock', and 'Bristol Bulldog' from *Aeroplane Monthly*, June 1991 and August 1991 respectively. Reproduced by kind permission of Alec Lumsden and *Aeroplane Monthly*.

Miles McCallum. Article 'The Deadliest Myth' from *Flying*, March 1991. Reproduced by kind permission of Miles McCallum.

M.G. McDonnell. Letter to *Flight International*, August 1978. Reprinted by kind permission of *Flight International*.

Wing Commander Norman Macmillan, OBE, MC, AFC, AFRAeS. Four articles 'The Spin', 'More History', 'Aerospin Postscript' and 'Letter From Estonia' from *Aeronautics*, July 1960, September 1961, March 1962 and March 1962 respectively. Reprinted with gratitude.

Dave Martin. Article 'Going for a Spin? Call Gene Beggs First' from *Private Pilot*, February 1986. Reprinted with gratitude.

John Maynard. Article extract from 'John Cunningham' from *Aeroplane Monthly*, September 1994. Reprinted by kind permission of John Maynard and *Aeroplane Monthly*.

John Stanley Owen. Article 'To Spin or Not to Spin' in *The International Journal of Aviation Safety*, 1983. Reprinted with gratitude.

Derek Piggott. Extract from *Gliding*, by Derek Piggott published by A. & C. Black, 1972. Reprinted by kind permission of Derek Piggott and A. & C. Black. Also article 'Stalling or Low g' from *The Sailplane and Gliding Yearbook*, May 1991. Reprinted by kind permission of Derek Piggott and *Sailplane and Gliding*.

Richard T. Riding. Article 'In a flat spin' from 'Plane Crazy' in *Aeroplane Monthly*, October 1992.

Royal Air Force Manual, volume II, 1955 amended to 1958. Crown copyright. Extract reproduced by permission of the Controller of Her Majesty's Stationery Office.

Bill Scull. Article 'Teaching Stalling and Spinning' from *The Sailplane and Gliding Yearbook*, 1993. Reprinted by kind permission of Bill Scull and *Sailplane and Gliding*.

Darrol Stinton D.Sc., Article 'Anatomy of Spinning' from *Flight International*, 23 March 1972. Reprinted by kind permission of *Flight International*.

'UK Tomahawks Re-cleared for Spinning' from *Flight International*, February 1981. Reprinted by kind permission of *Flight International*.

John C. Ward, M.B.E. Letter from the *General Aviation Safety Committee*. Reprinted by kind permission of the *General Aviation Safety Committee* and John C. Ward, M.B.E.

Squadron Leader W.A. Waterman RAF, GM, AFC. Extract from *The Quick and the Dead*, published by Frederick Muller, 1956. Reprinted by kind permission of Random House.

Philip Wills. Extract from *On Being a Bird*, published by David and Charles, 1937 and 1977. Reprinted by kind permission of David and Charles.

I.K.A.C. Wilson. Letter, May 1994. Reprinted by kind permission of I.K.A.C. Wilson and the Safety Regulation Group of the Civil Aviation Authority.

John S. Wilson. Letter to *Aeroplane Monthly*, December 1994. Reprinted by kind permission of *Aeroplane Monthly*.

R.W. Wood. Newspaper report on the death of Otto Lilienthal from the *Boston Evening Transcript*, August 1896. Reprinted with gratitude.

Wilbur and Orville Wright. Extract from *The Papers of Wilbur and Orville Wright*, edited by

Malcolm McFarland, published by the McGraw-Hill Book Company, 1953. Reprinted with kind permission of the McGraw-Hill Book Company.

General Charles Yeager USAF. Extracts from *Yeager*, published by Century Hutchinson, 1986. Reprinted by kind permission of Random House.

My thanks also go to:
M.D. Richardson, Fleet Air Arm Museum, for assistance and illustrations.
Sandra V. Cox, British Library.
P.J.V. Eliot, Royal Air Force Museum, Hendon.
B.L. Riddle, Royal Aeronautical Society.
Peter L. Jakab, The Smithsonian Institution.
All these people offered helpful advice.

Contents

Part 4: The Pros and Cons of Stalling and Spinning

Part 5: Into the Nineties

Preface

When an aircraft spins it is out of control. Unless the pilot can regain control it will crash, most often with fatal results. In the early days of flying this was nearly always so. The pilots did not have parachutes and no way to recover control had been discovered. A spin was not always fatal because the crashing aircraft absorbed a lot of the force of the impact as it hit the ground and the pilot sometimes escaped. A number of pilots have spun into the ground and lived.

At the Royal Aircraft Factory, Farnborough, the aerodynamic theory of autorotation, which causes an aircraft to spin, was worked out and after a number of experimental flights it was discovered how best to recover from a spin.

How to spin, how not to spin and how to get out of a spin are all part of a service pilot's normal training. During the course of both service and civilian flying in various types of aircraft I have done about a hundred spins intentionally, in aircraft designed to be spun safely, and two unintentional spins, in aircraft not intended to be spun. Spinning is viewed with some awe by pilots and non-pilots alike. With some aircraft it is possible to recover from a spin quite easily, with others it is not, and some, more especially large aircraft, no pilot would ever dream of spinning intentionally, although they might have been spun by test pilots either on purpose or by mistake. Training aircraft are usually designed to be spun and to recover fairly easily or else designed not to spin at all, but even these might be made to spin under extraordinary conditions.

Tales are told which make the hair stand on end and curdle the blood. There is the tale of the pilot of a Halifax bomber who was thrown into a spin by a close burst of anti-aircraft fire. By closing the throttles of both engines on the outside wing of the spinning aircraft and fully opening up both engines on the inside wing the combined efforts of himself and his co-pilot, who each had both feet on one side of the rudder pedals, managed to get it out after falling 12,000 feet. It must have aged them.

Flat spins, inverted spins and spins in cloud all bring to mind visions of peril. It must be worse diving to earth in an aircraft on fire, as one of my instructors had done and for which he proudly wore a medal, but a spin has a reputation all of its own.

I was introduced to a spin in a de Havilland Tiger Moth on my second flight by Wing Commander Edwards, Commandant of the Oxford University Air Squadron at the time. 'It is,' he said, 'about the worst thing that can happen to a pilot. It is important, therefore, to learn how to get out of one. You will find, that you have to go against your natural instincts. In a spin the aircraft is stalled and falling out of control. The only way to recover is to increase speed in what may seem a desperate manoeuvre, by making the aircraft dive.' This certainly sounded like a desperate manoeuvre. In the circumstances I thought perhaps it did not matter. He then explained that by increasing speed we restored the normal airflow over the wings and tail, and the aircraft could be brought back under control.

'Height and speed,' he said, 'are the pilot's best friends. Do not believe your old granny when she tells you that you will be safer if you fly slowly and stay close to the ground.' I said I wouldn't. 'So,' said my instructor, 'we will climb up and do a spin.' There was a lull in the conversation for a while, then he came on the air again.

'Accidental spinning results from misuse of the controls. An aeroplane spins only if stalled. We are at 5,000 feet now, which is plenty of height for a Tiger. First we make a 360-degree turn to see that we are over open country and that there are no aircraft underneath, then we close the throttle and, keeping the nose above the horizon, we wait for the speed to fall off.' He did, and it did. 'Just before the stall apply full rudder, ease back the stick and hold it fully back—'

The bottom fell out of the world. It was awful—a terrible feeling of falling, strapped tightly to this shuddering gyrating thing, a nightmare come to life. As I stared down, the only things I could see were fields whirling round and coming closer every second. I felt fear, and sweat began to form. Caught in this dreadful kaleidoscope I was conscious only of a cow grazing contentedly at the hub of the vortex. It looked calm and peaceful. I doubted if I would ever enjoy peace or calm again. The voice of my instructor had been droning on unheard. Now I became dimly aware of it. In calm unhurried tones he was saying, '. . . full opposite rudder, ease the stick forward. When the spinning stops centralise the rudder then gentle back pressure on the stick to recover from the dive. Note the loss of height.'

Our Tiger Moth came out of its dive smoothly, crushing me further into the seat by centrifugal force, known as g. Well, I thought, that's it. I shall never, ever, be able to fly after all. I've had it if that's what I have to do. How can anyone fly?

My instructor was babbling on: 'Now we have regained the height we lost, nothing below, we'll do one to the right this time.'

I scarcely had time to realise what he had said before we had lurched into another spin. The same horrible falling, whirling, yet this time somehow it did not seem so bad. I could see the same cow below but felt that I might live to join it safely on the ground after all. We recovered uneventfully.

'Right,' said Nemesis: 'Now you do one.' We climbed up and circled round again to have a look below. 'You've got her, you know what to do, carry on and do a spin to the right.'

This time I enjoyed it. Perhaps everything would be all right and I would make a pilot after all. It was a thrill, like going over the top on a roller coaster, then hitting a bend. It is always a thrill, even in the safest most reliable aircraft, because you can never be quite sure.

This book is a collection of some of the things that have been written about spinning. Some of it is history, some technical explanation. There are views on policy and the recorded experiences of pilots who, for various reasons, have found themselves in the spine-chilling situation of an accidental or deliberate spin from which recovery has seemed unlikely or proved to be impossible. There is a good deal of controversy about spins, so fasten your seat belt and enjoy yourself.

Part I

The Beginning of Spinning

Lilienthal and Wilbur and Orville Wright

Who has not seen a bird partly stall one wing and abruptly drop down to grab some morsel of food dropped by another bird? The bird is briefly out of control but it can recover in less time than it takes to blink an eye. Its reaction is instinctive. When the early pilots accidentally spun their machines they had little idea how the spin had come about and their instinctive reactions did not usually enable them to regain control. A few, perhaps by letting go of the controls to hold on to their spinning aircraft more firmly—who knows, many were not strapped in—survived, because some aircraft will recover by themselves if allowed to. Others crashed because of their failure to regain control, but lived to tell the tale.

Spinning is as old as flying itself. When the airspeed is reduced below a certain point, lift from the wings is lost, the aircraft stalls and may spin.

Otto Lilienthal, the first successful pilot, died following what was probably a spin, as reported by R.W. Wood of the *Boston Evening Transcript*, who witnessed it.

"On 9 August 1896 he took off from a hill in the Rhinower range in one of his standard monoplane gliders. A sudden sharp gust tossed his machine upwards at an acute angle. Lilienthal immediately threw his legs forward and tried to bring the nose down, but the glider stalled, a wing dropped and the glider plummeted to the ground breaking the right wing and Lilienthal's spine. He died next day.**"**

Many of Lilienthal's predecessors spun into the ground while trying to fly without ever gaining flying speed.

Wilbur Wright also spun, as recorded by Orville Wright in *The Papers of Wilbur and Orville Wright*.

"Saturday, 20 September 1902.
In the afternoon we continued gliding, Will making one glide of 11 seconds covering a distance of a little over 200 feet in which the machine began to slide to the side of the right wing, which was the lower one. The wind getting under the left wing from the side, on account of the flight being made a little to the right of the direction of the wind, raised it higher and higher, when he suddenly, by mistake, while attempting to alter the wing tips, turned the front rudder down at the rear, causing the machine to 'pierce the ethereal' to all

appearances at an angle of over 45 degrees. In the descent from this position the height of the left wing became still higher as compared with the right, and the machine made a fast downward plunge directly towards the right wing, the wind now being in line with the lateral axis of the machine. However before striking the ground, the torsion of the wings brought the left wing down considerably, and the machine, running almost directly at right angles with the wind, struck on the right wing and swung round, with the wind blowing from the rear.**

Although not recognised at the time this is a classic description of an unintentional spin entry from which, happily, Wilbur recovered, largely by good luck although he still hit the ground. Three days later Orville had a similar experience.

I was sailing along smoothly without any trouble at all from the fore and aft control, when I noticed that one wing was getting a little too high and that the machine was slowly sidling off in the opposite direction. I thought that by moving the end control mechanism (wing warping) an inch or so I would bring the wing back again to its proper position and, as I was going so smoothly with no need of changing the front rudder (elevator), I attempted to make the change. The next thing I knew was that the wing was very high in the air, a great deal higher than before, and I thought I must have worked the twisting apparatus the wrong way. Thinking of nothing else than the end control, after assuring myself as to what was the proper motion, I threw the wing tips to their greatest angle. By this time I found suddenly that I was making a descent backwards towards the low wing, from a height of 25 or 30 feet, as a result of the machine having turned up at an angle of nearly 45 degrees in front, which fact I had not noticed at all while occupied in the manipulation of the wing ends, but which had been witnessed by Will and Dan with alarm for several seconds before. The result was a heap of flying machine, cloth, and sticks in a heap, with me in the centre without a bruise or a scratch. The experiments thereupon suddenly came to a close till the repairs can be made. In spite of this sad catastrophe we are tonight in a hilarious mood as a result of the encouraging performance of the machine both in control and in angles of flight.

Later, during the night of 2–3 October while lying awake, Orville 'studied out a new vertical rudder'. A few days later they modified their glider and from then on had few control problems.

At that stage neither Wilbur nor Orville flew high enough for a spin to develop, but with their arrangement of a horizontal 'front rudder' the glider would probably have made a spontaneous recovery.

A.E. Berriman: Parke's Dive

By 1912 it was still not known what the cause of a spin was, how to prevent one, how to recover from one or even really what it was. A government body, the Advisory Committee on Aeronautics, therefore asked the Royal Aircraft Factory at Farnborough to investigate. One of the earliest accounts of a spin is 'Parke's Dive', reported by A.E. Berriman, Technical Editor of *Flight*, on 31 August 1912.

"*Salisbury Plain, Sunday, 25 August 1912.*

Here is the true story of one of the worst experiences in mid-air from which any pilot has extricated his machine in absolute safety, and as the circumstances precisely represent the hypothesis of the most debated problem among pilots at the present time, the following particulars should be studied with the closest attention by all.

At four minutes past six this morning Lieutenant Wilfred Parke RN accompanied by Lieutenant Le Breton RFC, as observer, started on the Avro biplane (60 hp Green engine) from Salisbury Plain for the three hours' qualifying flight in the Military Trials. At ten minutes past nine, having more than completed

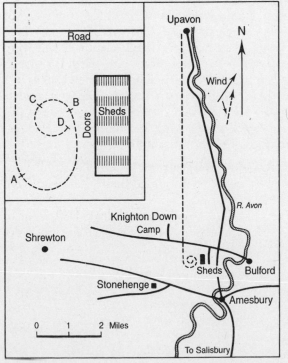

Fig 1   Key map illustrating the flight of the Avro biplane which terminated in the spiral dive. Inset on a larger scale is a lettered diagram of the dive to which reference is made in the text.

Flight copyright

the required duration, he was returning from the direction of Upavon for the express purpose of alighting in front of the sheds.

The direction of flight was practically towards due south; the wind was blowing approximately from the south-west, with a tendency to back south-wards. He was, therefore, flying virtually up-wind. The speed of the wind was estimated about 10–15 mph by the pilot, and the maximum airspeed of the machine with the present propeller is about 60 mph, as tested over the measured distance yesterday. The engine was pulling well, and the machine in perfect trim. There was bright sunshine and some clouds.

Throughout the flight an altitude of between 600 and 700 feet was main-tained, and the pilot, observing that he was still at this height, decided that he had sufficient room for a spiral glide. At the point A in the diagram [figure 1], he had closed the throttle without switching off (which kept the engine just turning) and immediately proceeded to glide round down-wind. At point B, having completed a half spiral, Parke thought the machine was in an unneces-sarily steep attitude, and was insufficiently banked for the turn he was making. He therefore elevated, and believes that he may also have given a momentary touch to the warp, which two operations were for the purpose of reducing the steepness of the descent and increasing the bank respectively.

The machine at once started a spiral nosedive.

At point C, Parke opened the throttle full out, in the hope that the propeller might pull the nose up, for he was aware (and had also confirmed the fact during the flight) that the machine was slightly nose-heavy with the throttle closed. The engine responded instantly, but failed to produce the desired effect on the machine; it may or may not have accelerated the descent, but the fall was already so rapid that the maximum engine speed was unlikely even to be equal to it.

Also at C, he drew the elevator lever hard back against his chest and put the rudder hard over to the left with his foot so as to turn the machine inwards, this latter being the principal of action that is accepted as proper in cases of incipient side-slip, and, therefore, naturally to be tried in an emergency such as this. The warp was normal, i.e. balanced with the control wheel neutral. These operations failed utterly to improve the conditions.

From C to D the machine was completely out of control, diving headlong at such a steep angle that all spectators described it as vertical and stood, horror stricken, waiting for the end. According to Parke, the angle was very steep, but certainly not vertical; he noticed no particular strain on his legs, with which he still kept the rudder about half over to the left (about as much as is ordinarily used in a turn), nor on his chest, across which he was strapped by a wide belt to his seat. His right hand he had already removed from the control wheel in order to steady himself by grasping the body strut forming an upright between the windows of the enclosed body. (The windows were not glazed.) This he did, not for support against the steepness of the descent, but because he felt himself being thrown outwards by the spiral motion of the machine, which he describes as 'violent'. The absence of pressure on the legs and arms appears to me, however, to be evidence that the machine was falling as fast as the pilot,

Lt. W. Parke emerging
from the Enclosed
Avro Biplane.
(From 'Flight', 31 August
1912.)

who was, therefore, unstable on his seat, and without a fulcrum until he
fastened himself to the framework by the grip of his hand.

It was his recognition, through this forcible effect, of the predominating
influence of the spiral motion, as distinct from the dive, that caused him to ease
off the rudder and finally push it hard over to the right (ie to turn the machine
outwards from the circle), as a last resource, when about 50 feet from the
ground.

Instantly, but without any jerkiness, the machine straightened and flattened
out—came at once under control and, without sinking appreciably, flew off in
a perfect attitude. Parke made a circuit of the sheds in order to get into position for landing in a good place up wind, and proceeded to alight in the usual
way without the least mishap. Thus did he and his observer, who, having no
belt and rather cramped accommodation, was thrown up against the front wall
of the cabin, escape at the last moment from what looked like certain death and
effect a perfect landing with the machine none the worse for the severe

straining save for a slight stretching of some of the lift wires under the main planes.

Like the majority, I was at breakfast when the dive occurred; for having watched the Avro during the earlier part of its flight and up to the end of its second hour, its uniform behaviour inspired a confidence that one was not loathe to translate into an excuse for leave. Very soon afterwards, however, I saw Lieutenant Parke on the field, and, together with G. de Havilland and F. Short, of the RAF [the Royal Aircraft Factory, not the Royal Air Force—Ed.] adjourned to the competitor's mess, where we held an informal, but extremely close, inquiry into the whole affair. It was so obvious to all that the problems of the accident were so near to having to be discussed under the shadow of the pilot's absence, that the opportunity of recording on the spot the essential facts and impressions as he understood them was not only unique, but of the utmost consequence to aviation. His own anxiety to facilitate this work for the benefit of others, and the fact that he retained his presence of mind from first to last in the emergency—although admittedly terribly alarmed—so that he was conscious of each operation and the effect produced, serves to give to the aviation world at least one definite experience of extreme character for its guidance.

The seriousness of the situation there is no denying. Parke himself stared death in the face; most of the spectators sickened for the crash, and among them were those who were also furious in the belief that he had attempted a 'stunt' and failed. There was some reason for this belief, because the machine behaved throughout in a perfectly smooth, normal manner, despite its extremely exaggerated attitude, and when it flattened out so nicely at the last moment even those who had been convinced they were witnessing an accident were left in doubt, whether, after all, it had not been intentional.

If disaster had followed, all manner of 'explanations' would have been forthcoming, and, among them, de Havilland would have given it as his opinion that the control had become jammed, having regard to the fact that there was no excuse otherwise for a pilot of such experience to get himself into that position. With this latter observation Parke himself heartily agrees; but it happened all the same. He was not tired after his flight, but he was naturally pleased at its successful termination after all the previous misfortunes that the Avro firm had borne in such good spirit, and had in mind merely the finishing of the flight safely, but in good style.

Of the many important and interesting aspects of the case, one is obviously related to the value of flying high. But for the room available for the fall, disaster was unavoidable. For the first 100 feet the descent was normal, but, afterwards, acceleration to something in the order of 90 mph (speed suggested by de Havilland) took place, and the machine fell about 450 feet, whilst more or less out of control—which is a lesson those who have not yet learnt would do well to bear in mind.

The next and most important point is that affecting the popular discussion on the proper method of recovering from side-slip in the air, particularly with reference to ruddering inwards and ruddering outwards in an emergency. In

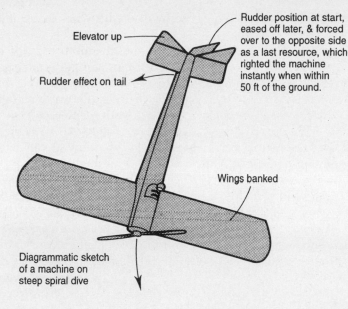

Elevator up

Rudder position at start, eased off later, & forced over to the opposite side as a last resource, which righted the machine instantly when within 50 ft of the ground.

Rudder effect on tail

Wings banked

Diagrammatic sketch of a machine on steep spiral dive

Fig 2   The above sketch was drawn from a paper model of a monoplane, as it is exceedingly difficult to convey an impression of a spiral path and banking on one view, and at the same time to show the position of the controls.
('*Flight*' *Copyright.*)

the first place it is necessary to differentiate between the present circumstances and a side-slip in the incipient stage as ordinarily understood. A side-slip (which means the machine slips inwards), is caused, fundamentally, by over-banking, insufficient speed and a cabré attitude (tail down), may be incidental to the occurrence. Ruddering inwards in such an emergency brings the machine on to its accidental line of motion in a flying attitude (instead of side-ways), and promotes a dive, from which the pilot obtains both the position and the velocity necessary to recovery.

In Parke's dive, the machine was not side-slipping in the above sense (even supposing that the term could properly be applied to any phase of the occurrence) when ruddering outwards proved to marvellously effective. It was flying on a true helix of an excessively steep pitch, and to obtain a proper understanding of the effect produced it is necessary to have a clear mental picture of the tail in its line of flight. It is illustrated diagrammatically in the sketch [figure 2]. The elevator is hard up and the rudder over to the pilot's left. In common with the rest of the machine the tail as a whole has a spiral motion downwards through space, but leans inwards somewhat towards the centre of the vertical path in such a way as might produce a side-slip if the machine lacked velocity.

The present position of the rudder (to the pilot's left) supports the tail, and as the speed increases tends to make it chase round outwards after the nose of the machine, thus turning the machine still more about its vertical pivot, increasing the steepness of the dive, and also, by maintaining the outer wing at its high velocity, accentuating the bank.

By throwing the rudder over to the right, this accentuation of the centrifugal action of the tail is checked, and a virtual acceleration of the inside main wing tip takes place in consequence, so that the machine tends to change its spiral direction of motion into a straight line, and at the same time to recover its lateral trim. These conditions at once release the elevator from the neutralising influences that have rendered it inoperative, and being already hard up it brings the machine onto an even keel at that high speed with extreme rapidity. The warp was not used consciously at this time; the wheel could have been turned with one hand, but Parke thinks he did not do so; i.e. the entire phenomenon is related to elevator and rudder action only.

Such is the gist of the explanation as we argued it on this occasion, and I believe the others who were party to the discussion are in agreement therewith, unless I have misunderstood their meaning on any point. There was a question as to whether the draught off the rudder being directed onto one half of the divided elevator could have exercised an appreciable torque through the backbone of the machine, first to increase the bank and afterwards to reduce it, but there seemed absolutely no evidence one way or the other on the subject. Later it was suggested that the machine might have made an automatic recovery, such as models do when launched vertically from the hand, but here it seems necessary to remember that a model is in the process of picking up its flying speed, whereas in this case the phenomenon is related to an occurrence that took place when the flying speed had been far exceeded. If it were it would have been a most extraordinary coincidence, for the response of this machine to the right-hand swing of the rudder was instantaneous and indeed with only 50 feet to go, it would have been quite useless otherwise.

Yes, on the whole I think we may consider it a genuine practical lesson in aeroplane control, and one, moreover, of the most important order. There has been endless discussion on this very subject and much conflicting opinion, but no one is voluntarily going to risk losing control of his machine in mid-air for the sake of demonstrating the facts. Now that it has happened to Lieutenant Parke by accident, and he is safely through it to tell the tale, let no one forget the rule to 'rudder outwards from a spiral dive that has already acquired a high velocity'.

In conclusion, a word to the credit of the Avro biplane and Green engine. That the machine stood the strain of flattening out at 90 mph or thereabouts, is no more than any pilot has a right to expect of any machine. Nothing must break in mid-air, and nothing did break. That it recovered in the long run is at least evidence in support of the design. The tail is the same on Parke's machine as on the Avro biplanes supplied to the Army, which are fitted with Gnôme engines; but two of those machines have been refitted, by instruction, with larger tails than the designers and pilot consider necessary, although they see no objection to their use. One of the Army Avros still has the original tail.

By courtesy of the firm, a scale drawing of the machine is reproduced. [figure 3] From this drawing the general lines of the machine and proportions

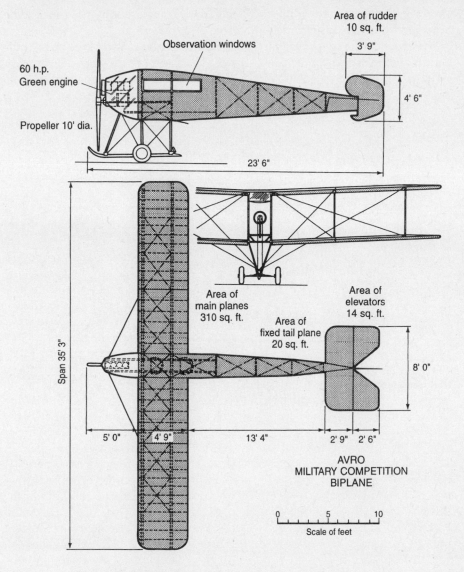

Fig 3   THE AVRO MILITARY BIPLANE.—Plan and Elevation to Scale.

of the surfaces are self-evident. The fuselage or backbone is entirely surfaced and rectangular; its sides narrow to a knife edge at the rudder-post, and present a considerable vertical surface to the wind. It appears, however, that this fin effect is balanced on either side of the vertical pivot about which the machine naturally swings in space, because Lieutenant Parke has found no tendency for it to be slewed off its course either into or out of the wind.

This is an important consideration, because the large extent of the surface thus presented by the backbone, which is most easily arranged this way as a natural extension of the cabin-body, was thought to be a possible source of trouble in windy weather. Under normal conditions the machine takes a natural bank when turning; its wings have a large dihedral angle and are quite rigid in the ribs. Equal-sized spars are used.

In winds the machine appears to be very steady and weatherly.**"**

In view of the fact that scarcely anything was known about spinning in 1912 this is a first-class description. It is hard to be sure but it looks as if Parke stalled and spun while making a gliding turn then fortuitously applied the correct spin-recovery technique, entering a dive from which he made an instant recovery.

There is no mention anywhere in the account of the fact that he stalled, and nobody realised that he had, because the aircraft flicked into a spin so fast. The whole episode occurred from somewhere below 500 feet down to 50 feet, surprising in itself. It is remarkable too that the aircraft had a totally enclosed cockpit—almost unknown in those days—and vision was totally obscured straight ahead by the engine bulkhead. To look forward the pilot would have to put his head partly through the windows either side. However, this would not be such a disadvantage as might at first appear as the total width of the fuse-lage was only 14½ inches. It was said that 'the only wind experienced by the pilot is a side one on banking!' At least he would have recognised at once when he was side-slipping.

Reading all that and trying to understand what was going on takes time. Try to imagine it happening in the time-scale in which it actually took place. Parke, approaching to land in a gliding turn to the left at about 500 feet, eases back on the stick—momentary touch of left warp—suddenly:

> Machine stalls.
> Spins to the left.
> Full throttle.
> Full back on stick.
> Full left rudder.
> Dive steeper.
> Thrown outwards by spin.
> Lets go stick with right hand.
> Grabs strut.
> Getting worse.
> Going to crash!
> Full right rudder.
> Machine straightens—flattens.
> Grabs stick—back in control, 50 feet above ground.
> 'Crikey! What happened then?'

If you read that very fast it takes eight seconds, about as long as Parke had. I doubt he would even have had time to swear.

Parke was killed on 15 December of the same year, flying a Handley Page monoplane.

Geoffrey de Havilland: From Sky Fever

Also at Farnborough on that day (and later to be knighted) was Geoffrey de Havilland. By 1913 he had not only designed and built aeroplanes, he had also taught himself to fly them, and to loop the loop. This extract comes from Sky Fever, his autobiography.

❝Looping became quite the thing just before the outbreak of the First World War. It was not really dangerous except in aircraft that were dangerous anyway . . . Spinning, however, was in a different class altogether from looping, and was a dangerous and mysterious involuntary evolution right up to 1915. I have had only one flying crash worthy of that name, and that was caused by a spin, in March 1913 at Farnborough. The aeroplane was a BS I, a small single-seat scout, the first of its type, fitted with a double-row fourteen-cylinder 100-horse-power Gnôme engine. This machine has since been referred to as the prototype of all single-seat fighters. Aerodynamic knowledge was limited at that time, and in making the drawings I relied largely on scaling down the successful BE2. This method was good enough for wings and tail-plane but not for rudder, which looked obviously too small when the machine was assembled, and I arranged for a rudder of greater area to be put in hand. I did not think the small rudder would lead to any serious trouble, but it might not be sufficiently effective in sharp turns. I did the first test flights with the small rudder and noticed that big rudder angles were required to correct a turn. In doing a rather sharper turn than usual the aeroplane suddenly took charge and went into a spinning turn which full opposite rudder movement failed to halt. As I was below 100 feet there was no hope of getting out of the spin, which luckily was fairly 'flat' when we hit the ground. I remember the sensation due to centrifugal force of being pressed hard against the side of the cockpit during the spin, and knew nothing more until dragged from the wreckage. The chief damage I suffered was a broken jaw and the loss of many teeth (later found in the wreckage and kindly returned in an envelope by a mechanic) and some bruises, but the aeroplane was a total wreck. While recovering in the Cambridge Hospital at Aldershot I had a visit from one of the technical people from the Factory who said, with a certain note of triumph, that they had made extensive calculations and the results proved that the rudder was too small. I tried to show interest. The aeroplane was reconstructed—with a larger rudder—and I did a lot of flying with it before it was sent to France on war service . . .

That was an involuntary spin, of course. The voluntary spin, however, comes under the heading of aerobatics and is today thoroughly understood; but in those early days the spin was a difficult condition to correct and caused many fatal crashes. Briefly, spinning is caused by trying to make a turn when safe flying speed has been lost and the 'plane stalls. Autorotation then occurs and the aeroplane rotates about a point near to its centre. Recovery can be made provided there is sufficient height so that the 'plane can be dived to regain speed, at the same time ruddering against the turn. Too small a fin or rudder makes recovery more difficult. In fact, the danger from spins continued right up to the end of the war, and remains to this day a potential danger if the pilot makes the unforgivable error of losing flying speed at an insufficient height for recovery by diving. This applies as much to the giant airliner as to the cheapest light 'plane, and a fatal crash is almost always the result . . .

Around 1915 Lindemann became interested in the problem of the involuntary spin, worked out a theory and apparently decided to put it to practical test. By then at least two pilots, Sir Vernon Brown and Brooke, knew how to recover from a spin, and as early as August 1912 during the Military Aeroplane Trials on Salisbury Plain I had watched Wilfred Parke recover from an accidental spin.

It is claimed by some that Lindemann obtained permission from O'Gorman (The Director at Farnborough) to learn to fly and within three weeks went up in a BE 2 and did spins and recoveries! One of the main points of controversy is to obtain firm evidence of the date when it happened. Over thirty years later, when nearly eighty years old, O'Gorman suggested it took place in 1916. I found O'G's memory relating to Farnborough days was often at fault or nonexistent, and feel it quite possible that he was confusing Lindemann with Goodden the chief test pilot, who did test spins at Farnborough in 1916. O'Gorman's references to Lindemann, incidentally, are far from complimentary, but he admitted that he was an able physicist. It is said that Lindemann had a 'meticulous' memory and 'quite exceptional powers of memory', and yet when asked by someone about his spinning experiences at a later date he said, 'I really cannot remember any details about my spinning experiments', and he does not even mention spinning in his memoirs. This was said to be due to his 'deep modesty'. This 'deep modesty' prevented his suggested discoveries connected with spinning being generally and quickly known as they should have been in order to save young pilots from fatal errors . . .

Major F.M. Green, who was closely in touch with Lindemann at Farnborough, puts the matter in sounder perspective when he says, 'I do not think it quite fair to rob Lindemann of his contributions to the problems of spinning . . . Major Goodden was an exceptionally good and experienced pilot and was my authority on aeroplane flight behaviour. He certainly used to do all sorts of aerobatics which must have included spinning . . .

Lindemann worked out a theory of spinning far enough to encourage him to experiment in the air. This he did, and I believe had some success, but I cannot remember exactly what he reported. I do not think this had any immediate result in giving guidance in all conditions of spin, nor, I think, did it make much impression on Goodden.**

Edward Busk

Another man to try spin recovery was Edward Busk. Ted Busk was a Cambridge man who graduated with a first in engineering from King's College then did postgraduate work on airflow. At Farnborough he was taught to fly by Geoffrey de Havilland whom he then assisted in designing the RE 1 which flew in November 1913. Flying soon after this he discovered how to recover from a spin but was killed later that month when the aircraft he was flying, a BE 2C which he had converted from being an unstable to a stable machine, caught fire in the air and crashed, witnessed by Geoffrey de Havilland.

L.K. Blackmore: Harry Hawker

L.K. Blackmore, in his biography of Harry Hawker in 1990, quotes an article from *Aeroplane*, 1 July 1914.

"One of the most extraordinary accidents in aviation, and a still more remarkable escape from death, occurred to Mr Harry Hawker at Brooklands on Saturday evening last. Mr Hawker went up about 7 pm in the Sopwith Scout (100 hp Gnôme) and, at about 1,200 feet, he made one of his famous loops with the engine cut off, by diving steeply and then pulling back. He made the loop perfectly, but over the Byfleet Road, as he came out of it, he started a vertical dive with a spin in it.

When I first caught sight of him from the paddock he was doing a perfect tourbillon spin, that is to say the wings were revolving round the centre line of the fuselage, and the machine was standing vertically on its nose. It was coming down quite slowly for such a fast machine, the pace being nothing like its ordinary diving speed. Then the tail seemed to swing out and the vertical path became an irregular spiral to the right, until finally the machine seemed to be doing a banked turn with the fuselage nearly horizontal and the left wing up. The speed of descent had by then decreased noticeably, but it was obvious that the machine was not under proper control, for it seemed to flutter round like a falling leaf. At this point it disappeared behind the trees on St George's Hill.

As quickly as possible a number of people from Brooklands rushed to the spot and, after considerable difficulty, found the machine on the ground in a thick coppice, with Mr Hawker standing alongside it absolutely unhurt. A few minutes afterwards he went off back to Brooklands, sitting on the carrier of a motorcycle, leaving the machine in charge of the Sopwith machine crew.

Apparently the machine had struck partly sideways and partly nose-on into the top of a tall tree, into which it had flown rather than fallen. It had then fallen vertically, bringing several big boughs of the tree with it, and had finally sat down right side up, flat on its chassis, on top of sundry saplings and under-growth. The wings had folded up neatly as it fell through the trees, and had come down like a lid on the cockpit. How Mr Hawker got out is a mystery. The chassis had telescoped into the front of the fuselage. The cowl was dented and bent, but not torn off. Two or three valve tappets had been wiped off the engine, which was evidently revolving when it struck the trees. The propeller was broken at the ends, but not at the boss. The fuselage, aft of the tank, together with the elevator and rudder, were absolutely untouched.

The first thing we did was to test the controls, and found the elevator and rudder worked perfectly. The warp wires were also undamaged, so there can be no question of controls going wrong. What then, was the cause of the accident?

For some time previously, Mr Hawker had been proving the extraordinary stability of this machine. He used to take it up to a thousand feet or so, switch off the engine, and let the machine glide. Then he would apply back stick slowly to stall it. With the controls hard back it would neither tail-slide, nor dive, or side-slip. It would simply descend on an even keel like a parachute, but moving gently forward and rolling slowly first to one side then back to the other. Occasionally, in a gust, it would slide to one side, descending sideways at about 45 degrees, in a side-slip. On moving the stick forward it would pick up its gliding angle promptly. In fact it seemed absolutely stable in every direction. It recovered promptly also from a straight dive which was almost vertical.

Now comes the smash, and it is worth studying. The nose did not appear to come up as expected when the stick was moved back. During the afternoon Mr Hawker had been arguing with an officer of the Naval Air Service about the need for more vertical surface aft on these small, high-speed Scouts. The officer in question was of the opinion that, owing to the short tail, if a Scout started to spin it perhaps would not be possible to regain control.

When Mr Hawker disappeared behind the trees he undoubtedly had his stick right back and, as he was then banked well over to the right, his elevators were acting as if they were rudders, and so were forcing his tail round and increasing the spin. In this position the rudder should act as an elevator and throw the nose of the machine down, so causing a straight nosedive from which it should be easy to recover. Mr Hawker tells me he tried to do this, but could not get it round against the air pressure. He put this down to the rudder being of the unbalanced type. He thinks that with a balanced rudder and no fin he could have done it.

Also, he admits that if he had moved the stick forward after application of rudder, as soon as he found the spin developing, and he had made a straight dive, he could have pulled up straight, but he thought he was too near the ground to risk doing so.

It must be remembered that the Caudron aeroplane, in which Chanteloup does his tourbillon dive, has a tail that warps in unison with the wings and that it has two big balanced rudders, so that it really has more control than the Scout class and, as it is a much slower machine, it changes its attitude in a much shorter distance even if it takes the same length of time to do so. Still, it looked to me as if Mr Hawker was getting the machine under control just as she disappeared, and I believe that if he tries the experiment again at 3,000 feet, instead of 1,000, he will have regained control before reaching 1,000 feet.

Anyhow he is very lucky to be alive, and only for that opportune clump of trees he would not have been. Still, to please the Navy, it might be worthwhile trying one of the Scouts with a bigger rudder and fin, and a proportionately strong rudder tube, so as to see how it affects their normal flying. If it does not slow the machine appreciably, it might be well to adopt the larger size simply to give extra directional stability and control, and simplify the flying of the type by less clever chaps.

Has it struck anybody that there may be a very good reason for the old Antoinette system of having vertical fins and rudders exactly equal to the tail fins and elevators?**

Blackmore also quotes an account of the incident by a fellow Australian, Horrie Miller, who arrived with the search party after the accident.

**Again he was in the cockpit, reliving the moments of suspense and panic, the struggle to defeat the unknown, the last despairing burst of engine power and the plunge to earth. 'I know what I should have done.' He paused. We hung on his words. 'If only I'd had the guts to do it . . . I'll have a new plane ready in four days. I'll get it into a spin and get out of it.' All eyes followed him as he turned away.

I helped put the finishing touches to that new plane. It was similar, except for the engine, to the one in which Hawker had crashed and, like all Sopwith's landplanes at that time, it had been brought by truck for assembly at Brooklands.

I was there to swing the propeller on that mist-laden morning of the fateful test. As St George, in ages past, had slain the dragon, so Hawker, a modern knight, leather jacket and goggles in place of shining armour, would renew the encounter in which he had been vanquished a few days earlier. Again, over St George's Hill, the battle was to be joined and no quarter given. The miracle of escape could not be repeated.

There were no spectators beside myself. Hawker, cap on back to front, goggles ready, stood quietly beside the plane as I turned the propeller. He took a long look around and up into the sky, then swung his body into the cockpit. 'I'll go to 8,000 feet, get into a spin and come out. Switch off! Suck in! Contact!' With the cloud of white smoke usual to a rotary engine, she started at once. Hawker ran the engine up to full revs then waved for 'chocks away'. The roar of the engine brought a few sleepy people out of their beds. The plane swung into a graceful bank at the end of the airfield up into the cold morning air. Hawker was part of this sweet, new plane, with its smell of fresh varnish. How beautifully she climbed above the ground haze! There lay the misty Thames, 4,000 feet beneath. A lifetime yet to swing up into the lovely morning sky. There was the oval saucer of Brooklands and the forest. How comforting the motor's steady beat! Only that dull ache of anxiety, this thing that must be done against every natural instinct. Six thousand feet. Away to the left lay the mighty city, London, in its blanket of smoke and, further on the sea, the land a mosaic of villages, roads, railways and pastures. He cut the petrol a little as the mixture became richer.

Seven thousand feet, 1,000 to go. It was growing cold but at this great height he met the enemy on better terms, 8,000. Over with the stick, on with the rudder. Cut the motor! She whipped into the spin, nose down, wings whirling down and down. The earth was a spinning bowl beneath. What to do now? Is this the moment? Push the stick forward, not back. Every nerve rebelled against this desperate action. The nose was down, must one send it further down? Perhaps, after all one does not have the guts. Down she goes. Forward with the stick down, centralise the rudder, hold.

How sweet the glide, the long, sweet glide. He turned a little, gently dipped the wing. Where was the wind? Ah yes – the smoke from the chimneys. Softly the wheels touched the grass, the battle fought and won.

Hawker had mastered the spinning dive.**"**

This was written in June 1914. Harry Hawker was confident that he could get out of a spin when he took off on that second flight. Horrie Miller's account is dramatic but has the ring of truth.

Frank T. Courtney: Spins and Things

This is a personal account by Frank T. Courtney of the first test studies of the spin which he did in 1914 as reported in *Aeronautics*, November 1961.

"The perennial interest in the 'spin' and its origins seems to arise from the fact that spinning was the first manoeuvre in which abnormal aerodynamics, with abnormal control action, was found to be acceptable and even useful, instead of being a bugaboo to be avoided at all costs. It was almost as though the medical profession had found a use for pneumonia. Before World War I, aerobatics were relatively elementary, consisting mainly of loops, steep climbing turns (a la Chevillard) and vertical banks; but all these were performed within the bounds of the cardinal rule: never lose flying speed. Sometimes, as on the top of a loop, a pilot could legitimately lose flying speed, but only because he counted on regaining it in the ensuing dive. But normally one avoided stalling an aeroplane as one avoids steering a car into a telegraph pole.

World War I brought in thousands of new pilots and dozens of new aeroplane types; hundreds of crashes resulted in some fashion from stalling, simply because stalling and its after-effects were hardly understood. But, with the accidental discovery (it had to be originally accidental) of spins, their causes, consequences and cures, stalling was reduced to a normal practical problem, and a new approach to aerobatics, and hence to military flying, became possible.

For quite a long while I believed, as a matter of mild personal interest, that I was the first pilot to make an intentional spin and recover from it. As time went on, I came across stories of a few pilots in England who were credited with this original deed, and of dozens of them in the USA, especially around Hollywood. Most such stories were pure tripe, involving some hero who deliberately went into a spin at a time when nobody knew that there was such a thing as a spin to go into. I have always thought of my little effort as an interesting, but fortuitous, outcome of a routine test-flying job, not calling for any award of cigars, nuts or brass bands. So, for what interest it may have today, I have recorded my own experiences with early spinning and with other flying antics related to the spin.

When I went to Farnborough in 1916, as a Royal Flying Corps test pilot, the only real spin I had ever heard of was the famous Parke's dive of, I think, 1911. For the benefit of those who have not reached that far back into history: Lieutenant Parke RN had somehow got himself into what we afterwards knew to be a spin on an early Cabin Avro, and normal control action failed to get him out of it; when he had dropped so far that his outlook was desperate, he figured that he had nothing to lose by reversing his controls, whereupon he came out of the spin and lived to keep out of future spins. The incident was observed by numerous witnesses. I well remember that, as a student pilot in 1914, I was much impressed by Parke's effort as a bright sample of emergency thinking; but, from all I heard about it, the whole affair was regarded simply as an obscure and freakish piece of aircraft behaviour, and I am pretty sure that nobody then recognised or described it as a spin.

One day in the summer of 1916, at the Royal Aircraft Factory (as it was then called), I was doing some low-speed tests on the very pronounced yaw characteristics of the full length ailerons on the FE 8, following similar tests which I had been doing on the SE 4a. The machine suddenly dropped off into a diving turn without any instructions from me; when I went through the standard motions for pulling up the wing and nose, all I got was more turn. In a test pilot's job, especially in those days, the unexpected was always to be expected, so that I don't remember being too perturbed and, among the ideas which went through my head, thoughts of Mr Parke quickly showed up; probably I wasn't too keen about reversing controls, but I tried it and found myself in a nice straight shallow dive. Evidently I had got into something where the usual rules of control didn't apply and where you could profitably reverse the rules. This sort of thing was obviously too much fun to be left alone, so I decided to try again, and proceeded to collect some more altitude.

Aileron Yaw?

At first I couldn't get this spinning motion started, because I didn't know how I had got into the first one—I was under the impression that it had all been started by aileron yaw. After one of two experiments around stalling speed I eventually kicked the rudder to help the yaw (which is probably what I had unknowingly done in the first place) and I was off into another spin, which was just as easily stopped.

By this time I was definitely in the spinning business. On the third try I had no difficulty in starting the spin, so this time I let it go for what seemed like twenty turns but was probably about three; again there was no problem getting straight. After another check or two I had come to the conclusion that, once you had done it, there was really nothing very special about spinning, and I probably wondered why we had not seen more of it. I did not know then of course, that there was a lot more to be found out about it.

When I landed there was considerable excitement among the ground watchers, who seemed to think I had been in some sort of serious trouble. Among those was Captain Frank Goodden who, as chief test pilot, was also our Commanding Officer. Goodden was an old friend of mine—we had shared the same lodgings at Hendon before the war; he had long been one of the country's best pilots. We went into his office and discussed my discovery. Goodden couldn't wait to try it out himself, which he promptly did. He got so enthusiastic about it that he set up a regular spinning test programme on the FE 8, and decided to do the tests himself. A couple of days after my first effort I spun an FE 2d, an over-stable monster which was hard to hold in a spin. When Goodden made his first formal report he illustrated it with some ground photographs of the FE 8 showing the control surfaces in the appropriate positions for starting and stopping the spin (a cloud background was dubbed in to simulate flight photos). It would be interesting to discover if that report still exists in the Farnborough dungeons.

Later I heard criticisms of Goodden that his reports did not refer to my part in the business and that he took all the credit himself; actually it wouldn't have entered Goodden's head to withhold credit where there was any point in handing it out. But we were not in the show business, with everyone looking for credit lines. Remember that those were the days when none of us knew very much, and it was a dull week at Farnborough when someone didn't find out something new about something. This spinning business was just another of those somethings, and we could never have suspected that, years later, the whole affair would be inflated into a historic whodunnit of breathless heroism. We were all doing the same sort of jobs, and none of us could have cared less about who got the credit for doing something first. In this particular case, one of Goodden's subordinates, myself, in the course of some routine work, accidentally came across a phenomenon which, after a preliminary check, he reported to his Commanding Officer. The said CO was sufficiently interested to run a series of checks and tests himself, and he reported his findings in the usual way.

Between Parke's dive and 1916 I never heard of anyone getting into a spin which started high enough up to be identified as a spin. This was probably because, in those times, training and every flying conversation put enormous emphasis on not losing flying speed; it was a firm rule that, when you cut your engine, or when in doubt, you pushed the nose down. But the spin was there just the same, killing lots of people, only we didn't recognise it. The records of the period refer to numerous crashes due to side-slip. So many of these were serious or fatal that the daily press took to labelling it the deadly side-slip. When the facts about spins became understood, it was clear that this side-slip was simply an incipient spin which started too low down to develop. It was, and always has been, a favourite form of serious crash for pilots who ran into trouble too close to the ground to push the nose down.

Not a Menace at All

By 1917, spinning had become a general procedure. Naturally, as more people spun more aircraft, sundry complications began to appear: some aircraft recovered less quickly or less easily than others, different aircraft demonstrated different spin characteristics, and some of them were nasty, so that inexperienced pilots, who were in plentiful supply at the time, managed to confuse themselves into crashes which really shouldn't have happened. A particular example was the case of the RE 8, which somehow achieved a reputation as a spinning menace. I flew dozens of RE 8s, from the prototype through all its later variations, under all sorts of loading conditions, and I could never understand how it got its reputation. I can only suppose that, since the average pilot of RE 8s knew only the docile Avros or BEs on which he was trained, he was liable to be taken by surprise and become confused if the RE 8 showed (as it probably did) unfamiliar spinning habits. Anyway, the result of all such troubles was that research establishments everywhere set up programmes of special spin experiments principally with the object of eliminating abnormal spin characteristics from aircraft designs. For this purpose all sorts of strange things were tried out, leading to such studies as those of the unpleasant flat spin. Such tests went on for years, and pilots who made them often took quite considerable chances which, however, were nothing new in regular test work. However, it is probably out of all this that the romantic writers of later years evolved their wondrous spin stories; they selected, or invented, a composite hero who, first, whirled himself off fearlessly into the unknown perils of the spin and then, at dreadful risk, went on and on spinning to save our brave lads from a splintery fate.

The flat spin was a nasty business because it was often very difficult or impossible to recover from, especially if power had been lost; in later flat spin experiments drag parachutes were used to assist recovery. Moreover, the basic aerodynamics of the plain spin were clearly obvious, those of the flat spin were not. The first flat spin I ever saw happened to Christopher Draper on a BAT Bantam at Hendon probably around 1921. I watched him start a normal spin at about 610 m (2,000 feet). After a number of turns, the aircraft, almost suddenly, flattened out but kept on spinning. Then the propeller stopped and, by the time the Bantam reached 150 m (500 feet) it was clear that Chris no longer had things under control and was in for something sticky. He hit the ground in an almost completely flat attitude and, when we dragged him out, he was practically undamaged except for a broken ankle and a bad headache. I then decided firmly that, if a pilot of Draper's calibre couldn't get out of a flat spin, I didn't want to get into one. I never did. Later on, studying test reports on flat spins, I was horrified to find that the Bristol Fighter, if heavily loaded aft, was particularly susceptible to going flat in a spin. I shuddered to remember the numerous occasions when I had spun Bristols down into Gosport, Northolt or Shoreham with the back seat loaded with everything that could be crammed into it, including (Gosport pilots—remember?) cases of Harvey's Bristol Cream for the officers' mess.

Centrifugal Force

The inverted spin was possible, but I never knew anyone to make a habit of it. I got into one once, by accident, while trying to do something or other with a Camel on top of a loop. I didn't like it because, as in the case of an outside loop, centrifugal force was fiercely trying to unhorse the pilot. It was perfectly easy to recover from provided the pilot was firmly held in his seat; I had long made a point of always wearing a very tight belt, and shoulder straps were not standard equipment at the time. I heard of two or three cases where Camel pilots were killed in inverted spins; one Shoreham pilot who was chewed up but survived (he had spun into the steep side of the hill), gave an explanation which probably covered the less fortunate cases: he was not very tightly belted in and, when he got into his inverted spin, the only use he could make of the stick was to hold himself from being thrown out of the cockpit, incidentally holding himself in the spin.

If the romantic yarn-spinners want to produce a hero who did something first, they should look into the case of the snap-roll (or barrel-roll or flick-roll). The aerodynamics of the snap-roll are practically the same as those of the spin but, whereas the first spin could have been made only by accident, it is practically impossible to do a snap-roll otherwise than on purpose; therefore there must be, or have been, some sportsman who first decided to inflict this amusing form of violence on the structure of his aircraft. (The snap-roll is totally distinct from the 'slow roll' which is, aerodynamically, simply an elaborate form of normal flying.) When I went back to France late in 1916, nobody seemed to have heard of the snap-roll; when I got home about a year later it was already a common stunt, but I have never heard any suggestions as to who started it, not even in Hollywood.

A snap-roll takes a much harder kick at the structure than does a spin because, although they both do the same thing to the aircraft, the roll does it at a good deal higher speed. I learnt the hard way to appreciate this one day at Yarmouth when I had borrowed Egbert Cadbury's Camel. For no known reason, I proceeded to do a roll just as I pulled out from a dive, which meant that I had added an initial high angle of attack to the other ingredients. The right bottom wing decided, quite reasonably, to break; the front spar parted completely, the fabric split across the wing, the rear spar showed splinters but held, bracing wires flapped around. I wobbled somehow to the ground, mostly with full left rudder because of the drag of the broken wing; on the way down I solemnly assured all interested spirits that, if they would only see me safely to earth, I would in future be more respectful towards rolls. Actually I never heard of a fatal crash from a structural failure due to a roll, but I imagine it must have happened. Anyway, I think the man who did the first snap-roll deserves all the nasturtiums that some people are trying to throw at whoever did the first spin.

The Falling Leaf stunt was first cousin to the spin, and it evolved pretty much accidentally. I know very certainly (if it matters) that I was the first to do it because, after I had discovered it at Gosport late in 1917, I left the other fellows to find out how it was done, and it was about a week before somebody (it was Billy Williams I think) caught on to the gag. I suppose the reason for the mystery was that, from the ground, the action looked like a very fancy bit of aileron work whereas, in fact, the ailerons had nothing much to do with it.

I was pottering around on a Camel at several hundred metres, and got to wondering what would happen if you stalled near the ground, started to spin, checked the spin, but had no room to check the stall. So I stalled, allowed the right wing to drop in the start of a spin, checking it immediately in an effort to return to a level stall; of course the Camel flicked sharply over to the left. Another check, and it flicked smartly back over to the right—and so on and on. I never did get back to the level stall but, in the process of trying, I had found myself a nice new little stunt.

Spinning and its associated stunts are no longer customary, although I believe they are still permitted under a batch of official regulations as numerous as those of a coronation procession. Flying, apparently, has progressed in a circle; we are now back to the days of the straight and level.**"**

Frederick Lindemann: From Fifty Years at Farnborough

Since 1912 scientists at Farnborough had been trying to discover how a spin came about. By 1916 they had still made very little progress. In 1917 one of them, Dr Frederick Lindemann, (later to become Lord Cherwell) obtained permission to learn to fly. This extract, in his own words, is from *Fifty Years at Farnborough*.

"In 1916 many pilots were killed flying our recently designed RE 8s by spinning into the ground. Although various people had succeeded in getting out of a spin, nobody quite knew how, nor indeed how or why an aircraft spun at all. Anyone watching a spinning 'plane could see that the rate of turn did not increase on the way down. I concluded therefore that the lift on both wings must be equal; and this could only be true—since the outer wing is beating against the air whereas the inner is not—if its effective angle of incidence was on the high angle side of the angle of maximum lift, whereas the inner wing was the opposite way round. This being so, if the speed were increased, the aeroplane would no longer spin. Experiments proved that the idea was correct, and the whole theory was worked out quantitatively and described in a paper by Glauert and myself published by the Aeronautical Research Committee in 1918.

Thereafter the pilots were taught to push the stick forward—the very opposite of the instinctive reaction of pulling it back in order to get the nose up—and to straighten out the rudder and then pull out of the dive in the ordinary way. The only merit I can claim in carrying out these experiments is that (unlike the professional pilot, who had usually not got a very good head for figures) I was able to remember the readings of the airspeed indicator, the bubble, the angle of incidence on the two wings (measured by tapes on the struts), the height of the beginning and ending of the spin, the time taken and the number of turns, and to write them down in my notebook when I had straightened out the 'plane again. I am glad of the opportunity to correct some of the absurdly dramatic stories which have appeared about this investigation.**

The following is a short extract from Part 1 of the experimental investigation carried out by Lindemann, Glauert and Harris into spinning. It is interesting and remarkable that the observations in Table 1 were made in the space of about half a minute as the aircraft fell about 2,000 feet. Similar observations were made for the first part of Table 2 as the pilot made ten complete turns of a spin.

**1.   A number of spins were performed on a BE 2E machine over a camera obscura so as to obtain a full series of observations and to determine the effect of small motions of the controls. It was found that in a normal spin with full left rudder and with the stick full back to the right, the time for one complete turn was approximately four seconds, the indicated airspeed about 55 miles per hour, and the radius of the turn about 20 feet. The attitude of the machine was such that the wing struts were horizontal and there was no appreciable sideslip. This motion of spinning could be kept quite steady and appeared to be a stable motion.

Observations were taken in the aeroplane of the indicated airspeed and the loss of height. Lateral and longitudinal spirit levels were fitted so that the direction of the resultant force could be determined, and the value of this force was also obtained by means of a spring accelerometer in the pilot's seat. The lateral bubble was found to be one or two degrees to the left, indicating an outward side-slip, but in all probability this was due rather to the fact that the bubble was a short distance behind the centre of gravity of the machine than to any side-slip of the machine as a whole.

2.   A number of spins were made with full left rudder but not varying positions of the control column to observe the consequent changes in the motion. The results are given in Table 1 opposite. It will be noticed that as the stick is moved across, the period of rotation, the airspeed and the total force all increase. When the stick is also moved a little forward the time of the turn is still further increased and the motion has developed into a steep spiral rather than a proper spin. In the last case when the stick was nearly central and a little forward, there was a considerable side-slip outwards. On another occasion it

Table 1
Effect of movement of controls

Position of control column	Period of rotation, seconds	Indicated airspeed mph.	Radius of turn, feet	Loss of height, feet per second	Number of times normal loading
Full back, right	4.2	58	30	66	1.6
Full back, central	4.5	70	45	83	2.6
Full back, left	7.5	70	115	56	2.7
Slightly forward, right	-	70	140	47	2.0
Slightly forward, central	10.0	75	190	-	2.2

Table 2
Conversion of spin into spiral

No. of turn	Time of turn	Indicated airspeed, mph.	No. of times normal load	Radius of turn, feet
1	4.9	-	1.9	31
2	3.8	54	-	-
3	3.8	-	-	27
4	4.1	-	-	-
5	5.2	-	-	77
6	8.0	70	2.5	-
7	8.4	-	-	130
8	7.1	-	-	115
9	4.4	-	1.8	-
10	4.0	55	-	-
1	4.5	55	1.6	35
2	5.6	-	-	62
3	7.0	65	2.6	110

was found possible to convert a spin gradually into a spiral and back again to a spin (see Table 2)."

The following extract from Part 2 of the report concerns the forces likely to be exerted on the aircraft.

"The only times apparently during which dangerous forces are likely to be exerted on the wings are when getting into or coming out of a spin. The stalling angle must be passed in these cases and if it is passed at a high speed the stresses will certainly be great. Thus if the spin is started from a spiral by pulling the stick in without taking care to keep the speed down with the rudder, the stalling angle is passed at a comparatively high speed. At 80 mph the loading will be four times normal and at 100 mph the machine might break. The same of course applies to the conversion of a spin into a spiral. Starting a spin in the usual manner, by stalling the aeroplane when flying straight and then crossing the controls, is scarcely likely to put any stress on the machine, as the speed never rises above some 60 mph. Coming out of the spin by putting the controls central and converting the spin into a nosedive is probably quite safe so long as care is taken to pull out of the dive gently. The speed of course is likely to increase very rapidly during the dive and it is found in practice that the stress coming out of the dive is greater than during the spin. It might be desirable for pilots engaged on spinning tests to use an accelerometer and to avoid letting the loading rise above 3 g. If the aeroplane spins faster than the BE 2E with which the experiments were carried out the factor of safety might be less, but it does not seem likely that the conditions would be seriously aggravated.**"**

Norman Macmillan: The Spin

The following three articles by Wing Commander Norman Macmillan, OBE, MC, AFC, AFRAeS describe in detail the history of spinning. They cover the first twenty years of the twentieth century, commenting on the episodes already described and adding further information. This first article appeared in *Aeronautics* in July 1960. Wing Commander Macmillan was himself a test pilot.

"Before men tried to fly, even in gliders, they watched the birds and sought to copy their flight. Wilbur and Orville Wright watched pigeons and buzzards in particular. They saw the wonderful manoeuvrability of the pigeons, the soaring ease of the buzzards. The fundamental feature of their observation was their decision that the birds turned by pivoting about one wing tip and that they would have to emulate their avian skill by the use of aerodynamic controls and not by weight shifting, as so many previous experimenters had done.

The one thing the brothers did not see these birds do was spin. A bird does not intentionally spin because it prefers to fly under control and spinning is an out of control motion during its continuation.

I myself have watched buzzards. They flew over my garden. I have seen them full roll when attacked by herring gulls, I have seen them half roll off the top of a loop. But I have never seen them spin. The only bird I have seen spin is a disabled bird. Birds shot in the wing do spin. But I have seen no reports of the Wright brothers spending their time out shooting birds.

The Wrights copied the birds faithfully by incorporating lateral and longitudinal controls in their first three gliders, the second and third of which were man-lifting. They purposely flew at a low height, deeming that the safer way. They found that during some glides for no apparent reason they ceased to have proper control. The glider then descended in a forward and downward sideslip and the lower wing struck the sand with a turning motion. If they tried to raise the depressed wing tip by applying more warp to it they found the contrary happening; the depressed wing tip dropped still lower and the turning motion was exaggerated.

They assumed by reasoning that their wing warp lateral control could work efficiently only if they had some means of sustaining each wing tip at the same forward speed through the air. They appreciated that the wing tip with positive warp slowed speed because of its increased resistance and that the lateral differential in wing resistance must be overcome. To achieve this, in their third man-lifting glider of 1902 they fitted a fixed vertical tail behind the wings. Usually this was effective. But if some unusual disturbance in the air or excessive movement of the pilot's lateral controls were not rapidly corrected the heavily worked wing then dropped. When this occurred with the fixed tail the side-slip was more pronounced and the rotary motion was greater.

Many times they ended their glides by striking the sand in this rotary motion which began with the side-slip. They gave no name to this uncontrollable movement. Nor do they appear to have analysed its full implications. They sought a cure for the initiatory causes without once considering what might occur if the uncontrolled movement were allowed to amplify. Without doubt only the low height at which they always flew saved the brothers from developing a proper spin during their trials with their two-axial control gliders.

The Hinged Rudder

Orville discovered the solution to the problem in the fitting of a hinged rudder whose appropriate face could be so turned to the relative wind as to counteract the wing tip drag. Thereafter the brothers had complete control at all times and the side-slip and its development into a rotary movement troubled them no more. Their aeroplane was unstable both longitudinally and laterally and so had to be flown by continual attention to the air controls. But this was what they had set out to achieve—to overcome the instability of the air—and they appear to have regarded it as normal to fly by perpetual attentiveness to the controlled maintenance of stability.

What is important here is that the Wright brothers (and in particular Orville) by pure reasoning had created the antidote for an incipient spin by providing a hinged vertical rudder (they called their elevator a horizontal rudder) such as no birds possess. Here one must observe that birds do not require a vertical rudder because they have independently flexible wings whose surface, plan form, incidence can be altered differentially as can also the muscular power applied to each wing in wing beat. A bird's tail can also apply correcting forces because it can be partially oscillated in its longitudinal axis and thus turned into a combined rudder and elevator and birds do so use it, often when flying in very unstable conditions.

It has always seemed strange to me that the Wrights' means of curing the incipient spin was not fully investigated either by themselves or others afterwards, especially when spinning began to cause fatal accidents. Indeed, so far as I know, I am myself the first to have called attention to this important feature of the Wrights' early experiments and developments. The point appears to have escaped others.

The Rolls Disaster

There is no record (so far as I have been able to discover) of anyone being killed in a Wright biplane through spinning. Lieutenant-Colonel Alec Ogilvie told me he believed Rolls's death in 1910 was due to the same cause as that affecting Orville Wright's crash at Dayton (two years before) when Lieutenant Selfridge was killed. At Dayton a propeller, vibrating loose, broke a tail stay wire (not stranded cable, but piano wire); this allowed the vertical rudder to twist horizontal and forced the machine to dive. [This accident happened not at Dayton but at Fort Myer, near Washington DC—Ed]

But many crashes (and deaths) occurred through spinning during the years 1910 to the end of the First World War. The cause of spinning and the procedure for recovery were both established before the end of that war, yet pilots still killed themselves afterwards through taking deliberate chances during intentional spins. There was, moreover, always the risk of spinning when flying blind until blind flying instrumentation was introduced into the cockpit a decade later.

The question has often been asked (but never satisfactorily answered) who first discovered the cause of spinning and (more importantly) made the first voluntary spin because he had found the assured method of recovering normal flight. I set myself the task of investigating this question with a view to presenting my findings as an historical record and I do so here for the first time.

Raynham's Experience

F.P. Raynham, then a pilot at the Avro school at Brooklands, is sometimes credited as having been the first pilot to recover from an unintentional spin. The facts appear to be that he left Brooklands on 21 September 1911 to fly to Hendon, ran into a bank of fog (not very deep because church spires and other prominent features were visible above the fog). He climbed to 1,500 feet (457 m) to ensure ample clearance and increase his visual range, and steered by compass. Thinking the compass card was not floating he bent over to pull the fixing screw down and simultaneously flew into an 'air pocket', the term then given to any disturbance in air flow. What followed he described as the most hair-raising incident of his flying career up to that date. The machine dived almost vertically, so that he was standing upright on the rudder bar and before he could regain control it had described two complete circles. When he straightened out he was at 500 feet (152 m) on his altimeter.

From my own experience of flying not as early, but early, types of aeroplanes I do not believe that was a spin, but a power spiral (the engine was running throughout). He would not have lost 1,000 feet (300 m) with only two turns of a spin. There is no evidence of a stall (the prerequisite of a spin). Bending down to fix his compass would induce a dive, not a stall. Personally, I disallow this experience as that of a true spin, without in any way decrying its unpleasant excitement. Certainly it left no imprint on the development of pilotage control over the spin, and any unamplified references to it should be disregarded as genuine spin history.

A Documented Spin Recovery

The first fully documented recovery from a spin is the only one which can stand critical scrutiny. The incident occurred on 25 August 1912 during the British Military Trials at Larkhill on Salisbury Plain. The pilot involved was Lieutenant Wilfred Parke RN who took his RAeC certificate No 73 on 25 April 1911. He had undertaken to fly A. V. Roe's enclosed-cabin Avro biplane with a 60 hp Green engine, whose designer, Gustavus Green, celebrated his ninety-fifth birthday in 1960. In this aeroplane occurred what was contemporaneously called 'Parke's Dive'.

Accounts of Parke's Dive vary greatly. Sir Alliott Verdon-Roe in his book *The World of Wings and Things* deals briefly with it, but states that Parke 'was the first aviator who had ever got out of a spiral nosedive which previously had always ended in fatal results'. *The Aeroplane* does not use the word spin, but writes of a slight side-slip and an almost vertical dive. The reason was almost certainly that few spectators saw the almost fatal descent because Parke had taken off at about 0600 for his three hours' qualifying duration test with Lieutenant Le Breton of the RFC as passenger–observer, so that when he was returning to Larkhill at about 0910 most people were at breakfast. Thus most accounts were not those of eye witnesses. Probably the best account is that in *Flight* for 31 August 1912, p 787 [see 'A.F. Berriman: Parke's Dive' page 17].

Engine and aeroplane were running and flying well. Maximum airspeed of the Avro was about 60 mph (95.5 kph). Wind speed (estimated) was 10–15 mph (16–24 kph). Weather was sunshine and broken clouds. Height was between 600 and 700 feet (180–200 m).

Parke decided to descend to land in a spiral glide. He closed the throttle. After a half-circuit downwind he thought the glide too steep and insufficiently banked. He pulled back the stick and may also have warped the wings. The Avro instantly began a left-hand spiral nosedive (the term then given to a spin). Within half a turn he gave full throttle, thinking this might bring the nose up since the Avro was nose-heavy engine off. It did not do so. He then pulled the stick back against his chest and applied full left rudder in accordance with the accepted theory of the time that one should always turn into a side-slip. The speed of rotation increased. Watchers on the ground waited, horror stricken, for the apparently inevitable fatal crash. They described the descent as vertical. Parke said it was steep but not vertical. Parke was judging the fuselage angle, the spectators the course made good; both were correct, as one can observe by watching a spin, by spinning, or from what follows below. Geoffrey de Havilland, watching, estimated the Avro's speed at about 90 mph (145 kph), probably an over-estimate.

Centrifugal Effects

Possibly for an instant of time Parke was in a condition of free-fall. Acceleration could not have been great but the conditions made it appear to him to be very pronounced. Centrifugal force tended to throw him outwards from the turn although he was strapped in by a single belt. He took his right hand from the warp control wheel on the stick, to steady himself by gripping a fuselage upright strut. It seems he still held the wheel with his left hand, kept the stick back and maintained half-left rudder.

Parke's quick reasoning gave him the idea of turning the Avro outwards from her circling motion in order to neutralise the centrifuge in which he flew. He estimated his height to be about 50 feet (15 m) when he centralised the rudder momentarily—then pushed it hard right. Reaction was instantaneous. The Avro ceased turning. She levelled out at 5 or 6 feet (1.5–2 m) above the ground under perfect control. (Remember the cg appears to have been well forward, which would help quick spin recovery). Parke made another circuit and landed normally. Le Breton, without belt, had been thrown about within the cabin, but was unhurt. Stretched lift wires were the only consequence to the Avro.

Although it occurred during government trials 'Parke's Dive' produced no official investigation—for the purpose of reaching conclusions whose propagation would have helped other pilots faced with similar danger—into the important question of how Parke had recovered from a spiral nosedive. But, in the competitors' mess at Larkhill, Parke, Geoffrey de Havilland, A.E. Berriman (Technical Editor of *Flight* and F. Short of the Royal Aircraft Factory held an informal discussion. This was fortunate because Parke was killed soon afterwards when a Handley Page inherently stable monoplane he was flying over Wembley suddenly dived to the ground and crashed; as with so many accidents in that period the cause of Parke's death was not discovered.

To summarise the findings of this unofficial private board of inquiry:

1. De Havilland said he would have thought the controls had jammed if Parke had crashed and been killed. He would have seen no other reason for a pilot so experienced to lose control.
2. Such loss of control was dangerous at low heights. In this case the Avro fell about 450 feet (140 m) out of control. Thus it was safer to fly at heights which gave room to recover.
3. It was now necessary to distinguish between a side-slip and a spiral nosedive.
    (a) Ruddering inwards had been and still was regarded as the correct control movement to restore a side-slip to normal flight.
    (b) The spiral nosedive had been thought of as a special kind of side-slip

which should receive similar control movement for recovery. Parke's experience showed this to be wrong.

4.   Parke was descending in a true helix of excessive pitch. In this case ruddering inwards tended to make the rudder support the tail to chase round outwards after the nose, the effect was to increase the rotation speed, steepen the dive, keep the outer wing at high velocity and accentuate the bank.

   (a) Ruddering outwards checked the centrifugal action of the tail, accelerated the inner main wing tip, and so changed the spiral motion into straight-line flight with recovery of lateral trim.

   (b) The action and reaction described in 4 (a) above released the elevator from the influences that had made it inoperative and Parke, having held the elevator hard up, rapidly brought the Avro onto an even keel.

5.   Parke regarded the whole phenomenon as of elevator and rudder only. He could not recall having used warp at all during recovery.

6.   The discussion group (for that it what is really was) reached the conclusion that no one would voluntarily go up and risk losing control of his aeroplane in mid-air for the sake of demonstrating the fact of recovery, but that it should not be forgotten that from then on the rule must be to rudder outwards from a spiral dive that had attained high velocity.

Spinning Defined

The conclusions of that post-actum discussion group are remarkable for their clarity and there is no doubt that they defined the first theory of spinning and of recovery from the spin in the history of aviation, based (as it was) on Parke's observation of ineffective control movements and their results.

Yet is must be noted that *ten years before on pure theoretical reasoning Orville Wright had reached the same fundamental conclusion as that in 4(a) above* and even before the Wright gliders possessed a rudder and without knowing that the initiating turning movement could develop into a spin. But his theory referred to stability, the prevention of unequal wing tip speeds, not recovery from a spin. Thus the second paragraph of the Parke discussion must be modified, because it was only through the extremely low heights whereat the Wrights flew that they did not crash in spins before they fitted their vertical rudder. The Wrights' experience can have played no part in the Larkhill discussion group's deliberations, for it is certain that the Wrights' reason for equipping their last man-lifting glider with an anti-yaw rudder was not then known to any in the Larkhill group.

The Royal Aero Club made the next move by its decision (reported in *The Aeroplane* for 5 December 1912) to approach the Advisory Committee for Aeronautics with a contribution of £50 to obtain co-operation and experimental assistance at the National Physical Laboratory in the elucidation of the principles involved in 'Parke's Dive' and similar experiences of other (why unnamed?) pilots. Little seems to have been done then, but the NPL later made experiments (referred to in R & M 618 mentioned below) on the rotation of stalled aerofoils. The essential work was all done elsewhere under other urges and in full-scale free-flight.

The Pickles Crash

Meanwhile, spinning continued to catch out experienced pilots, not only novices. In May 1914 Sydney Pickles crashed in a spin at Hendon aerodrome with a Mrs Stocks (herself a pilot) as passenger. He was flying a Champel biplane and thought his heel had jammed in the rudder control. He then pulled the stick back. He tried engine off and on as he came down without effect. Both were injured. The spin remained a mystery. Nothing was learned from this accident.

During the brief period he flew for Sopwith at Brooklands Fred Raynham taught Hawker to fly. That was in September 1912. If Raynham had really recovered from a spin and was cognisant of the method of recovery it seems strange he did not impart his knowledge to his pupil. Nearly two years later, on 27 June 1914 Harry Hawker crashed into the trees just outside Brooklands aerodrome in a spin in the Sopwith Scout with 100 hp Gnôme Monosoupape rotary engine. (The first aeroplane loop was performed by Lieutenant Petr Nikalaevich on 27 August 1913 in a Nieuport 4 monoplane at Kiev. Unlike Pégoud's Blériot monoplane, in which the Frenchman made his first loop in the following month, the Nieuport was not specially braced. Thus we may observe in passing that the spin preceded the loop, but the loop became a practised manoeuvre before the spin.)

Spin from the Top of a Loop

Hawker had dived with engine off, then looped. It was his habit to perform a loop in this way. This time he stalled on the top of the loop and spun coming out of it. It has been suggested that this was an inverted spin, but my examination of the contemporary evidence shows that this was not so. It was a normal right-handed spin. He would have had to push the stick forward to have produced an inverted spin and he would not have done so in a loop. I have several times seen an inexperienced aerobatic pilot spin when coming out of a loop on which he had stalled and Hawker was not then noted among the aerobatic pilots, but as a straight competition winner.

According to his own subsequent account of the incident Hawker held that he could have recovered if he had pushed the stick forward, but he thought he was too low to risk that, which confirms that he was in a normal spin. So he held the stick back and applied inside (right) rudder to try to straighten the nose by making the machine dive at slow speed. As we know (and as the Larkhill discussion group assessed nearly two years before) this merely held the aeroplane in its right-handed spin. It is important to remember that Hawker was then regarded as one of the ablest test pilots of his time. From this we know that the theory of spinning and of spin recovery was not then established and was still unknown in the flying schools and even to outstanding professional pilots.

It is astonishing that pilots of the quality of Pickles and Hawker should have crashed in spins as late as 1914, long after 'Parke's Dive' and the resultant discussion group's deliberations had been discursively reported in *Flight*. Apparently neither Pickles nor Hawker had read that particular issue nor had the conclusions sunk into the practising world of flying.

In 1914 a French pilot named Chanteloup performed a tourbillon dive as his special contribution to the aerobatic displays which then delighted aeroplane audiences. He flew a Caudron with two large balanced rudders and with the elevator warp and wing warp interconnected. It is not quite certain from available accounts whether Chanteloup's tourbillon dive was a dive with warp (aileron) turn or a real spin. It receives no mention in contemporary issues of *Flight* and is referred to but casually by C.G. Grey in *The Aeroplane* issue of 1 July 1914 in connection with Hawker's crash at Brooklands. In that account Charles said that it looked to him as if Hawker were regaining control just as his Sopwith Scout disappeared behind the trees and C.G. thought if Hawker tried to spin again at 3,000 feet (900 m) instead of his involuntary spin off a loop at 1,000 feet (300 m) he would regain control after a drop of 2,000 feet (600 m). But Hawker evidently felt much as the Larkhill discussion group had felt two years earlier and did not then attempt a voluntary spin. [See page 27]

It is confirmed that in mid-1914 the method of recovery from a spin was not generally known. C.G. Grey's writing that Hawker's smash is worth studying, because according to the rules of the game the machine should have come up when the elevator was pulled back. During the afternoon Mr Hawker had been arguing with an officer in the Naval Air Service about the need for more vertical surface aft in these small high-speed Scouts. The officer in question held that, owing to the short tail, if a Scout started to spin round its own nose 'it would never come into control again'.

Grey voices the opinion that Hawker's elevators, being held back, were acting (if at all) as rudders, so increasing the rate of spin. He continued that in this position the rudder should act as an elevator 'and throw the nose of the machine down, so causing a straight nosedive from which it should be easy to recover'. Hawker told C.G. that he had tried to do this but could not move the rudder against the air pressure and ascribed this to the rudder being unbalanced. He thought with a balanced rudder and no fin he could have done it. But was this due to his own sensations in a condition of free-fall?

Here, again, is the theory of applying inside rudder to turn the spin into a dive as advocated for a simple side-slip. It would appear from this account that neither Hawker nor Grey at that time appreciated what Orville Wright and the Larkhill discussion group had both independently discovered, namely, that opposite rudder was required to recover from a spin because only so (from that motion) could equal air speed be restored over both wing extremities.

Beginning of the Cherwell Myth

Sir Walter Raleigh in volume 1 of *The War in the Air*, p 261, writes: 'The spin, at the outbreak of the war (of 1914–18) was regarded as a fault in an aeroplane, due chiefly to bad construction; later on Dr F.A. Lindemann (later Lord Cherwell), by his researches and courageous experiments at the Royal Aircraft Factory, proved that any aeroplane can spin, and that any pilot who understands the spin can get out of it if there is height to spare. During the war the spin was freely used by pilots to break off a fight, to simulate defeat, or to descend in a vertical path.' This statement is liable to misinterpretation because it is couched in too general terms. The last sentence in it applies only to the last two years of the war. The part played by Professor Lindemann requires much amplification, not least in its relation to others, and this will be enlarged upon presently.

Four aeroplanes (at least) were notoriously evil spinners early in the First World War. These were the Sopwith Two-Seater Scout, better known as the 'Spinning Jenny'; the DH 2, sometimes called the 'Spinning Incinerator' because some spun, crashed and caught fire; the FE 8; the 110 hp le Rhône-engined Sopwith Camel.

The first voluntary spin and recovery I have been able to authenticate was made in a Spinning Jenny. It is sometimes written (even today) that before this voluntary spin was made in the Spinning Jenny the corrective action was not known. We have already seen that this is incorrect. It would be true to say that it was not sufficiently known, but no more than that. Orville and Wilbur Wright, Parke, Geoffrey de Havilland and a few others certainly knew. In retrospect it is astonishing that the gospel of spin recovery was not widely preached before it was. But one must remember that there was no systematic method of flying instruction until Smith-Barry started his School of Special Flying at Gosport in August 1917 as the first school to instruct instructors how to instruct pupils, the genesis of all flying instruction throughout the world ever since.

John Callaghan Brooke took his RAeC certificate No 908 on 21 September 1914 and entered the RNAS. In the First World War he gained a DSC and ultimately retired from the RAF as a Squadron Leader. In midsummer of 1915 he was a flying instructor at Killingholme in Lincolnshire aged 22. Norman Blackburn, who was at Killingholme, said of Brooke at that time: 'There was not much of him then, or even the last time I saw him, about 9½ stone I should say; but what grits the lad had.'

The Avro 16

Norman W.G. Blackburn (brother of Robert, founder of the Blackburn Aircraft Company) took his RAeC Certificate No 1311 on 5 June 1915. In that month or the next (he told me) he took off from Chingford aerodrome in an Avro 503 with a 100 hp fourteen-cylinder Gnôme engine. Designated by Avros the type H, this aeroplane originally was built as a float-plane. Norman Blackburn says two were built for the *Daily Mail* Seaplane Circuit of Britain which was scheduled for August 1914 and cancelled by the war. They were taken over by the Admiralty. It was in one of these two, with wheels instead of floats, that he took off from Chingford. 'From my log book,' he told me, 'it seems that the official name was the Avro 16.

'The trouble started by "seizure", in presumably one pot of the fourteen-cylinder Gnôme, and a con rod broke.

'I was over the reservoir at about 1,100 feet [330 m] and in trying to nurse the kite back to the aerodrome stalled and spun [as he now called it] . . . Knowing little about the job, the young, of which I was one, naturally pulled back the stick to bring up the nose. *It was the only thing to do!*

'I crashed on the bank of Chingford Reservoir, still spinning comparatively slowly . . . and was lucky to hit the built-up slope of the reservoir bank with the lower port wing tip, which swung her around just right and all I got was the wheel in my face . . . and a broken thumb and nose, a lot of bruises and the loss of three teeth where I still wear a plate.

'I have my log books, which include Killingholme, and I see that I did one or two trips with Brookie.

'Now the Sopwith Gnôme 80 had a much tighter and nose-downer spin and Brookie got one—a beauty!

'The date would be about October or early November 1915. When Brookie "came out" to our astonishment and relief, and landed, seemingly not too shaken, he declared to a bunch of us that he knew how he had done it . . . There was a lot of chatter and "come off it" but Brookie was certain he could do it again (BF). But he did, and on his next flight on the same machine . . .'

Brooke's own story of his spin says it was in June or July 1915 when he was at Killingholme, where, as at most RNAS stations in those days there was a strange mixture of aeroplanes and seaplanes—Forman box-kites, FBA flying boats, Short float-planes and two Sopwith Two-Seater Scouts with 80 hp Gnôme engines (Spinning Jennies). Brooke gave pupils dual instruction in a Maurice Farman Longhorn.

'One day I was giving a joy ride to a pupil, Flight Sub-Lieutenant G.G. Hogge in one of the Sopwiths,' he told me, 'and was coming down from about 2,500 feet (760 m) in a spiral glide, considered 'aerobatics' in those days. I must have gone too slowly for the Jenny suddenly went into a very fast spin.

'I remembered the story of "Parke's Dive" in the enclosed Avro in the Military Trials and put the rudder central and pushed the wheel control hard forward, whereupon the Jenny came out into a glide almost as quickly as she had flicked into the spin.

'When I landed some of the pupils including Norman Blackburn, asked me what had happened and I told them and said I would try and do it again. Next day I went up alone and at about 3,000 feet (915 m) started a spiral as before. I went slower and slower until I again went into a spin at about 2,000 feet (600 m) and came out as before. It was probably about two or three turns, but it felt like dozens.

'Afterwards my CO Lieutenant Osmond RN was not at all pleased as there had been some orders from the Admiralty about unnecessary stunts and dangerous flying. The second in command was J.P. Wilson (A "gentleman player" for Yorkshire cricket before the 1914 war, a major in the RAF with a DSC and AFC at its end and the winning rider of Double Chance in the Grand National a few years later).'

No Report

Brookie's feat was not reported to the Admiralty Air Department—probably (he thinks) because at that time Commodore (later Rear-Admiral Sir) Murray Sueter's post of Director of the Air Department was abolished on 1 August 1915 and Rear-Admiral C.L. Vaughan-Lee (who had no experience of flying) was given the new post of Director of Air Services. The vagrant, upstart RNAS was simultaneously ordered by the Board of Admiralty to be an integral part of the Royal Navy and Vaughan-Lee clamped down hard on punctilious observance of strict naval discipline.

But Norman Blackburn says, 'there is, to my mind, no doubt that Brookie was the first man to put an aeroplane into an intentional spin and recover from the situation by using the controls in such a way as he had declared he would do before taking off . . . I feel quite sure that Brookie was the first to "spin" on purpose! Other blokes who would see the first spin would be Elliot, Shanks, Startup and some of the ratings.'

Certainly there is justification for the claim that Squadron Leader J.C. Brooke was the first British pilot deliberately to spin an aeroplane and recover normal flight having first announced his intention to do so. He may well be also the first pilot in the world to have done so, but it is always possible that there might be other claimants. If there are it is hoped that the publication of this article will bring them to light and the writer of the article (who has spent much time on research for its subject matter) will be pleased to learn of any such claims.

We now come to the British official story of the investigation of the spin. We have already seen that volume 1 of the official history of the first war in the air mentions only Dr Lindemann.

Goodden and Lindemann

In an extract from Sir Roy Harrod's personal biography of Lord Cherwell which appeared in the *Sunday Times* for 23 August 1959 is the statement that 'In the early part of the First World War any pilot who got into a spinning nosedive invariably crashed, and was lost together with his aeroplane.' Clearly Brooke's deliberate spin was then unknown at the Royal Aircraft Factory, where Dr Lindemann worked on the staff under Lieutenant-Colonel Mervyn O'Gorman. Many years ago I asked O'Gorman for a list of his staff there with brief biographical comments. Only two were mentioned as concerned with spin investigation. These were Major F.W. Goodden, who was chief test and research pilot at the RAF at the time and part designer with Kenworthy and Folland of the SE 5 (in the prototype of which Goodden was killed), and Dr F.A. Lindemann. In his notes on these two members of his staff O'Gorman wrote of Goodden; 'Not the first to get an aeroplane out of a spin, but joint discoverer with Lindemann of the reasons and method. Spinning in his time was almost always fatal', and of Lindemann, 'Learnt to fly to test spinning calculations. Invented aeroplane accelerometer.'

O'Gorman of course knew about 'Parke's Dive' and that may have been the reason for his qualifications of Goodden's priority in spin recovery.

Glauert's Investigation

In his spare time (according to Sir Roy Harrod) Lindemann converted the aerodynamics of spinning into algebraic formulae from which he decided how a pilot ought to recover normal flight. After reporting this to O'Gorman he asked to be taught to fly in order to put his theories to practical test. After three weeks' instruction (so it is said) he flew solo to a great (but unspecified) height, spun, recovered, went up again and spun in the opposite-handed direction, recovered, then came down and landed. (This is wrong. All his spins were left-handed—Norman Macmillan). It was implied in the extract published in the *Sunday Times* that Lindemann was the first man deliberately to spin. The professor would never have made such a claim, because he must have been well aware that Goodden had made experimental spin tests in 1916 while his (the professor's) spins were made in 1917. What then are the facts?

Reports and Memoranda (R & M) No 618 of June 1919 of the Advisory Committee for Aeronautics published *The Investigation of the Spin of an Aeroplane* by H. Glauert. The reader is referred to this document for its complete report. Here it is possible only to extract the essential features that concern our story.

First it is stated that 'It is believed that the method of coming out of a spin was evolved first by Mr H.G. Hawker on a Sopwith aeroplane, but the manoeuvre was not generally known until Major F.W. Goodden carried out some spins on an FE 8.' This statement in an official document shows that its compiler was not aware of historical facts. I asked Sir Thomas Sopwith about Hawker spinning, but he is unable to add to what we know, that Hawker crashed in a spin outside Brooklands aerodrome. I have been unable to uncover any evidence that Hawker ever deliberately spun until long afterwards when the manoeuvre had become common. The method first evolved in 1912 by the discussion group at Larkhill relied chiefly on rudder movements with elevator up. Brooke evolved independently his recovery procedure at Killingholme in 1915, involving chiefly elevator movements with rudder centralised. Note the difference in method.

Goodden in the FE 8

Goodden reported spin tests made by him at Farnborough on 23 August 1916 in an FE 8 with 100 hp Gnôme Monosoupape engine. He began each spin (thrice to the left, thrice to the right) by applying full rudder and opposite stick. The aeroplane flat turned, engine on. When it was almost stalled he pulled the stick back. This increased the turning speed and started the spin. The right-hand spin began after about 300 degrees of turn, the left after about 540 degrees. To recover he first switched off the engine, next put the stick laterally central and pushed it forward and finally centred the rudder. This resulted in a nosedive, from which having increased speed, he pulled out easily with the stick slightly back. He stated that, when the aeroplane dived, spinning could not continue provided all controls were central. He reported the FE 8 to be perfectly stable and its controllability very great. He could make it spin only by the misuse of the controls described and concluded that the spinning accidents to FE 8s were due to such misuse.

Goodden lost his life at the end of January 1917 when the prototype SE 5 he was flying suffered wing failure and crashed. Hence no doubt, O'Gorman's quandary over air tests of Lindemann's spin theories and the latter's offer to make them himself.

The R & M report continues by stating that the first scientific experiments on the behaviour of an aeroplane in a spin were carried out in 1917 by F.A. Lindemann with a BE 2E aeroplane. Previously little definite information had been available on the behaviour and attitude of an aeroplane in a spin. Goodden had merely reported that the whole aeroplane was turning about a point midway between the right-hand wing tip and the body during a spin to the right. Nor was much known scientifically about the effect of the control surfaces. Analysis of the results obtained by Lindemann gave full information of the path and attitude of the aeroplane and established the continuity of a spin with a normal spiral glide when Lindemann changed from a spin to a spiral and back to a spin in one continuous helix.

Noakes and Hill

Following Lindemann's experiments on the BE 2E and FE 2B aeroplanes much additional information was collected as the result of further research flights by Captain J. Noakes, Captain J.G.S. Candy, Lieutenant R.K. Muir, and Major R.M. Hill (apparently in that order), on aeroplanes which included the Sopwith Camel with 150 hp Bentley 1 and 130 hp Clerget engines, the Vickers FB 14 aeroplane with 150 hp RAF 4A engine, the SE 5A with 200 hp Hispano-Suiza engine, and the Bristol Fighter.

The general conclusion was reached that the best way to bring an aeroplane out of a spin was to push the control column forward and give opposite rudder for an instant then central.

The Accidents Committee of the Advisory Committee for Aeronautics issued the following method in its report: 'The normal method of coming out of a spin is with the control column slightly forward and the other controls neutral. In this position the spin will soon stop, but the nose of the aeroplane must be held down until flying speed is attained, when the stick should be pulled gently back and the aeroplane is flattened out. In case of emergency (ie low height) the spin can be stopped more rapidly by putting the stick forward and reversing the rudder, but in this case a violent manoeuvre is induced and want of skill may lead to the aeroplane dropping back into the reverse spin.' I have myself seen pupils in the First World War drop into a reverse spin on Camels through that very cause.

The Gosport Method

The method of recovery from a spin taught at Smith-Barry's School of Special Flying was stick forward, rudder central. This was obviously based on the Farnborough experiments. But in flying progress is seldom static. Between the two world wars the technique changed. Pupils were then taught that the correct method of recovery was just to apply full opposite rudder and then move the control column forward until the spinning stopped. The controls were then to be centralised and the aeroplane levelled out from the resultant dive by easing the control column gently back. It was specifically enjoined that the control column was not to be moved forward before the rudder was moved because with elevator surface down, the shielding effect of the tail-plane on the rudder became worse. A full forward movement of the control column was seldom needed; to avoid over-steepening the dive with greater loss of height it was to be moved forward just far enough to stop the spin.

Here we return close to the conclusions of the 'Parke's Dive' discussion group and particularly so in the procedure recommended for recovery from stable spins. Because of the time factor in gaining height in relatively slow-climbing aeroplanes, pilots in the original Farnborough experiments began their tests comparatively low, between 3,000 and 4,000 feet (900–1,200 m); it was thus unusual for them to spin for more than about three or four turns before recovering. So it was not discovered until several years after the First World War that some aeroplanes tended to stabilise in spins after completing more than about four turns. When the stable spin condition was discovered test pilots of prototypes were required to spin each new type for not less than eight turns, in order to prove either that a stable spin did not develop or if it did that the aeroplane could be restored from it to normal flight.

In the stable spin the fuselage angle was much less vertical and when in the 'flat spin' (as it was called) the control column was often forced back. Brisker control movements were required to recover and more time had to be allowed for response. Full opposite rudder was maintained after its first application. If the flat spin had not steepened or decelerated after 1,000 feet (300 m) drop, it was recommended that the control column be held back while the aircraft dropped a further 500 feet (150 m) to remove the elevator's shielding effect on the rudder; or conversely, the pilot might simultaneously rock both the elevator column and throttle lever full forward and full back, with a second's pause at each extreme.

The inverted spin was discovered in the First World War. Sometimes it came from stalling when fully inverted or in a half-roll off a loop; it might happen when overcorrecting a Camel's ordinary spin. Correction was by centralising the controls or (if necessary) by opposite rudder and pulling the stick back; the aeroplane recovered into a slightly inverted dive, which demanded a longer time for recovery to normal flight.

Phases in Flight Safety

Thus we see that the 'Parke's Dive' analysts, Hawker's theorising after his spin crash, Brooke's intentional spin, Goodden's tests and Lindemann's experiments were all phases in flying safety progress. Each contributed something. None contributed everything. None remained the ultimate standard practice for recovery. What, then, stands to Lindemann's credit? This—the first really scientific full-scale analysis of the behaviour of an aeroplane when spinning to be made (so far as one can ascertain) anywhere.

Only a few months before Lord Cherwell's death I wrote to him and asked him what precisely it was that he did in his spinning tests. His reply constitutes the best and most authoritative statement of his contribution to the history of spin investigation. He wrote, 'I really cannot remember any details about my spinning experiments, but I think they will all be found in the Proceedings of the Aeronautical Research Committee.

'Briefly, various people had got out of a spin without exactly knowing how or why. Since the rate of turn appeared to be constant, it was clear to me that the lift on both wings must be about equal which could only be the case if the angle of incidence on the one wing was above the maximum lift angle and the other one below. What I did was to take appropriate measurements so that this could be checked quantitatively.'

In the R & M 618 mentioned above, the statement is made that the earliest experimental results available were those obtained by Dr Lindemann in 1917, on BE 2e and FE 2b aeroplanes. The data he obtained were:

1. rate of turn
2. rate of height drop
3. radius of turn, by means of the camera obscura
4. indicated airspeed
5. resultant force, by means of an accelerometer (Lindemann invented for the purpose)
6. readings of longitudinal and lateral levels

Dr Lindemann's spins were all made to the left with full rudder. Owing to the high angle of incidence of the wings in a spin the ordinary airspeed indicator installation met the relative wind at a considerable angle of pitch and little value could be attached to the readings. A pressure head was therefore fitted pointing approximately along the direction of the relative wind during the spin. In analysing the data obtained by Lindemann to determine the nature of the motion of the cg of the aeroplane in a spin the forces on the fin, rudder and tailplane were neglected and it was assumed (in accordance with the readings of the lateral level) that there was no side-slip. The observed radius of turn and rate of height drop were considered the least satisfactory observations, owing to aneroid lag and the difficulty of correlating the camera obscura record with the aeroplane's height.

Spin Characteristics

The analysis revealed the characteristics of a spin to be as follows:

1. The path was a steep helix with a radius of 10–20 feet (3–6 m).
2. The central portions of the wings were above the critical angle, and incidence along the span of the wings varied rapidly, possibly as much as 1 degree in 1 foot (30 cm).
3. The speed of the aeroplane was roughly equal to its rate of fall, and in the case of the aeroplanes tested was usually between 55 and 70 mph (85–110 kph). Since the angle was above the stalling angle the drag was very large; the greater part of the weight was supported by the drag, while the lift was used to turn the aeroplane in its path.
4. The resultant force on the aeroplane from gravity and rotation was roughly equal to 2 g.

In the BE 2E the angle of dive was from 52 to 72 degrees, the angle of incidence from 15 to 37 degrees, and the radius of turn from 18 to 40 feet (5.5–12 m). The same characteristics in the FE 2B were respectively 80, 78 and 35 degrees and 8 feet (2.8 m).

The general result of the analysis showed that a spin was merely a spiral dive with a large angle of incidence on the wings, above the stalling angle, with a resultant very large drag. During later experiments, following Dr Lindemann's, with other types of aeroplanes, the phenomenon of the elevator control locking back on a spin was observed, indicating (as mentioned above) that at that time the flat spin was encountered but the R & M 618 does not make specific mention of the stable or flat spin; at that time it had not been recognised as the special form of spin it is.

The 1917 Period

The actual date or dates of Dr Lindemann's spin tests is not given in the R & M, but if we take the date line of Goodden's death and add the time Lindemann took to learn to fly, it is unlikely that these tests took place before the end of February 1917, perhaps rather later. At that time the writer of this article was stationed at the Central Flying School at Upavon. He remained there until 19 March 1917. He well remembers seeing four crashes, only one from a spin. The second in command was killed in a downwind stalled turn in a Vickers Bullet; a pupil was killed in a Sopwith 1½-Strutter when he overstressed the machine in a dive, pull-out and zoom and the tail came off; a flight commander crashed when taking off in an Avro with crossed aileron controls. The writer contracted a spin in a Gnôme-engined Avro 504 over 'Death Valley', but came out again, largely owing to the stability of the 504, for he had never been taught to spin or recover from one. He recalls seeing Major E. Leslie Foot MC fly over Upavon aerodrome and demonstrate spinning in (he believes) a Sopwith Pup in the campaign of visits that were arranged to different flying schools to show that spinning was a safe manoeuvre and not a death trap. That must have been about contemporaneous with Lindemann's tests and most probably was a consequence of the earlier empirical tests made by Goodden.

To sum up, the sequence in the history of spinning (in Britain certainly) would appear to be:

1. 25 August 1912 Parke made the first recovery from an involuntary spin.
2. May and June 1914 Pickles and Hawker failed to recover from involuntary spins.
3. July or August (or October–November?) 1915 Brooke successfully recovered from an involuntary spin, ascended on the following day, deliberately spun once and recovered.
4. 23 August 1916 Goodden made six spins (three left, three right) while testing an FE 8 for its spinning proclivities.
5. Late in (probably) first quarter of 1917 Lindemann made specific spin characteristic tests (all left hand) on BE 2e and FE 2b aeroplanes.

Thereafter several Royal Aircraft Factory test pilots test spun a variety of aeroplanes.

Gosport perhaps excepted, flying training schools in England did not teach spinning in the first quarter of 1917, but that was the period of their awakening. From August 1917 Smith-Barry's School of Special Flying taught pilots selected to be instructors how to spin so that they could teach pupils how to do so and recover safely. The spin appears to have been first used intentionally in combat (as far as can be ascertained) early in 1917, usually as a ruse to feign disablement in order to escape. Compulsory spinning of prototype aircraft by manufacturers' test pilots before acceptance by RAF military test pilots began about 1925. The stable or flat spin was tracked down to reality between the wars; some failures to recover from it introduced the aircraft anti-spin tail parachute for assured recovery, in order to avoid the loss of the aircraft even if the pilot could otherwise survive by use of his personal parachute.

Recovery Styles

During the course of spin history the recommended method of recovery was changed more than once. This memoir should establish clearly the part played by Lord Cherwell when he was Dr Lindemann and in what sense his spin tests were original scientifically but not empirically. The certainty of recovery from a normal spin was established and the method was known before he made his first spin. It is remarkable how closely analogous were the distinctive methods evolved by the 'Parke Dive' discussion group of 1912 with those recommended in the RAF Training Manuals shortly before the Second World War.

All the tests so far described involved only landplanes. But several years after the First World War in some RAF flying accidents Fairey IIID float-planes crashed into the sea. It was thought the cause might be pilot's loss of control in a spin begun too low for recovery to be possible. But no one knew how much height was necessary for a float-plane to recover because float-planes had never been spun intentionally nor had one spun accidentally with survivors able to do what Parke did in describing what happened. Float-plane spinners died. So it had always been the rule that float-planes should not be spun intentionally because of the potentially dangerous nature of the extensive forward side area of their main floats and the dispersed load distribution inherent in their flotation undercarriage, especially marked in the IIID five-float system.

After the float-plane crashes into the sea the manufacturer was asked by the Air Ministry to provide information of the minimum height necessary to recover from a spin in the IIID. This could not be obtained by theorising or by mathematics; even modern mathematical computers or analogues could have supplied no answer. Perhaps today radar-controlled robot pilotage might provide the clue. But in those days full-scale empirical tests by a human pilot were the sole sources of the knowledge then required in the interests of aircrew safety. The writer made these tests at Hamble, Hants, on 15 March 1926, at different cg loadings. They were the first (and so far as is known only) British spin tests on float-planes. The large forward side area of the main floats and the flywheel effect of all five floats during spin rotation made recovery response very sluggish even with full opposite application of the powerful rudder and rocking of the elevator. It was established that the absolute minimum height required to recover level flight from even a quickly and fully corrected spin was 1,500 feet (460 m). This almost certainly confirmed the suspected cause of the accidents because of the much lower height whereat float-planes usually flew over water. The knowledge gained was disseminated and the subsequent history of the IIID proved that it successfully prevented other accidents from occurring. On these tests the pilot flew solo and wore a parachute. All the First World War spin tests were made without personal parachute protection against failure to recover, which adds to the gallantry of those who made the tests that others might live. **"**

Norman Macmillan: More History

After that article in *Aeronautics* Wing Commander Macmillan did not rest on his laurels. Fourteen months later a further article appeared in *Aeronautics*.

"My original research into the history of the spin, first published in *Aeronautics* for July 1960 aroused worldwide aviation circles interest. A considerable correspondence resulted. In December 1960 a second article by the same author epitomised some of this correspondence and brought to light further information. In that issue also appeared the evidence of Sir Roy Harrod, the unofficial biographer of the late Lord Cherwell, in support of his claim that Cherwell, when Dr F.A. Lindemann, first spun in a BE 2c aeroplane on an unspecified date in June or July 1916.

There has been a long-cherished belief in some quarters, not excluding the official history of the First War in the air, that Lindemann was the first man to spin deliberately. Others have claimed that Major F.W. Goodden, chief test pilot at the Royal Aircraft Factory, was the first, the date given in the R & M being 23 August 1916. Sir Roy Harrod would antedate Goodden by Lindemann who, he says, deliberately spun after about three weeks of clandestine tuition, which would have been given by ignoring regulations against scientists and engineers being taught to fly. Are we really to believe this?

Even if the Lindemann spins in 1916 could be accepted (their improbability being hereafter examined) they would not give Lindemann priority as first to spin intentionally, knowing or believing he could recover from the spin. Several British pilots deliberately spun before mid-1916. If, as the present writer believes, Lindemann did not spin until mid-1917, he was far behind in what had by then become an accepted manoeuvre, widely practised. His place in the history of spinning can then be only that he gave the spin—as the spin was then known—a completely analysed description derived from piloted experiments and mathematical exposition; but afterwards his theory had to be much modified and amplified.

Theory before Practice

It is important to observe from all his accounts that Lindemann constructed his theory first and made his empirical flight tests to confirm his theory. He himself has stated that he evolved the theory from watching aeroplanes spin. Whose aeroplanes? Was he, a physicist at the Royal Aircraft Factory, so much out and about that he actually witnessed several spins? Or did he see others spin at Farnborough deliberately and then formulate his theory? If he first spun in June or July 1916 why did another whole year pass before he ever spun again? And why was it that the first paper on spinning in which his name appears as one of three co-authors was not published as an R & M until March 1918? If he had already spun in June or July 1916, why was it, having completed his licit flying training before mid-November 1916, that he did not initiate his empirical spinning tests in flight until June 1917?

The whole case for Lindemann having spun in June or July 1916 rests on old-age memory. Sir Roy Harrod places implicit faith in a letter dated when its writer Mervyn O'Gorman was seventy-eight years of age. But I am assured by a life-long friend of O'Gorman's that in his later years O'Gorman's memory was unreliable (as is the case of so many men). Lord Cherwell who, earlier, had a reputation of having a wonderful memory, about two months before his death, wrote 'I really cannot remember any details about my spinning experiments . . .'

In *Aeronautics* for December 1960 I referred to recollections written by O'Gorman after the First World War to assist the preparation of the official history. These included post-war additions to a paper about spinning which he had sent to the War Office in 1915 with no mention of Lindemann. But when O'Gorman appended to his recollections 'typescript paper post-war notes' about spinning experiments made by Lindemann these afterwards could be misinterpreted as meaning that those experiments occurred before O'Gorman left the Royal Aircraft Factory. If, in 1949, O'Gorman referred to his post-First-World-War-thus-added notes, they readily could lead him into mnemonic error (see extracts at end of this article.)

That no note was made at the time of the alleged spins in 1916 by Lindemann himself (on the grounds—according to protagonists—that he was secretive), O'Gorman, or any member of the staff of the Royal Aircraft Factory, is beyond understanding. If Lindemann had only flown three weeks as a pilot and was being watched in flight by both superintendent and his assistant (as is suggested) is it not most strange that even the mechanics who handled the aeroplane were so disinterested in this queer behaviour that none of them ever breathed a word about it? Were they sworn to secrecy? How did O'Gorman, Smith and Lindemann prevent all other pilots, observers and scientists from seeing this unusual flight, either from the ground or the air?

There are other anomalies. In his own reminiscences of Farnborough, written for the fifty years anniversary of the Establishment, Lord Cherwell wrote: 'I am glad of this opportunity to correct some of the absurdly dramatic stories which have appeared about this [spinning] investigation.'

Lindemann's Denial

What can this mean if it does not mean his own refutation of the tale of his 'sublime courage' in going up after only three weeks' flying training and spinning first one way then climbing up and spinning the other way in June or July 1916? There is no other 'absurdly dramatic' story about his spinning that I have ever heard of. All other records of his spinning are purely factual records of his theoretical and 1917 flying work on spinning. Surely this is his own categorical denial of the romantic story of the spinning professor of 1916, strangely enough the only one known to Lord Hailsham, who writes that he was ignorant of the 1917 series of constructive experiments.

But in the same reminiscences Lord Cherwell also stated that 'In 1916 many pilots were killed flying our recently designed RE 8s by spinning into the ground . . . Anyone watching a spinning 'plane could see that the rate of turn did not increase on the way down. I concluded therefore that the lift on both wings must be equal . . . This being so, if the speed were increased the aeroplane would no longer spin. Experiments proved that this idea was correct and the whole theory was worked out quantitatively and described in a paper by Glauert and myself, published by the Aeronautical Research Committee in (March) 1918. Thereafter the pilots were taught to push the stick forward—the very opposite of the instinctive reaction of pulling it back in order to get the nose up—and to straighten out the rudder and then pull out of the dive in the ordinary way.'

That statement can be analysed by those who flew in the 1914–1918 War.

First the prototype RE 8 had a woefully small fin and rudder area, which gave scant correction in yawing moments. The fin was afterwards much enlarged, following which the spinning propensities of the RE 8 were much reduced, but never eliminated. The first RE 8 built at the Royal Aircraft Factory bore the number 7996. The records show that Goodden as pilot flew it with Lindemann as observer on 1, 4 and 25 July 1916 on climb and speed tests. Lindemann again flew in this machine twice on 7 September 1916 on climb and stability tests, with Tait Cox as pilot. The professor did not fly in that or another RE 8 during the remainder of 1916.

If it was the spinning of the RE 8 which directed the close attention of those at Farnborough to the question of spinning in 1916, why is it alleged that the professor with 'sublime courage' went up in a BE 2c to make two spins in June or July 1916? The BE 2c, as I know from personal experience, which is corroborated by Sir Vernon Brown, was absolutely stable and came out of a spin if one merely shut off the engine and took hands and feet off the controls. If there were to be 'sublime courage' surely the RE 8 was the mount for its display?

Secondly, it appears from Lindemann's reminiscences that the student of the 1914–1918 War in the air, who was not there, would be led to believe that it was not until after the publication of the Glauert, Lindemann (and Harris) paper in March 1918 that pilots began to correct for spins by pushing the stick forward and centralising the rudder.

The Crucial Question

Now we have seen that the prototype RE 8 was flying at Farnborough with Lindemann as observer to the Factory's chief test pilot on three days in one of the months when it is alleged he with 'sublime courage' made his spins in a BE 2c. If he had found the answer to spinning and his purpose was to save the lives of pilots less scientifically minded than himself, why did he not spin an RE 8, or ask Goodden to do it with himself on board as observer, so that he could observe the phenomenon in the aeroplane then most afflicted by it? None has suggested he did either. Moreover, we have seen that the RE 8 was improved against spinning by fitting a larger fin. Central rudder and forward elevator were not good enough antidotes to spinning on the prototype RE 8 and its early successors in production. And in the 1930s the Royal Air Force Flying Training Manual discussed the varieties of spins and stressed that opposite rudder was the first proper corrective action, to be followed by moving the centralised stick forward only far enough to regain flying speed without stalling in order to prevent too much loss of height. I believe this was first discovered in the Camel, whose fore-and-aft instability rendered excessive use of forward elevator in spin correction dangerous because of the risk of entering an inverted spin (or dive) from a normal spin. This must be compared with the Lindemann theory that speed (hence the forward elevator and central rudder) was the corrective answer to spinning.

In any event, pilots were correcting spins long before the publication of the Glauert, Lindemann, Harris paper of March 1918. In *Aeronautics* for December 1960 I described Edgar Percival's first involuntary spin. His next was in a Nieuport 17 Scout of No 60 Squadron on a lone escort of a BE 2c on artillery observation over the river Scarpe, in the early months of 1917. Sighting two enemy aircraft he tried to climb through a heavy cloud layer to superior height. After climbing through about 1,500 feet (475 m) of cloud his Baby Nicup flicked over. It spun fast, fairly whistling round. After several turns Edgar applied the corrective action he had discovered in his involuntary spin at Port Meadow, Oxford, in an Avro 504. The Nicup stopped spinning, then spun again in the reverse direction. Edgar waited until he came below cloud when he quickly stopped the second spin. He had self-learnt the art of spin and recovery. He spun voluntarily many times thereafter with No 60 Squadron, a stint concluding with his invaliding out of France at the end of May 1917, before Lindemann had begun his spinning experiments over Farnborough.

My own experience was not dissimilar. Like Edgar Percival I was never taught to spin by an instructor, but I saw Leslie Foot fly over Upavon aerodrome early in 1917 and spin down to demonstrate that spinning was not fatal. He landed and told us to centralise controls and ease the stick slightly forward of neutral. Other skilled pilots did the same at other airfields at that time. It was the only spin instruction there was, because the training squadron instructors never spun. I was never spun, looped, rolled, half-rolled off the top of a loop by anyone but myself. I went to the Gosport School of Special Flying in March 1918. There I suppose I ought to have been so taught, but when less than halfway through my course I was ordered to fly an unarmed Camel to Hounslow to have it fitted with guns and then go to France. Not until 'Mary' Cunningham stunted me in a two-seater Snipe at CFS in 1921 did anyone ever demonstrate all he could do with an aeroplane in which I flew. I had long since learnt it all for myself.

Thereafter spinning became increasingly common and it was widely practised and used by pilots in front-line squadrons during the first half of 1917, before the series of spinning tests by Dr F.A. Lindemann began at Farnborough. His flight tests are given in Table 2.

Table 1
List of pilots known to have made early intentional spins.

1.	Between 27 April and 24 November 1914
	Geoffrey de Havilland in a BE type aircraft from Farnborough
2.	Between August and October 1915
	J.C. Brooke in a Sopwith two-seater 'Spinning Jenny', Killingholme
3.	September to December 1915
	Vernon Brown in a Vickers 'Gunbus', Martinsyde Scout and BE 2c No III, Upavon (It is not known whether Brooke or Brown was the first of these two to spin intentionally.)
4. ⎫	
5. ⎬	September to December 1915
6. ⎭	Kennedy, Cochran, Patrick, 'Nobby' Clark, Balcombe Brown, BE 2; order of precedence unknown, Upavon
7.	4 and/or 5 July 1916
	F.T. Courtney, FE 8, Farnborough
8.	22 August 1916
	F.W. Goodden, FE 8, Farnborough
9.	About August 1916
	Unknown French pilot, Nieuport 17, Issy-les-Moulineaux
10.	About August 1916
	C. Draper, Nieuport 17, France
11.	September 1916
	K.K. Artzeulor, Nieuport 17, Sebastopol
12.	Latter part 1916
	C.T.R. Hill, DH 2, France

It has sometimes been suggested that Mons Chanteloup and Chevillard spun at pre-1914 War flying meetings during their stunt performances. C.G. Grey referred to Chanteloup's as a 'tourbillon dive'. But the answer is that these French pilots did not spin. Sir Philip Joubert told the writer recently that a number of pilots including himself performed a 'spiral nosedive' before the war of 1914. He said that during a turn they pulled the stick back and applied top rudder (that is opposite to the rudder direction required for spinning), thus descending in a tight spiral, which, with the light wing loading of those days, had a very small radius. There appears to be no doubt that this was the tourbillon dive flashed at public exhibitions by Chanteloup and Chevillard. It is essential to add this footnote in order to confirm the priority of the above list.

A 1917 Experience

My first involuntary spin was over 'Death Valley' near Upavon on 23 January 1917 in a No 435 Gnôme Avro 504. I came out by centralising controls and shutting off the engine. My next involuntary spins were in a Nieuport 12 two-seater in France. On 24 April 1917 I tried to climb through the clouds while on patrol over the Ypres sector. I entered cloud at 1,600 feet (500 m). At 2,000 feet (600 m) I began to spin, corrected successfully when I came below cloud. Two days later I spun three times in another Nieuport 12 through stalling on turns when trying to follow my climbing flight commander through thick clouds. Each time I came down out of the clouds spinning and each time recovered successfully. On 4 May 1917 at the end of another patrol I spiralled, spun and nosedived voluntarily from 6,500 feet (2,000 m) and spinning thereafter never had any terrors for me.

Percival and I (and others like us) were lucky. Many embryo pilots died in spins they could not correct. But by mid-1917 pupils at flying training schools were being taught how to spin and recover by instructors who had returned from overseas and had there learnt the trick in the same way as Percival and myself. Before Lindemann began his series of experiments in June 1917 to measure the speed, rate of turn, incidence and side-slip in spinning BE 2c and FE 2b aeroplanes at Farnborough, we were all spinning regularly in France in all sorts of aeroplanes. It is nonsense to write that, after the publication of the March 1918 R & M pilots were taught how to recover from a spin by the Lindemann method. One cannot help believing that Lindemann had seen voluntary spins before he began his mid-1917 series of tests and from observing other pilots' voluntary spins had evolved his theory. And that his series of tests in flight had for their chief object the empirical confirmation of his theory, a matter which ordinarily delights every scientist, many of whom display little concern over the ultimate use which is made of their work because they live in a world of their own. Whether true or untrue, the picture drawn, of Lindemann supposedly being amused that his fellow scientists at Farnborough knew nothing of his alleged spins in June and July 1916 and nursing his knowledge with secretive delight, indicates him to have been of that pattern of scientist.

Major Chris Draper, writing a letter to The Aeroplane (p 730, 28 November 1952) told how he and Reggie Marix, when on their way across France to join No 3 Wing RNAS saw a French ace (un-named) deliberately spin a Nieuport 17 Scout at Issy-les-Moulineaux about August 1916. Reaching Villacoublay, Draper borrowed a Nicup from the French and after some experiments, spun, eased the stick forward and came out. Marix did the same, but he spun in and lost a leg.

Air Vice-Marshal S.F. Vincent wrote to The Aeroplane (21 November 1952, p 702) that he first saw a deliberate spin in the latter part of 1916 when G.T.R. Hide flew in a DH 2 of No 29 Squadron to show his discovery to his brother, Roderic Hill, a Lieutenant in No 60 Squadron. Then No 60 Squadron pilots themselves began to spin.

A more recent letter in The Aeroplane of 3 March 1961 from R.G. Jackson states that Tait Cox (who, as reported by me above, piloted Lindemann in an RE 8 in September 1916) claimed that the recovery from a spin was worked out aerodynamically by Lindemann. The latter continues: 'After a time he got a pilot to carry out his theory, centralise controls and apply slight opposite rudder. I think he must have been a brave man because he tried it out on none other than an

FE 8 pusher. He started at 4,000 feet (1,220 m) and was successful. Date 1917.'

If this letter is a correct account of Tait Cox's recollection of the matter, his memory was wrong in certain particulars. Lindemann advocated centralised rudder and forward stick. The date of the FE 8 spinning was 1916 not 1917. What is important here is:

1.   that the first aerodynamic theory of spinning was that formulated after Parke's recovery from a spin on 25 August 1912
2.   that Tait Cox apparently believed that Lindemann found a pilot—not himself—to make the FE 8 experiment

This indicates that Lindemann was not then a pilot. The story that he spun a BE 2c in June or July 1916 is based on certain assumptions. First, that he was taught to fly by a pilot at Farnborough. Sir Roy Harrod in *Aeronautics* for December 1960 quoted certain dates when, according to the *Farnborough Flight Log Book* Lindemann was an observer flying mostly with Lieutenant W. Laidler (but twice with Mr James) mostly in BE 2c 2029 (but twice in FE 2b 6360) with all flights entered as 'climb'. Sir Roy Harrod suggested that during these flights, totalling eight and three-quarter hours, Lindemann was taught to fly (19–26 May 1916); and that this was the instruction which preceded the 1916 spins said to have been made in June or July 1916 by Lindemann.

But Sir Roy Harrod has brought forward no evidence to show that there were any dual-control aeroplanes at Farnborough at that time which would enable such instruction to be given.

No Dual Control

I have been unable to find any evidence that dual-control aeroplanes were at Farnborough then. One scientist, who was there at that time, says that none of the aeroplanes in which Lindemann and the other scientists flew in 1916 at Farnborough had dual controls. He and others had asked O'Gorman to provide dual-control aeroplanes, but O'Gorman refused. Another writes that he is practically certain that none of the 'Chudleigh' crowd—Farren, Taylor, Lindemann—flew solo before going to CFS.

It is useless to suggest that flights entered as 'climbs' were really flights to teach Lindemann to fly unless it can be proved that the aeroplanes involved (whose numbers are given above) had dual controls.

The available evidence is against their having been so equipped. One cannot just assume for the purposes of a story that they were so equipped. Proof is essential. So far it is not forthcoming. If Lieutenant W. Laidler is alive he could answer this question unequivocally. If he or anyone who knows of him should read this paragraph I hope they will communicate with me.

Courtney's Experience

Frank T. Courtney was a test pilot at Farnborough from March to September 1916. He has informed me: 'I can state categorically that Lindemann did not do any spinning tests, or any other (piloted) tests, in that time . . .

'The first authentically recorded and witnessed performance of what was later known as a 'spin' was the famous Parke's Dive . . . As a student pilot I was much impressed by this event . . . because of Parke's decision, when all normal action failed, to reverse all normal action and so save himself; it seemed to me to be a great thing to remember, and I read all accounts I could find of the affair.

'In the summer of 1916 I was given a series of tests to do on the SE 4a which had full-span ailerons which could also be pulled down as flaps. As you can imagine, this aeroplane did the damnedest things at slow speed with all the ailerons pulled down, and it kept me too busy keeping out of trouble to allow any unscheduled research. Soon after I was assigned to tests of the FE 8 which . . . had full-span ailerons, but without the flap gear. In the course of some slow-speed flying, I was trying out something which I never remembered, when the machine suddenly flicked into a spin. I did probably a couple of turns during which normal control action did me no good and immediately I remembered Parke's Dive. I reversed the controls and promptly came out straight. This was utterly wonderful!

'So I climbed up higher and, after some fiddling with the controls at low speed, I got into another spin, and as easily came out. I repeated this a couple of times and then landed. I already had some reputation as an aerobatic pilot, and I found great excitement among those who had seen this from the ground who wanted to know "what I had found out this time". Amongst these was Frank Goodden, who was our chief pilot. He took me into the office and we discussed the matter; I was not quite clear how I got into the spin, but was quite sure how I came out. So, of course, Goodden had to go up and try it himself, which he did with complete success.

'I then tried it on the FE 2d, because I had associated the start of the spin with the full-span ailerons, and their drag, on the FE 8. I got the FE 2d into a spin and out again without difficulty. So it wasn't the ailerons, and I then found that all I had to do was to stall, kick on hard rudder and off she went.

'Meanwhile Goodden was instructed to put in a full report on this spin business, which he did . . . The report was signed by Goodden and I was for some time very upset that my part in the business was not mentioned; later, however, I figured that it was Goodden's job as chief pilot to report a technical flying matter as he had tested it, and there was no real call for him to report what I had done in an accidental and unscheduled effort.'

Now, here is just the sequence of events around which the Lindemann legend (of his alleged 1916 spin) could arise. Courtney would have had to obtain permission to try the spin on the FE 2d. O'Gorman would no doubt watch him. There is only one letter to distinguish the FE 2 from the BE 2: memory over the two could easily miscarry. Courtney preceded Goodden (as

Lindemann was alleged to have done). The circumstances are too alike not to arouse comment on their similarity. It is improbable that two such sets of circumstances could have arisen simultaneously. For Courtney, accidentally substitute the name Lindemann, and everything about the legend becomes as clear as crystal. The suppression of Courtney's name by Goodden made it possible for those who had heard some version of the story to give the credit to the man who was working out the theory of spinning at the time. It explains in a rational way why, if Lindemann did spin in June and July 1916 he never spun again until June 1917. The explanation is that it was Courtney, not Lindemann, who preceded Goodden.

I checked Courtney's flight dates from the *Farnborough Flight Log Book*. His own log books were lost, some after he was shot down by Immelmann on Trafalgar Day 1915 when piloting a Morane Parasol, others later. Incidentally I saw him shot down when I was an infantryman. Both Courtney and his observer were wounded. Here are his Farnborough recorded flights apposite to his spins:

> SE 4 No 3—29 June, 1 and 3 July
> FE 8 No 7456—4 July (twice), 5 July
> FE 2c No 6370—7 and 8 July
> FE 2b No 6360—14 July
> FE 2c No 6370—18 July
> FE 2b No 4256—19 July
> FE 2b No 6360—20, 21, 22, 26, 28 July

In his letter he referred to the FE 2d, but it is clear he has written *d* for *b* or *c*, a simple slip after all these years. The dates correspond to those of the Lindemann legend. In the absence of positive proof that Dr Lindemann was taught to fly at Farnborough in a dual-control aeroplane (which scientists who were there then either say did not exist at that time or cannot recall having known of) one must conclude that here is a case of mistaken identity.

To support the dateline great importance has been attributed to the professor's alleged 1916 spins having occurred shortly before O'Gorman left the Royal Aircraft Factory at the beginning of August 1916. But that is precisely when Courtney's spins were made. Courtney writes, 'Take it as about 500 per cent certain that Lindemann wasn't even remotely connected with any such tests and probably, at that time, hadn't done a solo flight.'

Scientists as pilots

We are not here concerned with the reasons for O'Gorman leaving Farnborough, but similar reasons lay behind the setting up of the first Air Board under Lord Curzon of Kidleston. The formation of this Board was announced on 17 May 1916. The Board assembled for the first time on 22 May. It was only after the formation of this Board that Farnborough scientists and engineers

The world's first successful pilot, Otto Lilienthal, flying his monoplane glider. Albeit with a few errors, he worked out the theory of flight. He was also the first pilot to spin in. On 9 August 1896 his luck ran out, and he was fatally injured. *(National Air and Space Museum, Smithsonian Institution)*

Wilbur Wright flying the 1902 glider. It was with this glider that the Wright brothers finally solved the problem of three axis aerodynamic control of flight, demonstrating at the same time Wilbur's adage that if you 'fly slowly and stay close to the ground when you are trying to find out how it is done you will not come to much harm'. They spun into the ground twice, once each, but suffered no injury. *(National Air and Space Museum, Smithsonian Institution)*

Avro Enclosed Biplane. The aircraft that Lt Wilfred Parke was flying when he made his 'Dive', the first successful recovery from a spin. *(Fleet Air Arm Museum)*

Sir Geoffrey de Havilland sitting in a BE3 (50 hp Gnôme) 1912. *(Aeroplane Monthly)*

Harry Hawker, pioneer Australian pilot, who spun deliberately in a Sopwith Tabloid in June 1914. *(Mrs Patricia Blackmore)*

The Sopwith Scout – 'Tabloid'. This is a 1916 aircraft but similar to the one Hawker was flying in 1914 when he did his spins. *(Fleet Air Arm Museum)*

Sir Geoffrey de Havilland sitting in a BE2c (70 hp Renault). The fin, the rear engine cowling and front cockpit cowling have been removed. This was the aircraft known as 'The Spinning Jenny'. *(Aeroplane Monthly)*

Major F. W. Goodden, the Royal Aircraft Factory Chief Test Pilot at Farnborough in 1916. He was killed in a crash of an SE5 aircraft on 28 January 1917. *(Crown copyright)*

The FE (Fighter Experimental) 8 prototype, (Gnôme). It had no fin and a rather long nose and was prone to spin. *(Aeroplane Monthly)*

Leslie Irvin. Designer of the Irvin Parachute which has saved so many airmen's lives. *(Aeroplane Monthly)*

The Armstrong Whitworth Ape. With a name like that it was asking for trouble! It was a variable configuration experimental biplane. The whole empennage, elevators and rudder, was hinged to the top of the fuselage. This was the cause of the aircraft's crash, as 'tailplane up' incidence, wound on from the cockpit during stalling tests, could not be reversed rapidly enough to aid recovery from an unexpected spin. *(Philip Jarrett)*

The Gloster Gamecock. A natural spinner. *(Fleet Air Arm Museum)*

The Bristol Bulldog. Early Marks were OK, but later Marks 'gave a little bother'. *(Fleet Air Arm Museum)*

Miss Margot Gore (Commandant Women's Ferry Pool, A.T.A. Hamble.). On one occasion she spun deliberately to avoid hitting a building. *(Aeroplane Monthly)*

The North American Harvard II. Literally tens of thousands of pupils were safely taught spinning and spin recovery in this magnificent aeroplane. Its predecessor, the Harvard I, had to be taken out of service after a number of fatalities caused by its unreliable spin recovery. *(Author's collection)*

Self standing beside Fairey Barracuda II in 1943, the aircraft in which I inadvertently spun. *(Author's collection)*

The Fairey Barracuda II in the landing configuration suffered from a surfeit of drag, which although was a help when deck landing, proved to be a disadvantage if the pilot found it necessary to go round again. *(Author's collection)*

were given permission to learn to fly, 'thanks I like to think,' wrote Lindemann, 'to a somewhat journalistically phrased application concocted by myself.' Clearly that Board would have weightier matters than that to take priority on its earlier agendas.

'With George Thomson, William Farren and Keith Lucas I went to the Central Flying School in 1916,' wrote Lindemann. But Sir William Farren (as he is now) says Thomson went later. When did they go? Lindemann's flying as an observer at Farnborough in 1916 is fairly consistent until 16 August; from that date until 9 November he made only the two flights in the RE 8 with Tait Cox on 7 September. Thus we may assume that the flying course took place between mid-August and early November 1916. They flew Maurice Farman Shorthorns and Longhorns at Netheravon, BE 2cs and Avro 504s at Upavon. Lindemann went as a civilian, Farren and Lucas as commissioned officers. Lieutenant Keith Lucas was killed in a collision at Upavon on 5 October 1916. All three were there then. One of their associates at Farnborough has written to me: 'I am quite certain none of them flew solo before their course there, and the stories put about re "The Prof" flying while O'G turned a blind eye are all nonsense.'

If Lindemann had already spun a BE 2c at Farnborough before going on his flying course, he would have created a sensation by spinning when a pupil at Upavon. Such an occurrence could not have been missed. There is no record of it. His first recorded spin appears in the *Farnborough Flight Log Book* on 12 June 1917 when Mr H.L. Stevens flew with him as observer. Mr Stevens has told me that he is quite certain that Lindemann flew solo and spun within a few days preceding his going up with the professor. It would be a rational proceeding to spin solo before taking passengers. It was not recorded as 'spinning', so the date cannot be fixed with precision, but it was almost certainly in June 1917.

Thereafter the professor made his series of spinning tests in flight to confirm his theory of spinning. These are shown in tabular form (Table 2).

Table 2

Spinning test flights by Dr F.A. Lindemann at Farnborough in 1917

1917	Aircraft	Time	Observer	Weather	Wind
12 June	BE 2e 2029	1930–05	Mr Stevens	Gusty	
5 July	BE 2e 2029	1820–30	Capt Renwick	Gusty	NE
7 July	BE 2e 2029	1145–40	"	Gusty	NE
10 July	FE 2e 4256	1915–40	"	Gusty	NE
12 July	BE 2c 1688	1215–25	"	Hazy	SW
17 July	FE 2b 4927	1145–45	"	Hazy	SW
27 July	BE 2c 1688	1640–30	"	Gusty	SW
28 July	BE 2c 1688	1025–35	Mr Jenner	Calm	SW
5 August	BE 2c 1688	1455–55	Capt Renwick	Cloudy	N
18 August	BE 2c 1688	1605–35	Mr Thompson	Gusty	SW
21 August	BE 2c 1688	1855–30	"	Fair	SW

The above flights (Table 2) are the complete list of flights by Dr Lindemann which appear in the *Farnborough Flight Log Book* with the specific entry that they were spinning tests. It is, however, possible that a flight on 13 June lasting for forty minutes with Mr Stevens as observer and described as a diving test might have included spins. It is also possible that Dr Lindemann may have spun while flying solo on gyro tests on BE 2c 2029 for fifty-five minutes on 6 June and thirty minutes on 11 June 1917; and possible when making a compass test for thirty minutes in FE 2e 4256 on 11 June 1917.

Sir William Farren summed them up succinctly in his biographical memorial notice to Lord Cherwell in the *Biographical Memoirs of Fellows of the Royal Society*, volume 4 p 54 as follows: 'Lindemann's experiments on spinning were made in June and July 1917 on BE 2e and FE 2b aircraft. It is impossible to say how much flying experience he had by then, and I never asked him. But from my own log book it appears that I had then done about eighty hours' flying on half a dozen different aircraft. I had greater opportunity to fly than Lindemann had, and more interest in flying for its own sake, so it is probable that he had not done more than about fifty hours. His courage in undertaking systematic spinning, involving continuous spins of anything up to a dozen turns, has been widely recognised, but to anyone who has flown it is, to say the least of it, astonishing that he should have undertaken such an arduous and difficult, not to say dangerous task, after so little experience as a pilot.'

It would be invidious to compare what Lindemann did with the infinitely more dangerous flying undertaken by the younger and even less experienced pilots who joined squadrons at the front at that time. The two tasks are quite different, demanding a different temperament, outlook and training for their fulfilment.

The First to Spin

We are left with one question. Who was the first pilot to spin intentionally, knowing he could recover? In *Aeronautics* for July 1960 I put forward the name of Squadron Leader J.C. Brooke. In December 1960 this had to be coupled with that of Air Commodore Sir Arthur Vernon Brown. Which of these two spun first cannot be judged, for neither has produced evidence of the exact day, but both spun intentionally in the autumn of 1915.

I have since discovered that Sir Geoffrey de Havilland had previously spun intentionally knowing he could recover. He was mounted in a BE 2 possibly (but not certainly), a BE 2c. According to a paragraph in *Flight*, which provided the material for an entry in *The Historical Summary of the Royal Aircraft Establishment 1878–1918*, G. de Havilland and Norman Spratt looped a BE aircraft at Farnborough on 27 April 1914. It was not on that date, but later that Geoffrey de Havilland intentionally spun the BE. Unfortunately he has no extant record of the precise date. No record of that spin is recorded in the *Farnborough Flight Log Book*. It is thus possible only to say that Geoffrey de Havilland's first intentional spin occurred between 27 April and 24 November 1914, for the second of these dates was the last day Geoffrey de Havilland flew at the Factory. Thereafter he was at the Aircraft Manufacturing Co Ltd for the duration of the war, flying Airco-built DH aircraft of his own design.

These dates establish Sir Geoffrey de Havilland as the first British pilot to have spun intentionally knowing he could recover; and until any earlier claim is discovered and verified it stands as both the British and world record for the earliest known deliberate spin.

Finally, it can be stated with assurance that all the early intentional spins were started from flat turns in the belief that aileron drag played an important part in the phenomenon. But, as a flat turn approaches the stalled condition, the stick must be brought further back, when the real conditions for spinning—a stall with stick back and rudder applied—were produced. From this it was not difficult to deduce that reversal of the elevator and rudder controls would check an incipient spin or stop one that had been started and many hundreds of British pilots were spinning regularly as a normal manoeuvre months before Dr Lindemann's experiments in mid-1917 began.

Near the beginning of this article I referred to Lieutenant-Colonel Mervyn O'Gorman's recollections. They contain two significant paragraphs and one footnote, as follows: 'Latterly [1916] the discovery has been made by Mr Lindermann [original spelling—N.M.], that spinning is an evolution which all aeroplanes may perform, that the rate of rotation during a spin is the chief difference between one spin and another, and that the ease with which a pilot can get out of a spin is partly physiological and is in some measure determined by the degree of longitudinal stability, which the aeroplane possesses. None of these things were suspected in July 1914.'

'Not only was the firing of bullets through the disc of the airscrew an untried idea, but also single-seater tractor "scouts" of the time were unstable so that the pilot could not be called upon effectively to aim a gun to the side of his cockpit without risking his precarious control of the aeroplane and endangering his balance with the chance of falling into a spin.'

'Footnote. The occurrence of a spin was equivalent to a crash. [Not always, see actual history above and in previous articles—N.M.]. When Mr Lindermann analysed the movements of a spin, made instrumental observations during a spin voluntarily started in the air, he by great personal courage gave aeronautics a new military manoeuvre.' [As we have seen this last clause is quite incorrect, because others preceded him by many months and even years—N.M.]

These two paragraphs and the footnote are misleading. The first paragraph refers to a 'discovery' by Lindemann in 1916. Taken in conjunction with Lindemann's own written statement, 'In 1916 . . . anyone *watching* [my italics, N.M.] a spinning 'plane could see . . . I concluded therefore . . .', it appears that this 1916–dated statement by O'Gorman refers to Lindemann's initial theoretical interest in spinning and his theoretical deductions from terra firma observations of spinning aeroplanes.

The footnote includes no date, but the reference to 'instrumental observations during a spin' clearly dates the references as of 1917, for it was not until then that Lindemann modified his instruments to read correctly during the conditions of a spin.

It is, however, unfortunate that a cursory reference to the first-quoted paragraph of this paper and the quoted footnote might readily induce any unwary reader to assume that the year of the 'instrumental observations during a spin' was the same year (1916) as the 'discovery . . . made by Mr Lindermann'. Here, I believe, lies the root of the hitherto flourishing, but factually un-supported, story that Dr Lindemann spun as a pilot in mid-1916. I have given the matter a vast amount of research and I would be only too happy to confirm the story if I could, but I have been unable to discover anywhere a single shred of factual evidence to show that Dr Lindemann ever flew solo before he pro-ceeded to Netheravon and Upavon for flying instruction in the autumn of 1916 or that he spun an aeroplane (or spun in one) before mid-1917.**

Norman Macmillan: *Aerospin* Postscript

Six months later, twenty months after his first article on spinning, Wing Commander Norman Macmillan wrote his final words on the subject in another article in *Aeronautics*, March 1962. During this period he received much correspondence on the subject from many countries so that it is fair to say that the history of the spin must now be well beyond doubt, except that he appears not to have heard of Hawker's deliberate spin in 1914.

**It was perhaps inevitable that my full investigation into the history of the spin published in the September 1961 issue of *Aeronautics* should have brought some further correspondence on this subject.

A correspondent drew attention to an extract from *Flying* by Gustav Hamel and Charles C. Turner, published in 1914 by Longmans, Green and Company. On pages 191–195 of this book the joint authors describe what the correspondent thought might have been a deliberate and controlled spin performed by Garros, Hamel, Gilbert, Chevilland (who are all named by the authors) in mid-1912. The manoeuvre they made is fully described and the description might well lead some to believe it was a spin. But it was not. It was a controlled spiral.

The authors call it a 'corkscrew descent' or a 'spiral descent'. Nowhere in their description do they give it the name by which the spin was contempora-neously known, that is, the 'spiral nosedive'. It was the manoeuvre which I had already mentioned as having been well known before the 1914 War began, when it was practised by military as well as civilian pilots. I spoke with Air Marshal Sir Philip Joubert about it and he confirmed this and said it was not a spin and that pilots did not then spin, but performed only this tight spiral, in which aircraft were always under control and not in a state of autorotation.

The extract is too long to quote here and he who is interested must refer to it in the original book. There he will read that to begin this manoeuvre the nose of the aeroplane was first pushed down by the controls and so will realise that the aeroplane was never stalled. Since the stall is the prerequisite of the spin it is obvious from the description that a spin could not result from the control movements described by Hamel and Turner. Moreover the turning circle they mention, twice the machine's length, is much greater than that in the spin quantitatively measured at Farnborough by Professor Lindemann in his experiments in June and July 1917 and recorded in the resulting R & M.

I have been quite unable to find any pre-1914 War pilot who saw a controlled spin deliberately made by any stunt pilot of those days. Sir Geoffrey de Havilland saw Adolphe Pégoud stunt, but he does not recall that he ever spun and is sure he did not. Contemporary descriptions of his stunts do not include the spin. Yet Pégoud was the star stunt pilot of his time.

The spin in those days meant a complete and unaccountable loss of control and resulted in a crash. That was why 'Parke's Dive', in the course of the Military Aeroplane Trials at Larkhill, so impressed those who saw it, because he was the first pilot ever to recover from an accidental spin.

If the manoeuvre described by Hamel and Turner as relatively common in mid-1912 really had been a spin it is quite incredible that Hawker should have crashed in a spin in June 1914, ignorant of how to recover from a predicament in which a faulty loop had placed him. [Page 27]

Quite definitely the manoeuvre described by Hamel and Turner was never the autorotation of a spin, but just (for those days) a clever nosedown spiral.

Mr E. Meos, a correspondent in Estonia, USSR wrote to me that it has been found recently in Russia that Ensign K.K. Artzeulor was not (as previously believed) the first Russian pilot to make a deliberate spin and recover. He states that Lieutenant-Commander V.V. Dybovski of the Imperial Navy deliberately spun at Ivangorod, Poland, in 1915. He gives no more precision to the date than the year, nor does he mention any witnesses or the type of aircraft. While not disputing the possibility that this may be correct it is equally impossible to substantiate it without further information for which I have written but which has not so far been given.

Dybovski had designed an aeroplane and was the inventor of the synchronised gun-gear bought by the Admiralty and perfected by Warrant Officer Scarff, when it became known as the Scarff-Dybovski gun-gear. It was fitted to some of the early Sopwith 1½-strutters used by the RNAS, some of which were transferred to 70 Squadron RFC and flew to France for the Battle of the Somme in 1916. Dybovski became Air Attaché in England from 1915 to 1917 and continued to live here after the revolution in 1917.

Mr Meos also wrote: 'The French write that A. Pégoud in 1913 performed the premeditated spin in France, also Charles Nungesser in August 1915 at Nancy for which he was arrested for fifteen days. Gerhard Fiesler writes that the first premeditated spin in Germany was performed in early 1916.'

Deliberate spinning by German pilots first in 1916 coincides with my own information, but I have found it impossible to discover who it was among German pilots who first (and where exactly and when) deliberately spun. But it is certain he did so long after British pilots had done so.

I have referred to Pégoud above. I have been unable to find any historical reference to Pégoud having spun. If he had done so it would (with such a contemporaneously famous pilot) have been reported. But where is such a report? Legends grow and are given credence. But legends are not facts. Until some proof is presented I discard the story that Pégoud spun before the First World War. I believe he performed the corkscrew descent or controlled spiral and that his having done this has been the source of the legend that he deliberately put his aircraft out of control and into an autorotative spin. The Blériot monoplanes he flew were under-ruddered and their rudder was shrouded by the elevator in the conditions of a spin. None of the records shows the Blériot monoplane among aeroplanes in which early spins were spun by intention and from which recovery was made.

Mr Meos's story of Nungesser's spinning does not accord with recorded detail. In August 1915 Nungesser was given eight days' arrest, but the offence was that of being absent when on duty; but during that absence he brought down an Albatros biplane near Nancy, for which he was awarded the Croix de Guerre. It was in November 1915 that Nungesser was given eight days' simple arrest (our equivalent of confined to camp) for aerobatting at a low altitude. The 'low altitude' I think definitely rules out spinning from that performance in a Nieuport. I have no information that Nungesser spun at that date and it was not until 1916 that I have found positive information of French Scout pilots spinning.

In *War in the Air*, volume V by H.A. Jones, pages 429–434, appears an account of the origins of the Gosport School of Special Flying which, founded by Smith-Barry, became the source of organised flying instruction in the RAF and in all the air forces of the world and in civilian flying schools, too. After the First World War Trenchard reverted the name to that of Central Flying School, but the CFS system of flying instruction was initially and essentially that of Gosport. By the change in name Smith-Barry never received the full credit which was his due and the only British decoration he ever had was the Air Force Cross, the most richly earned AFC of all time.

Jones wrote that the appearance of the 100 hp Mono-Avro in the autumn of 1916 was appropriate to Smith-Barry's ideas. 'It was also of help that the problem of spinning had been solved. Up to the autumn of 1916 not many pilots who had the misfortune to get into a spin in the air had ever regained control. One exception with Major J. A. Chamier who, while in France, found himself spinning as he came from a cloud. While he was falling he recalled [the] incident on Salisbury Plain before the war when Lieutenant W. Parke RN had recovered from a spin near the ground. When people had crowded round to congratulate Parke on his luck, he had explained that he had stopped spinning by doing "everything wrong". Major Chamier likewise did the opposite of what his experience as a pilot suggested and he also recovered. He subsequently related his adventure at Royal Flying Corps headquarters. Whether any spinning experiments were made as a result there is no record.'

This rather suggests that Chamier was one of the first to recover from a spin, but it does not give a date clearly. I therefore wrote to (now) Air Commodore

Sir Adrian Chamier for details. He informed me that the incident occurred in September 1916, but as it was not an intentional spin it does not affect the list of pilots known to have made early intentional spins, [see page 60], wherein it will be seen to be about collateral with Artzeulov's intentional spin at Sebastopol in a Nieuport 17 and that Artzeulov was eleventh in that list. Chamier's aeroplane was a BE 2c and the observer was either Cotton or Minchin: the squadron was No 34, with Chamier in command. Returning from a reconnaissance, he found a cloud bank over the lines, too low to fly under ('we liked to have several thousand feet in those days over the front-line trenches') and too extended to fly round or over because of fuel shortage. Chamier flew into the cloud with care, could not see his wing tips. Speed rose until the needle jammed against its stop. He thought, 'This is a stable machine' and let go the controls. When he came below the clouds low down he saw the ground rotating like a roulette wheel. He had seen Parke's Dive and after Parke landed heard his explanation of how he had recovered from his spinning nose-dive. Chamier acted accordingly and flared out about 300 feet above the enemy front line, from which he was heavily fired on. A French 75 battery opened fire on the enemy lines to make them keep their heads down and they aided Chamier. The French shells burst so close to the BE 2c that Chamier thought he was being fired at by an enemy field battery. He landed behind our lines and was ordered to report to RFC headquarters. He taught his squadron pilots how to recover from a spin.

About the same time New Zealand Captain R. Balcombe-Brown, who was in No 1 Squadron, flew to 60 Squadron then commanded by Major R.R. Smith-Barry and said he knew how to spin and recover. S-B laughed and said, 'A true spin is an act of God.' But he tried Brown's recipe, spun, recovered: so did several other 60 Squadron pilots.

About the same time Lindemann at Farnborough began the theoretical study of spinning which culminated in his spin tests in flight in July and August 1917.

Those who have read in *Aeronautics* my previous articles on spinning will appreciate how inadequately the official history of the 1914–1918 War in the air dealt with this subject, which has only now been fully analysed for the first time.

Since the publication in *Aeronautics* for September 1961 of my documented article on spinning history I have heard from the RAE that R & M 411 published in March 1918 was in fact compiled from four 1917 ARC reports (971, Experimental investigation of spinning, July 1917; ARC T 97a, note on ARCT 971, August 1917; ARC T 971b, note on the stresses on BE 2e wings during spinning, August 1917; and ARCT T 988, Mathematical investigation of spinning, August 1917).

Further support for my dating of the spin as a manoeuvre in air combat prior to Lindemann's experiments in flight is to be found in Glauert's statements in R & M 618 of June 1919 (originally RAE report BA 317, May 1919): 'About this period [August 1916] . . . the spin became a recognised manoeuvre in air fighting', and 'The first scientific experiments on the behaviour of an aeroplane in a spin were carried out in the following year by Dr F.A. Lindemann with a

BE 2e aeroplane.'

Smith-Barry commanded 60 Squadron in France from 3 July 1916 to 24 December 1916, when he came home to command No 1 Reserve Squadron at Gosport. Then Smith-Barry came into his own. He knew then that the spin was not an act of God, but a manoeuvre whose mystery was revealed by under-standing. He developed his method of teaching pilotage by the full explanation of each and every control movement and its corresponding reaction. He was first in this field and received full encouragement and a free hand from Major-General J.M. (now Marshal of the Royal Air Force Sir John) Salmond, commanding the RFC Training Division, who recommended that Smith-Barry's squadron be developed as a school of special flying. Nos 27 and 55 Training Squadrons were added to No 1 Reserve Squadron at Gosport, thus making Smith-Barry's establishment equal to that of the newly created depot stations and in August 1917 was born the Gosport School of Special Flying (the Adam of efficient flying instruction throughout the world) where the previously dreaded spin was just another thing.

C. Draper: The Flat Spin

That should have been the end of it, but a letter to *Aeronautics* from Major C. Draper kept the blaze going a little longer.

"'Spins and Things' by Frank Courtney, in the November number of *Aeronautics* I have studied closely.

Three main points arise from the article: First, the reference to the 'flat spin'. I do not know what is meant by this. In all these years I have never witnessed two distinct types of spin nor ever experienced them myself.

Second, each machine I have spun takes up its own particular angle.

My third point concerns what Frank Courtney writes when he witnessed what happened at the time I spun into the ground at Hendon in March 1920 (not 1921). He writes that after a number of normal turns in the spin 'the aircraft almost suddenly flattened out but kept on spinning.' This is most interesting.

As is well known I had deliberately gone into this spin in the usual way, and after a few turns had fainted. What then actually happened to the controls I do not know for I did not 'come to' for eight days. (This is also the first time I have been told the propeller had stopped.) Other pilots, including Graham White's chief test pilot who also saw the accident, never mentioned this, but a change in the angle of the spin could perhaps have occurred by some move-ment of the controls at the time of the faint.

The first spin I ever saw was performed by a Frenchman at Issy-les-Moulineaux, Paris, in the summer of 1916. Neither Reggie Marix, who was with me at the time, nor myself had the slightest idea how it was done, but the same day I borrowed a Nieuport and found out.**"**

Wing Commander Macmillan was prompt in his reply.

"And a last word.

While not entering into controversy concerning Chris Draper's crash in a spin in the Bantam at Hendon, which I did not witness, it may be wise, in this ultimate word in *Aeronautics* to say that there is a condition of spin which is referred to as 'flat'. But the term 'flat' does not mean that the fuselage is horizontal, simply that the angles of attack of both wings are much greater than in the normal spin and the fuselage nearer the horizontal.

The terms 'steep spin' and 'flat spin' have been used in RAF Flying Training Manuals freely purchasable through HMSO.

If one takes a piece of string with a weight tied to one end and swings it slowly in a circle from the opposite end the angle of the string to the vertical will be small. If the string is swung faster the weight will rise under the influence of centrifugal force and the angle of the string to the vertical will be greater. This is precisely the difference between the steep and the flat spin. When a spin is prolonged the distributed weight in the aeroplane (particularly when the cg is too far aft) acts like the weight on the string. In the resulting spin the angle of attack may reach 60 degrees. In this condition the rudder and fin are shielded and recovery is more difficult.

Not all types of aircraft will develop the flat spin. It is associated with weight distribution, cg position and overall design. For example, the Fairey Fox of 1925 could not be kept in a steep spin for more than three turns because the stick load became too heavy. In the second half of the 1920s the Air Ministry required as a condition of acceptance of military aircraft prototypes of all but the larger categories that the manufacturers' test pilots had first spun the aircraft for not less than eight turns. This condition was laid down that it might be demonstrated at the risk of the manufacturer and his pilot that the aircraft was not prone after three or four autorotations to flatten the spin to a degree which made it too sluggish (or at the worst resistant) in recovery movements.

Every test pilot who carried out such spin tests knows only too well the risk he ran of recovery failure when making repetitive tests with repeated rearward extensions of the cg position produced by artificial loading until one more shift aft of the cg would have meant certain loss of recovery control.

The characteristics of the steep spin are a steep flying attitude with a wide spiral of spin, slow axial rotation and a rapid loss of height. Those of the flat spin are a relatively flat flying attitude with fast axial rotation, a narrow spiral and a gradual loss of height.

Sir Geoffrey de Havilland considers that his survival from his spin crash in the BS 1 of 1913 was due to its flat characteristic saving him from a nose-in finale. It does appear from what Courtney and Draper say, that the latter's survival in the Bantam crash was due to the same phenomenon. But those who have experienced it have no love for the treacherous flat spin which can develop sequentially from the normal steep spin when the requisite conditions are present.**"**

Norman Macmillan: Letter from Estonia

That would have been the last word from Norman Macmillan. However he eventually received a belated reply to his letter to Mr Meos in Estonia. As a result, he wrote one further contribution to *Aeronautics* in 1962.

"Mr Meos informed me he had received the following information from Moscow air historians: Lieutenant-Commander V.V. Dybovski was an ordinary (ie service) pilot in the air squadron of the fortress of Ivangorod in Poland. According to an air general (who lived in Moscow and was an eye witness) Dybovski deliberately spun in a Morane G (which Russian pilots called 'the 14-metre Morane') over the Ivangorod fortress in July 1915. The general does not remember the day in July when Dybovski did this, but Dybovski departed for England on 15 July 1915, so the spin must have been performed during the first fortnight in July. No written records or mentions in reports or orders exist to confirm this sole eye witness's memory, but this is (unfortunately) the usual difficulty encountered by air historians investigating that period of air history. One must, therefore, assume that Dybovski intentionally spun and recovered in the first half of July 1915.

Soviet air historians in Moscow are doubtful of the spin hitherto credited to Ensign K.K. Artzeulov. Records show that he arrived at the Sebastapol Flying School from the front only on the day before he has been credited with having deliberately spun a Nieuport. They have discovered that he had never flown Nieuports before. Nor have they discovered any school records of this spin; in October–December 1916, there are records of Artzeulov looping, but none of spinning. The first intentional spin recorded in the orders of the school is dated 27 February 1917 and names Lieutenant Biatov as the performer on that day. The Central House of Aviation in Moscow had planned to celebrate last autumn the forty-fifth anniversary of Artzeulov's previously accepted spin, but subsequently changed its mind and K.K. Artzeulov (a nephew of the famous Russian painter Aivazovski) was not so honoured.

In consequence of this information the list which I gave in *Aeronautics*, September 1961, page 75 should be amended as follows:

List of pilots known to have made early intentional spins		
1	Between 27 April and 24 November 1914	Geoffrey de Havilland in a BE-type aircraft from Farnborough
2	During first fortnight of July 1915	V.V. Dybovski in a Morane G at Ivangorod, Poland, air station of the Imperial Air Service
3	Between August and October 1915	J.C. Brooke in a Sopwith two-seater Spinning Jenny, Killingholme RNAS
4	September–December 1915	Vernon Brown in a Vickers Gunbus Martinsyde Scout and BE 2c No 111, Upavon RFC

It is impossible on the available evidence to say whether Brooke or Brown was the first of these two to spin intentionally, since neither is able to provide the exact dates within the period when he first spun.

5		
6	September–December 1915	Kennedy, Cochran, Patrick, 'Nobby' Clark, B. Balcombe Brown BE 2c; order of precedence unknown:
7		Upavon RFC
8	4 and/or 5 July 1916	F.T. Courtney, FE 8, Farnborough
9	22 August 1916	F.W. Goodden, FE 8, Farnborough

The R & M gives the date 23 August 1916, but this is probably an error in transcription, as there is no record of Goodden flying an FE 8 on 23 August. The date 22 August, when he flew FE 8 7456 for 40 minutes has therefore been adopted here.

10	About August 1916	Unknown French pilot; Nieuport 17, Issy-les-Moulineaux
11	About August 1916	C. Draper, Nieuport 17, France RNAS
12	About September 1916	J.A. Chamier, BE 2c, 34 Squadron RFC
13	Latter part of 1916	C.T.R. Hill, DH 2, 29 Squadron; R.R. Smith-Barry; Nieuport 17, 60 Squadron RFC France; and many other RFC pilots

It became a more common manoeuvre from this time on in squadrons serving in France, but was still untaught in flying training schools in Britain.**"**

Part 2

Spinning in the Twenties and Thirties

Richard T. Riding: In a Flat Spin

After 1918 the Royal Aircraft Factory at Farnborough became the Royal Aircraft Establishment and continued to carry out research and testing of all things aeronautical. Perhaps surprisingly spinning was still high on the list of things to be investigated. The Royal Flying Corps had been united with the Royal Naval Air Service and together they became the Royal Air Force, which was now a permanent arm of the fighting forces. Commercial flying was also about to begin. The following account of one of these experiments was gleaned from *Aeroplane Monthly*. 'Plane crazy', written by Richard T. Riding, October 1992.

"In December 1921 the Royal Aircraft Establishment, the RAE, carried out an experiment to ascertain whether, if an aeroplane got itself into an uncontrollable spin, a pilot might save himself by means of a parachute. Thus it was that a time-expired Sopwith Camel was hitched to a kite-balloon. In place of the engine a slab of concrete of the same weight was installed and the controls were lashed with the stick hard back and to the side to induce a spin. A dead bomb, simulating the pilot, was attached to a parachute and a time fuze was set to release the bomb and thus pull the 'chute out seconds after the Camel was released from the balloon. The kite-balloon cable was attached to a winch on a 7-ton lorry. In order to keep the vehicle well out of the danger area the cable was led through a fairlead on a smaller lorry about 300 yards away. The scene was now set.

The balloon hoisted the Camel up to 1,000 feet and released it. Soon afterwards it entered a slow, stately spin and out came the bomb, followed by the parachute. So far so good. The bomb, being streamlined, got well away, towing the 'chute at a rate of knots – so fast, in fact, that the 'chute Roman-candled, failing to open properly, and the bomb hit the ground with a resounding thud.

Meanwhile the Camel continued its stately spiral to earth, hitting terra firma ever so gently on its nose and one wingtip. Although the wings and undercarriage were slightly damaged a real pilot would certainly have survived, had he managed to prevent his face from hitting the instrument panel. Thus it proved, if one can trust the circumstantial evidence, that the safest thing to do in a spinning aeroplane is to sit with it.

But the story does not end there. While the spectators and investigators were watching the parachute and the spinning Camel an earsplitting crash from behind diverted attention to another spectacle. Relieved of the weight of the Camel, the kite-balloon shot upwards, yanked the smaller lorry off the ground and slid it by means of its own fairlead down the cable until it smashed into the 7-tonner.

What with the wrecked Camel, two smashed lorries and a parachute that failed to open, and the subsequent moral collision between the leading parachute experts, no doubt other spectators saw the funny side of the incident.**"**

Alec Lumsden: Gloster Gamecock

As time passed and the building and testing of aircraft ceased to be haphazard, regular test programmes were devised. These usually included spinning. Some observations on the spinning characteristics of the Gloster Gamecock, designed by H.P. Folland, which first flew in 1925 make interesting reading. This article, written by Alec Lumsden, is from *Aeroplane Monthly*, June 1991.

"Although its top speed of 150 mph at sea level when powered by a Jupiter IV hardly equalled that of the Grebe II, the Gamecock soon established itself, like its predecessor, as a very agile little fighter indeed. Its very agility became the cause for concern among squadron pilots because of a persistent tendency to wing-flutter. As on the Grebe, the upper wing, which had an overhang of nearly 3 feet, permitted too great an elasticity. The controls were also very light and sensitive and an unwary pilot who allowed flutter to develop could lose a wing. Another, unwelcome, similarity was its ferocious spin, which was timed at fifty revolutions per minute (no less than 300 degrees a second) and could become stabilised and flat when made to the right. The very short fuselage, tail blanketing and engine torque accentuated the reluctance to come out of a spin. The rudder of the production aeroplane was distinguished from the prototype by its horn-balance and the upper fin by its low-aspect-ratio curved shape.**"**

Originally from an RAE report comes the following alarming description of tests on flat spinning by a Gamecock.

"To make a convincing demonstration it was decided to use a Gamecock, a single-seater fighter, which although popular in the Royal Air Force had a reputation for spinning fast and flat. Apart from its reputation, it had all the features which were known to lead to flat spins: a short fat, round body . . . and a badly shielded fin and rudder . . . It seemed necessary to establish that it really had a dangerous spin. The aeroplane was accordingly loaded to what was thought to be its safest condition and provided with a few recording instruments. The pilot for this flight was Flight Lieutenant C.E. Maitland and responsibility for the experiment lay mainly with S.B. Gates. Gates went out to the tarmac and watched Maitland climb to 15,000 feet with instructions to do a few turns of a spin then recover.

The spin started, and Gates watched from the tarmac with increasing anxiety as the number of turns mounted; after no fewer than 40 turns the spin suddenly stopped. A few minutes later Maitland taxied in and gave a terse description of what must have been a most harrowing experience. After a turn or two the Gamecock had 'flicked' into a very fast and flat spin which had made him giddy and confused. He had immediately reversed the controls for recovery but this made no difference. The spin continued unabated (subsequent analysis showed a rotational speed of more than 50 rpm) and he had tried all the artifices he could think of—bursts of engine, rocking the controls and so forth—without success. Eventually he had chanced to look down at his feet and was amazed to discover that he was holding the aeroplane into the spin with the rudder. He had then reversed the rudder and the aeroplane slowly stopped spinning. So beyond establishing that the Gamecock spun unpleasantly fast, the experiment proved nothing. Maitland at once volunteered to repeat it.

After adding an instrument to record the rudder angle, spectators again repaired to the tarmac to watch another spin. This time Maitland completed thirty-four turns—the last twenty-five of them against his will. The instruments showed that there had been no mistake with the rudder this time and all were satisfied that they had a thoroughly dangerous spin to correct. For this courageous and useful test Flight Lieutenant Maitland was accorded the Air Force Cross.**

Gates continued to investigate spinning and in 1926 wrote a paper 'The Spinning of Aeroplanes' by S.B. Gates and L.W. Bryant, *RAE Report* of 1926. (Ed.)

Richard Dennis: Armstrong Whitworth Ape

One experimental aircraft which got itself into a mess was the Armstrong Whitworth Ape. This aeroplane had a variable incidence tailplane of an unusual type. The whole empennage was mounted on a hinge in the rear fuselage on the upper side. The angle of the tailplane was controlled by moving the whole after end of the aircraft, and could be controlled from the cockpit. Following is an extract from an article in *Aeroplane Monthly*, January 1994 by Richard Dennis.

**On 23 May 1929 Flight Lieutenant D.W.F. Bonham-Carter and Mr Stuart Scott-Hall had to make an emergency escape from an Armstrong Whitworth Ape "variable configuration experimental biplane" which stalled then spun into the ground at Cove Farnborough. It was a fortunate escape for both pilot and scientist, as they later went on to have distinguished careers in British aviation.

The special research aircraft was probably a good idea, enabling the effect of major changes in configuration to be investigated in a series of flights. But RAE legend has it that it was also the cause of the aircraft's downfall, as "tailplane up" incidence wound on during stalling tests, could not be reversed rapidly enough to aid recovery from an unexpected spin.**

Alec Lumsden: Bristol Bulldog

The Bristol Bulldog, which was tested in 1927, proved much less troublesome. The Mark I went into spins and came out quite easily. Here is a report reproduced from *Aeroplane Monthly*, August 1991.

"The Bulldog prototype performed well enough to be sent in June 1927 to Martlesham Heath in Suffolk (at that time the home of the Aeroplane and Armament Experimental Establishment). It appeared at the Royal Air Force Pageant at Hendon the following month. Initially, the spinning characteristics of the prototype Bulldog were unsatisfactory and tended to flatten but, in an A & AEE report dated 26 October 1927, following the preliminary tests, a larger fin and rudder had been fitted and the aircraft was spun with more satisfactory results. Loading, centre of gravity and power unit were all unchanged, but the tail-plane and elevator, fin and rudder volume coefficients had been increased slightly.

The pilot reported that the aircraft was put into a series of spins. At first, a left-hand spin was made with the tail adjustment fully forward. The aircraft was stalled and full left rudder applied with the control column right back and to the left. The aircraft was difficult to put into a left-hand spin and the rudder had to be applied just at the correct moment. The spin was fast with a jerky motion for the first two or three turns, after which it settled down to a steady spin with the nose well down. After nine turns the rudder was centralised and the stick put forward. The aircraft came out immediately.

The next spin was made with the tail adjustment 'half-back', the stick and rudder applied as on the previous occasion. The Bulldog did eight turns, after which the rudder was centralised, the control column put forward and the aircraft came out as before. The tail adjustment was next put in the 'right-back' position and the aircraft put into a spin. With the tail adjustment set like this, the spin was a little more flat. After eight turns the rudder was centralised and the stick pushed forward. After about three quarters of a turn the aircraft came out comfortably.

The first spin to the right was with the tail adjustment in the fully forward position. The aircraft spun much more easily to the right and a trifle faster. To start, the Bulldog was stalled, and full-right rudder applied with the control column hard back and to the right-hand side. The first two or three turns produced a noticeable jerk, after which the aircraft settled down to an even spin. On centralising the controls the aircraft came out of the spin almost immediately. The aircraft was next spun with the tail adjustment in the 'half-back' position. This spin was as before and, on centralising the controls, it came out after one half-turn. The last spin was with the tail adjustment in the 'full-back' position. This time, it was in a much flatter attitude than the others and not quite so fast. After nine turns the rudder was centralised and the control column pushed forward. After one turn the aircraft came out in quite a normal dive. There was no uncomfortable feeling in any of the spins and the Bulldog prototype came out of each quite easily.

The Martlesham pilot concluded that, with the larger fin and rudder and the cg on the aft limit, the aircraft was satisfactory in spins to the left or right, recovery being easy and comfortable. The report therefore recommended that the larger fin and rudder be standardised. However the larger area resulted in cross-wind taxi-ing problems and it was decided instead to lengthen the fuselage and retain the smaller rudder. This together with other modifications resulted in the Type 105A Bulldog II.

An order for a prototype was placed in November 1927. The aircraft was flown on 21 January 1928 as J9480 and was bought by the Air Ministry on 21 August for extended trials at Martlesham, becoming the winner of specification No F 9/26. It was ordered into production to spec 17/28 and the first was delivered on 8 May 1929. Spinning problems persisted, however, there being a right and a wrong way to stop a Bulldog spinning without considerable loss of height; these were covered by several further A & AEE reports. In this connection it should be noted that the Bulldog II and the improved Mk IIA had a relatively heavy exhaust collector ring whereas the Mk I did not. This and later versions of the Bulldog, some of which were also fitted with Townend cowling rings, acquired greater vertical area which reduced the problems associated with spinning the aeroplane. Wheel brakes, fitted later, balanced the weathercock effect of the larger tail."

The Bulldog Mk II however had problems of its own. The modifications to the exhaust system together with modifications to the undercarriage made the aircraft heavier. There were also alterations to the ailerons, wings and rudder, and by 1933 further spinning tests were needed. This extract is also from *Aeroplane Monthly*, August 1991.

"Early in 1933, further spinning tests were carried out in a Bulldog IIA with a partially mass-balanced rudder with the results little different, if at all, from the standard aircraft. Later in the year Martlesham put K2188 through trials with mass-balanced rudder and ailerons. These trials included spinning, diving and aerobatic handling tests and were made in comparison with the standard rudder and ailerons. It was found that there was no perceptible change in the spinning characteristics of the Bulldog as the result of mass-balancing the rudder and ailerons. The rudder was quite satisfactory in all diving and aerobatic tests. There was, however, a sluggishness of the lateral control which became more noticeable when the ailerons were mass-balanced.

Diving tests to the limiting crankshaft speed of 1,980 rpm were made with the engine on and off. That limitation did not allow the terminal velocity to be reached, the maximum speed achievable being at full throttle, 245 mph being reached at 10,000 feet from a dive started at 14,000 feet and recovery completed at 8,500 feet."

The Bulldog exemplified the painstaking elimination of problems by the A & AEE. Even by the 1930s, the dynamics of the spin were imperfectly understood and trial and error was very much the order of the day.

Richard P. Hallion: From Test Pilots

Of course others besides the British were having problems. In America there were many accidents due to spins. This next extract comes from *Test Pilots* by Richard P. Hallion, published by the Smithsonian Institution, Washington DC.

"An appalling number of prototypes crashed in the 1920s and 1930s as a result of losing their wings in dives or simply developing uncontrollable spins. As a result, companies, the NACA and the military devoted increasing amounts of time to studying load criteria for dive pullouts, and studying the phenomenon of aircraft spinning, first scientifically examined by Lindemann during the First World War. (The changes in aircraft design since the days of Lindemann demanded upgrading and re-examination of spin criteria—as is true today, in the era of the multi-Mach jet.)

The Army undertook a study of spinning at Wright Field, using specially instrumented test aircraft (and as a result of his piloting these hazardous test missions, project pilot H.A. Sutton received a well-earned DFC). So did the NACA, using a variety of aeroplanes equipped with modified control surfaces and various methods of varying the craft's inertias, characteristics and centre-of-gravity location, as well as an emergency 'spin-'chute' attached to the craft's vertical fin, which the pilot could deploy to break out of a spin and into a spiral from which a dive recovery could be effected. The intensive nature of these research programmes can be measured by a single statistic: during one year of testing NACA pilot McAvoy estimated that he had spun a grand total of over 300 miles vertically. As a result of his work, however, the mechanism of spin onset and the loads developed during spins and dives were much better under-stood, in time for these lessons to be incorporated in the generation of aircraft with which America went to war in 1941.**"**

And so it went on. In 1935 the first of Grumman's XF3 F-1 prototypes had disintegrated in the air following a nine g test dive recovery. This account also comes from *Test Pilots*

"In early 1935 Grumman sent the second XF3 F-1 to Anacostia for tests with company pilot Lee Gehlbach. On 17 May 1935, during a requisite Navy ten-turn right-hand spin demonstration, the plane entered a stable flat spin, and despite Gehlbach's best efforts, he could not recover. He baled out safely, reporting that the XF3 F-1 was directionally unstable. With two down Grumman built a third, modifying it by adding a short ventral fin to increase the effective vertical tail-surface area. The third XF3 F-1 passed its trials without incident, piloted by Lee Gehlbach and NACA's Bill McAvoy, the latter a natural choice because of his expertise in both dive and spin testing. Because of the loss of the second prototype, the Navy's Bureau of Aeronautics issued strict guide-lines that no manned spinning trials be undertaken in new naval aircraft until the designs had successfully passed tests in the NACA's newly created spin-research tunnel at the Langley Laboratory. This effective partnership of ground testing with flight verification aloft went a long way towards preventing the kinds of accidents that plagued the development of new military aircraft in the early 1930s. The third XF3 F-1 paved the way for a batch of production F3F fighters, which served with the fleet from 1937 until stricken from active service in 1943, when they had long been relegated to advanced training duties.**"**

Philip Wills: From On Being a Bird

The ten-turn spin appeared to have become the standard test. Unpowered gliders were also tested on their ability to spin and recover. The following account by Philip Wills from his book On Being a Bird explains how a parachute and a silver cigarette case saved his life when he found himself in a spin from which attempts at recovery had proved fruitless.

"In 1937 the Germans held the first International Gliding Championship ever organised. The venue was their famous soaring centre on the Wasserkuppe, in the Rhön mountains.

We decided to enter a team and, as it happened, Slingsby was at the time building at his works a new high-performance sailplane, named the 'King Kite', designed by Mungo Buxton, who had also designed my Hjordis. The Slingsby firm very sportingly decided to take the risk and complete three of these aircraft for us to take to Germany.

I say 'risk' because, in the normal way, a new design is usually built as a single prototype, which is thus exhaustively tested and modified until one is quite sure she is right; and not until then does quantity production start. There was no time for this in this case, but Hjordis, designed and built by the same people, had proved immediately successful, so everyone, including myself, had considerable confidence in the new type.

The first machine was finished in April, and I went north for her test flying, which took place from York aerodrome. She proved beautiful to look at and to handle, and everyone congratulated everyone else on her success. A month went by, and in Coronation week I again went north for her final trials, the last item of which was to be her test for spinning.

Even today, when the causes of spinning and the design requirements for successful recovery from a spin are fairly well known, every machine has to be taken to a great height and stalled and spun deliberately before the designer can be quite certain that it is satisfactory in this respect. But I had never heard of a glider spinning viciously, in fact my own Hjordis refused to spin at all, and the King Kite had behaved so beautifully on all her trials so far that any idea of trouble never entered my head.

I was strapped into the cockpit and the celluloid cover was put over my head. Three hundred feet of wire cable was strung from the tail-skid hook of the towing aeroplane to my own nose hook, and we took off.

It was a clear blue day with not a ripple in the sky. At 4,500 feet I pulled the release, the aeroplane put down its nose and dived away to the distant earth. I floated along for a minute or so in blissful quiet which is one of the abiding joys of the sport. Then I eased the stick gently back, and she started to climb. Slowly the speed fell off until, as the needle came back to just under 40, she gave a little shudder, and the stick went dead. I kicked on full left rudder, the nose rolled over, the earth tilted majestically up from underneath until it was right ahead of me, then started to revolve.

After half a turn the speed came up rapidly, I put on opposite rudder and centralised the stick in the normal way, the earth slowed down and returned quickly to its normal place beneath me. Good! I glanced at the altimeter, still 4,000 feet up, plenty of height for one more spin the other way.

I eased back the stick once more, she climbed, slowed, faltered. I kicked on full right rudder, she rolled over like a gannet onto the dive. I let her spin a little longer this time, all seemed well, then moved the controls again to bring her out.

Nothing happened, the earth ahead went on revolving like an immense gramophone record, objects on it growing perceptibly larger.

Quickly I put the controls back to the spinning position, adjusted the wing-flaps, and tried again, firmly. Still the spin went on, my speed increasing unsteadily and the hum of the wind outside growing to a roar. There was nothing more to be done, the time, so often anticipated, had come to abandon ship and take my first taste of the delights or otherwise of parachuting.

There was so much to do that I did not feel in the least worried, only faintly ridiculous that such a thing should befall me, a respectable city businessman, husband and father. There was some mistake, these experiences should confine themselves to our professional heroes. But my next movements had been practised so often in imagination that they took place almost without volition.

I reached above my head for the cord releasing the cockpit cover, pulled it, and pushed the cover upwards. The gale outside lanced in underneath as it lifted, caught it from my hand and whirled it away. The wind shrieked and tore at my clothes, caught my glasses and whipped them off. The nearing earth became a green, unfocused, whirling blur. I let go of the controls and my hands went to the catch fastening the safety strap, clicked it open, and gave a reassuring pat to the sheathed handle of the parachute rip-cord. The machine, freed of all attempt at human control, lurched about as it spun in a curious idiot way, a body without a mind. I drew up my knees, leant over the left-hand side of the cockpit, and dived head foremost over the edge.

And now a dreadful thing happened. As I went over the side, it seemed to swing round and up at me with a vicious jerk, struck me across my chest and flung me back helplessly into my seat. The spin went on.

A second time I gathered myself together and leaped over the side, and a second time I was caught and bounced childishly back. It was as if I was struggling to break through the bars of an invisible but invincible cage. The spin went on. The blurred earth seemed now very near, in fact it was scarcely 250 yards ahead.

It is curious but true that at a last moment such as this one's body, partly exhausted by former struggles, can nevertheless gather together sufficient physical energy to make a final effort surpassing previous ones. A third time I flung myself, still more violently, over the side. This time I got well out, head-first and well forward—almost free—the whirling outline of wings and fuselage was all around me, filling the sky. There was the most appalling bang, a violent blow, and I found myself once more back in my seat, hands and feet instinctively on the controls. The world swung violently overhead, slowed, stopped spinning, the machine was on its back, only centrifugal force was holding me in—but the controls were biting the air again, life had come back into them, life in them was life in me. I pulled back on the stick, she came staggering round on the second half of a loop, I steadied her and looked down.

The aerodrome buildings were a bare 300 feet beneath. The raging gale in the exposed cockpit sank to a friendly breeze, apologising for losing its temper. I put down the landing flaps, did a half turn and landed, not a hundred yards from the clubhouse. I looked out, and saw my wife running towards me over the turf. My recording barograph showed that I had spun down like Satan from Paradise, two thirds of a mile in one minute.

After a while I levered myself to my feet and stepped gingerly over the edge of the cockpit. As I did so I felt a violent cramping pain in my chest. Clearly I had strained my heart: you can't go doing things like this without paying for it, I thought.

I was helped into the clubhouse and lay down, waiting for the reaction. Every time I moved my heart gave a vicious tweak. Ten minutes later I put my hand to my waistcoat pocket for a soothing cigarette and brought out my metal case bent in a line across its centre to the shape of a three-dimensional 'L'.

My last jump had got my weight so far forward, had so materially altered the trim of the machine, that the hidden vice had been overcome. As the wings bit the air at high speed, the machine was swung round with such violence that we found the main wingbolts, great rods of steel holding the wings to the fuselage, all four bent. And the sides of the cockpit came round and hit my chest with a blow sufficient to break every rib in my body. But instead it caught my cigarette case fair in the middle, the force was distributed over an area, and I escaped with a set of internal bruises that kept me awake for the next three weeks, a cigarette case that will never open again, and a parachute that never had been opened, but nevertheless had given me the incentive to jump.

In the outcome, I was able to describe my spin sufficiently well for the experts to diagnose too small a rudder. A larger one was fitted, the machine was tested again with many safeguards. Although subsequent events showed that this was not the full answer, we took the three King Kites to Germany with two other machines, and in the fortnight the British team did cross-country flights totalling over 1,100 miles.

I was told that I should have known that you must always bale out on the *inside* of a spin, and that if, in a right-hand spin, I had dived over the right-hand side, I would have fallen clearly and instantly down the centre of the corkscrew and, once clear of the machine, released my parachute and watched the glider spin down to its wreckage.

As it happened it was fortunate I did not know this, one of the elementary rules of parachuting which no one troubles to tell you; for the machine was saved. Even the cockpit cover was picked up, but slightly damaged, a mile away. The only permanent loss was my spectacles, and perhaps a few days cut off my old age.**"**

As Philip Wills points out he would not have released his parachute, had he jumped, until he was clear of the machine and some pilots have had their parachutes entangled with the falling machine. Other accounts by pilots who have baled out have found themselves in a dilemma when they found they were falling at the same speed as the aircraft and have had to take a chance by opening the parachute and hoping it would check their fall before the aircraft caught them.

John Maynard: John Cunningham

The next extract from John Maynard's account of a spin by John Cunningham (now Group Captain John Cunningham, ex de Havilland chief test pilot) in *Aeroplane Monthly*, 1991 illustrates this point. It also has one or two other interesting features.

"Early in 1939 John was close to completing the flight testing of the first production Moth Minor. It occurred to him that since this was likely to differ slightly from the hand-built prototypes it would be as well for Geoffrey de Havilland Junior to fly it for comparative purposes, if for no other reason. The founder's son reacted rather impatiently to this suggestion—he was far too busy. Later he softened somewhat and suggested that he did the aft cg spinning tests with John accompanying him to provide a representative load.

No Safeguard

The prototype had had the benefit of an anti-spin 'chute fitted before embarking on the spinning programme, but recoveries had always been made without recourse to this safety device. The standard production aeroplane had no such safeguards. With John in the rear cockpit the pair took off, climbed to about 8,000 feet and initiated a left-hand spin, completing eight turns before recovery. Back they climbed to 8,000 feet and commenced a right-hand spin, at the first turn of which the engine coughed and stopped. At the same time the aircraft's nose reared up and the spin became totally flat. After a turn or two of this unpleasant manoeuvre Geoffrey spoke into the voice tube and reported that he was getting no response to control movements, perhaps John should try. He did so immediately and achieved nothing, whilst the ground panned round and rose towards them.

. John thinks that he suggested it was high time for them to get out and Geoffrey agreed, telling John to go immediately. He was somewhat concerned to be abandoning a straight-falling flat-spinning aeroplane, and reached down to grasp the trailing edge before pulling himself forcefully out of the cockpit. He waited before opening the 'chute, watched Geoffrey get out and, he thinks, pull his rip-cord whilst still standing on the wing. Thus he was snatched clear of the aeroplane by the rapidly developing canopy. At this moment the Moth

Minor, its cg dramatically changed, dropped its nose and recovered from the spin, whereupon its propeller windmilled and restarted the engine. This chaplinesque situation was in fact none too amusing, since the aeroplane began turning in aggressive circles round the descending airmen with the danger of either of them drifting into it. Happily, however, the Minor descended very quickly before hitting a large oak near Wheathamstead and burst into flames.

Having lost sight of his boss, John landed near the rapidly burning wreckage and, ever calm, fished out the camera he always carried to photograph both the remains as they were and his parachute neatly laid out on the ground. He assumed, rightly, that Geoffrey would be waiting for him at the nearby Crooked Chimney pub at Lemsford, folded his parachute and stopped a passing car which took him there! Various colleagues, including Martin Sharp, the public relations manager, turned up, having had the same hunch as John about Geoffrey's whereabouts; a few drinks were consumed!

Very recently John tried to find again the exact location of the crash and believes he may have done so. There were two lessons to be learnt. First, there are often significant differences between the behaviour of prototype and production aircraft. Secondly, when abandoning an aeroplane, always switch off the ignition before you go.

John spent many hours spinning Moth Minors during the early months of 1939. The rudder travel was increased as a result of the accident, as was the rudder area below the tailplane. Added to this, anti-spin strakes were placed on the upper fuselage in front of the fin.**"**

John S. Wilson: Flat Spins

Shortly after reading John Maynard's article I came across a letter from John S. Wilson, also in *Aeroplane Monthly*, December 1994, relating to flat spins.

"Sir, I was very interested to read of John Cunningham's description of the Moth Minor's entry into its flat spin during the production aircraft's flight test programme.

I learnt to fly with the Fairey Flying Club, whose students were trained by the instructors at the West London Flying Club at White Waltham. During this training the importance of studying the characteristics of the aeroplane under all flight conditions was impressed upon us.

An example of how such knowledge had been used by the previous CFI, Margot Gore, was often quoted. Miss Gore, it was said, took a new student up for his first flight in one of the club Moth Minors. She took off into wind and straight towards the RAF hangars on the southside of the airfield. The engine cut at a critical position close to a hangar when the conventional advice of continuing straight ahead in such a situation seemed inappropriate.

Knowing her aeroplane's flat-spinning characteristic, she hauled the nose up, kicked on full rudder and the aircraft spun flat, down on to the ground short of the hangar. Thanks to this, both occupants walked away from the resulting crash! What the student thought of flying after this was never reported.

Flat spins have always had a bad press, but here was one case where, very skilfully utilised, the characteristic proved beneficial.**

I think Margot Gore's exhibition of airmanship quite outstanding. In the split second at her disposal she not only decided exactly what to do but with tremendous courage did it with breathtaking skill and success.

Richard P. Hallion: From Test Pilots

The arrival of the emergency spin-'chute saved a lot of pilots and aircraft from destruction. A sudden jerk on the tail, even if the spin-'chute was wrecked, was enough to get most aircraft out of a spin. This is another extract from Hallion's *Test Pilots*.

The early test performance of the Chance Vought Corsair, the first American naval fighter to attain 400 mph in level flight convinced Bureau of Aeronautics officials to abandon two previously hallowed requisite tests for Navy fighters and dive bombers: holding a 'zero lift' vertical dive through a 10,000 feet loss of altitude, and demonstrating recovery in a ten-turn spin. Vought test pilot Boone T. Guyton had touched 550 mph during one Corsair dive but suffered hydraulic failure that caused the XF4U-1's propeller to overspeed, wrecking the engine. Following a perilous low altitude, high-g pullout, he skilfully swapped airspeed for altitude, then smartly dead-sticked down to a safe landing. During the standard ten-turn spin tests, the angular Corsair developed such control loads that Guyton discovered the forces were too high for him to recover; if the plane had not been equipped with an emergency spin-'chute, Guyton would have had to abandon it. Flight testing is a dynamic field, and the criteria for yesterday's aeroplanes are often not sufficient for tomorrow's—or even today's. The advanced fighters and bombers of the late 1930s demanded rewriting the test manuals of the 1920s. The high-speed dive would become a thing to be approached with caution, lest the refined subsonic aerodynamics of the day betray one into overextending the airplane into an as yet unknown realm, where the mysteries of transonic flight could tear it apart.

Spin-'chutes are now almost always fitted to new aircraft under test and some retain them to use normally as braking parachutes during landing.

Part 3

The Forties, Fifties, Sixties and Seventies

N. Roy Harben: From The Complete Flying Course

It is relevant at this point to describe how spinning was taught in 1942 by the Royal Air Force. It was considered essential that a new pilot should master this particular lesson before going solo. Failure to do so would have precluded a solo flight. Introduction to the spin usually came in the second flight and a total of about ten or twelve spins were usually carried out before the first solo. Anybody who became totally incapacitated by spinning or proved unable to master the recovery would be taken off the course. They might be given a further trial after a medical examination and if they were very keen to continue but they would have to demonstrate competence in spin recovery before any further training was undertaken.

The standard textbook of instruction was The Complete Flying Course by N. Roy Harben DFC and was intended for pilots learning to fly on such aircraft as de Havilland Gipsy Moth, de Havilland Tiger Moth, Avro Tutor, Miles Magister or similar primary training aircraft. The extract between pages 90 and 93 deals with the spin and going solo. Although scheduled as Lesson 10 in the book, spinning was practised intermittently throughout training both before and after solo.

John Kilbracken: Four Spins of Interest

While reading John Kilbracken's book Bring Back my Stringbag I came across two short accounts of spins which are of interest. The first is a Barracuda spin.

"On my way by motor-bike from my office to the mess. Watching this Barracuda out of the corner of my eye as it came in to land, seemed to be flying so slowly, banked steeply to port on its last turn for landing and at once whipped into a spin. At less than 400 feet the pilot hadn't a hope. The Barra had hardly time to complete a revolution before falling vertically into a field beside the mess. Not a hundred yards from me. The first flames sprouting at once from the half buried engine.**"**

This type of spin is not uncommon also among glider pilots who, due to inexperience or nervousness, may make the last turn into wind for the approach to land with insufficient bank or flying too slowly, due to being rather close to the ground. It is very dangerous and causes deaths almost every year.

AIR LESSON NO. 10   **SPINNING**

Action		Effect	Remarks
Accidental spinning results only from the misuse of controls. An aeroplane spins only if it is both stalled and 'ruddered'.			
DELIBERATE SPIN Climb to at least 4,000 feet. Look all round, particularly underneath. Note altimeter. Close throttle. Keep nose above horizon. Just before stall apply full rudder and opposite bank. Ease stick right back.		Aeroplane spins in direction ruddered. Great loss of height and control.	Thus stalling and applying rudder produces a spin.
RECOVERY FROM SPIN Apply full opposite rudder. Then ease stick forward. When spinning stops, centralise controls. Keep straight with rudder. Ease out of dive by gentle back pressure on stick. Note altimeter and loss of height.			Always apply full opposite rudder before moving stick forward.
STALL WITH RUDDER CENTRAL Close throttle. Ease stick slowly right back. Keep rudder central.		Aeroplane stalls. Nose falls and dives straight.	No rudder, no spin.
BANK AND STALL WITH RUDDER CENTRAL Close throttle. Apply bank and ease stick right back. Keep rudder central.		Aeroplane stalls and falls sideways.	No rudder, no spin.

These demonstrations show that, although stalled, 'Rudder Effect' must be present at same time to produce a spin.

GROUND LESSON NO. 10   **SPINNING**

Explanation	Instructor's Notes
For simplicity in the air the term 'ruddered' is used, as the rudder is the chief cause of a couple in the Rudder Plane, and it is a couple in this plane and a stalled condition which produces a spin. Aileron drag and keep surface both produce a couple in the Rudder Plane, and if large enough can produce a spin. Thus the application of opposite bank, although not starting the spin, produced aileron drag and a couple in the same direction as the applied rudder, so assisting the spin.	At RAF Flying Schools, recovery from spins and aerobatics must be at a height of not less than 3,000 feet. Even if you are not subject to this edict, it is a very wise one to observe. Dislike of spinning is no disgrace, therefore do not prolong a spin any longer than is necessary. Instruct the pupil to go into a spin each way and to recover without assistance. Warn pupil that he may go into a spin the other way if he holds on opposite rudder too long. The amount that the stick is eased forward varies according to the particular type of aircraft, and it should be made clear that the stick must only be eased forward sufficiently to produce desired result. Ask pupil how he feels. By this time he has probably had enough, in which case do not continue with 'Accidental Spins'. These demonstrations might well be termed 'The Effects of Rudder Abuse'.

Spinning axis

The shielding effect of the tail-plane on the rudder is greater when the elevators are down than when they are up so making the rudder less effective. That is why rudder is applied before easing the stick forward to that the maximum effect is produced by the rudder before using the elevators. The object of this demonstration is to show that banking when stalled is not the primary cause of a spin when the aircraft is stalled, although, as explained above, it assists a spin, and in certain cases of high aileron drag and keel surfaces it can be made to cause a spin.	The primary object of this demonstration is to show that a spin does not result from a straight stall. Straight stalls on highly loaded wing aircraft are not always possible without recourse to the rudder as a wing may drop and start a spin. If such an aircraft is being used let the pupil experience a spin resulting from this and then show that if he counteracts the wing drop with rudder and ailerons, so keeping the aeroplane straight, that it will not then spin. This lesson should also be used to demonstrate the 'wing dropping' possibility in a stall and the danger of approaching to land at too low an airspeed.

AIR LESSON NO. 10 (Cont'd)   ## SPINNING

Action		Effect	Remarks
ACCIDENTAL SPINNING FROM A TURN (ENGINE OR GLIDING) Go into a turn. Apply excessive bottom rudder.		Aeroplane skids out and nose drops.	
Try to bring nose up by easing stick back. Recover as before.		Aeroplane spins.	Note the stick is back and rudder on, just the same as a deliberate spin.
FROM A GLIDING TURN Glide at less than normal gliding speed. Go into a turn.		Nose and wing drop.	
Try to bring nose and wing up by easing stick back and away from low wing. Recover as before.		Aeroplane spins.	This shows the danger of turning with rudder only, particularly on the glide, and the necessity for extra speed for a gliding turn.

Final Conclusion
The rudder is an excellent servant but a wicked master, particularly near the stalling point.
Excessive BOTTOM RUDDER always leads to trouble.
Beware of excessive Bottom Rudder and lack of airspeed on a gliding turn.
Always have plenty of speed and sufficient bank, especially near the ground.

GROUND LESSON NO. 10 (Cont'd) SPINNING

Explanation	Instructor's Notes
As explained under the heading of 'Medium Turns, Wing Loading', the stalling speed increases with bank; thus, if the airspeed is lower than usual and the aeroplane is banked, it quickly stalls. Bottom rudder is already on, so that when stick is eased back to lift nose, we have all the spinning conditions, viz stalled, stick back, rudder, and aileron drag helping, as opposite bank has been applied.	These demonstrations are particularly useful in curing over-ruddering and heavy feet, and should be repeated if pupil persists in these faults.

AIR LESSON NO. 11

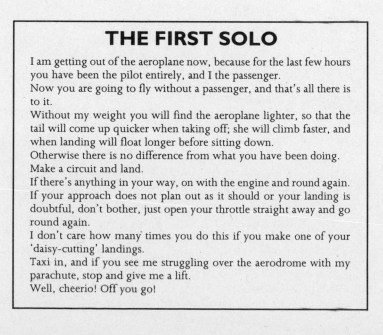

THE FIRST SOLO

I am getting out of the aeroplane now, because for the last few hours you have been the pilot entirely, and I the passenger.

Now you are going to fly without a passenger, and that's all there is to it.

Without my weight you will find the aeroplane lighter, so that the tail will come up quicker when taking off; she will climb faster, and when landing will float longer before sitting down.

Otherwise there is no difference from what you have been doing.

Make a circuit and land.

If there's anything in your way, on with the engine and round again.

If your approach does not plan out as it should or your landing is doubtful, don't bother, just open your throttle straight away and go round again.

I don't care how many times you do this if you make one of your 'daisy-cutting' landings.

Taxi in, and if you see me struggling over the aerodrome with my parachute, stop and give me a lift.

Well, cheerio! Off you go!

The second spin is this account of C.S. Staniland, Fairey's chief test pilot, spinning the TSR 1 9/30. It shows how an aircraft regarded as very safe and easy to fly can dismay its pilot be getting into a flat spin.

"One of the many remarkable facts about the Stringbag is that by all the rules it should have been very nearly obsolescent not long after reaching the first front-line squadrons in 1936, yet was still operational nearly a decade later.

It was largely designed to meet a specification issued by the Air Ministry (who then controlled the Fleet Air Arm) in October 1930. This resulted in Fairey's designing the prototype S 9/30, for which they received a go-ahead less than a year later. The aircraft closely resembled the Swordfish apart from its liquid-cooled Rolls-Royce Kestrel II engine, which gave it a pointed nose. It first flew in February 1934.

Meantime Fairey had been working on another prototype, known as TSR1 which was intended for the Greek navy. With its Bristol Pegasus II radial engine, it was even more like a Stringbag. Though work on 'the Greek machine', as it became known, started after that on the S 9/30, it flew nearly a year earlier, in March 1933. It promised well but one little design fault came to light. In September Fairey's chief test pilot took it up for spinning trials.

He experienced great difficulty in getting TSR1 to spin, as would later be the case with the Stringbag, but once he succeeded the aircraft went into a flat spin (with the nose only slightly below the horizon) and simply wouldn't come out.

After completing a dozen revolutions, Staniland decided to jump, but only jumped as far as the observer's open cockpit behind him. He thus became probably the only aviator to bale out twice from the same aircraft. S 9/30 was smashed to pieces.

Instead of persevering with this prototype, the Fairey design team under Marcel Lobelle now combined the knowledge gained from S 9/30 and TSR 1 to produce a new mark with a Pegasus III engine, at first christened TSR II. This historic aircraft, No K4190, the first Swordfish, made its initial flight in Staniland's hands on 17 April 1934.**"**

The third incident concerns a spin in a Miles Magister, one of the standard training aircraft in use during the Second World War.

"It's quite possible to spin off a turn by accident and you're dead if this happens below 500 feet. But with enough altitude you can get out of it, so every pilot is taught the drill and carries it out half a dozen times at safe height before flying solo. I loved aerobatics, and soon started spinning as well as loops and rolls, when flying solo, though this was forbidden at EFTS. I was totally self-confident. On this particular morning I first broke the rules by map reading my way to Eton: look at me, I'm flying. Then I climbed 5,000 or 6,000 feet till I was precisely over Windsor Castle, throttled back, full port rudder and over into a spin. The whole world revolving about the Round Tower, with College Chapel a bit off-centre.

But now I made the most appalling error. Always previously, with or without an instructor, I'd let her spin for not more than half a dozen revolutions. Today in case anyone was watching I kept her in it for over 2,000 feet. O.K., let's come out. I went through the usual drill and absolutely nothing happened.

Let there be no mistake, if I'd panicked I would quite certainly have plunged vertically into Windsor Castle, writing off not only myself but maybe most of the Royal Family if they happened to be at home. I gave the situation about three seconds of cool deliberate thought (the earth was rising towards me at about 200 feet a second). The only possible explanation was that I was now descending much faster than ever before and spinning much more rapidly; the only hope was to go through the whole drill again, very slowly and calmly, very deliberately, exaggerating each stage of it.

Below 3,000 feet now. Starboard rudder every inch she would go. Hold her there a full five seconds. For the love of Christ don't panic. The spin slowing at 1,200 feet, centralise controls, wait, I'm in a straight vertical dive. At 700 feet, haul back on the stick as hard as I dare, don't pull the bloody wings off, she's coming out. Nearly brushing the oaks of Windsor Great Park, slinking away to westward, hoping no one had taken my number, a long slow turn for home

Never a word to anyone.**"**

The fourth incident is a near-spin. Flying a Vought-Sikorski Chesapeake, John Kilbracken has another near miss.

"Exactly two weeks later I took off to fly to Lee but hit weather near Swindon that I thought just bad enough to justify turning back for another night in Oxford, where Angel was. Having arrived over the airfield—it was little more than a landing strip, at Starvell Farm, near Kidlington—I dived into a low-level downwind pass, pulled up steeply, would have landed in three minutes. It was not to be. My engine stopped dead at about 200 feet.

Fortunately I had plenty of speed but I'd reach mother earth in less than a minute and had to turn through almost 130 degrees if I was to get her into wind. The countryside was wooded with only a single field of any size upwind. It happened to be a potato field. To reach it I'd have to lose height in the shallowest glide possible, at the same time continuing an extremely steep turn towards it. On glancing at my airspeed indicator for a fraction of a second, I saw to my horror that I was several knots below stalling speed. Why hadn't I already spun in? It could now happen any second—curtains. But the even more certainly fatal alternative, I knew in a flash, was to gain speed by steepening my glide path or come out of my turn—either of which would have landed me in a dense forest. So there was nothing for it but to continue as I was until directly upwind. Somehow I just made it (flaps down, wheels up), ran 20 or 30 yards, hit an extra large potato ridge and turned on my back. End of Chesapeake AL936—but I could walk away.

You must spin off a rate-four turn at such a low airspeed; the only possible explanation is that my ASI was reading five or ten knots slow. And yet . . .**"**

D.L. Hadley: Barracuda Spin

While under training I learnt spinning and spin recovery like everyone else but I did not really expect that I would ever be caught out by an unintentional spin myself, such is the confidence of youth. During deck landing training, while I was serving in the Fleet Air Arm, one of the things we had to practise was slow flying. I was flying a Fairey Barracuda II and although I did not much like flying it slowly the Barracuda was quite good at it, but it became sluggish and I had the feeling that it might be just about to lose control of itself and bite me.

One day after a spell of this humming-bird stuff I thought that I would see just how slowly she would fly. So I climbed to several thousand feet, put the throttle at the usual 'approach to land setting' wheels and flaps down, then deliberately stalled. She stalled at 55 knots. I just kicked the rudder to pick up the dropped wing, opened the throttle a bit more and she came straight out. I tried again with a bit more engine and the same thing happened. Then I tried again on about half-throttle, or a bit more, and she did not stall until the speed had dropped to 45 knots! I could scarcely believe it.

Of course the Barra was mushing down, but when I kicked the rudder and opened the throttle a bit more she did not come out as she had before. She could not really fly at that speed I suppose and she just flicked into a spin. I'd lost quite a lot of height by this time and was only at about 1,500 feet and there was a 600-foot-high hill underneath covered with trees. However, I had no choice but to do a proper spin recovery. I closed the throttle, put on full opposite rudder and pushed the stick forward. The Barra came out of the spin at once but I could see that I was going to hit the trees during the pullout from the dive. I should have retracted the undercarriage and flaps but I do not remember whether I did then or later. I suppose your mind works faster on these occasions because it came to me in a flash that if I pulled the Barra into a steep turn I should lengthen my path to the ground. I did this and it worked, I was back in control doing a steep turn with one wing tip skimming the tops of the trees.

This little episode increased my respect for the Barra a good deal. I was not only surprised to find that with enough power it was controllable down to a speed of 45 knots, but the speed and ease with which it recovered from the spin I found most encouraging. With a normal deck landing approach speed of 60 or 61 knots I felt that perhaps we should get on well together.

The Fairey Barracuda was notorious for diving unexpectedly into the sea. There were several reasons for this. First, in the torpedo attack dive from 12,000 to 150 feet the dive brakes limited the terminal velocity to about 260 knots, no matter how steep the dive. The Youngman flaps were put into 30 degrees negative incidence before the dive for this purpose. But this had the effect of making the aircraft tail-heavy so that it had to be trimmed about four divisions on the cockpit indicator nose heavy for the dive. As soon as the aircraft was levelled at the end of the dive the dive brakes, which caused so much drag, had to be taken off. *At the same time* the nose-down trim had to be wound off too, because the sudden change of attitude caused by the brakes coming off would have pulled the aircraft into the sea. This happened to a number of pilots, no doubt distracted by having other things to do at the same time.

In addition, during the dive the rudder became very heavy and it was desirable to wind on about 3 or 4 degrees of left rudder trim too. Some pilots, with strong legs, did not do this but simply held on hard-left rudder. After dropping their fish the normal evasive action was to turn in a skidding turn, the idea being that a skidding aircraft was harder to shoot at, as it was not pointing in the direction in which it was moving—that was the idea anyway. When a pilot who had not put on rudder trim lifted his foot off the rudder the aircraft skidded violently to port.

A friend of mine while flying at 5,000 feet at cruising speed of about 130 knots, wheels up, flaps normal, started to push the rudder pedals alternately, inducing a series of flat skidding turns. The oscillations increased and after about five or six the tail suddenly shot violently up in the air and the Barracuda plunged down. He was so surprised and shaken by this that by the time he had regained control he had lost 4,000 feet. He told me about this and we discussed it and I decided to try it myself. At 5,000 feet, 130 knots, I began skidding from side to side as he had done. Suddenly the tail shot up and the nose went down so violently that my seat flew to the top of its travel and my head hit the canopy. An Aldis lamp on the floor rose up and floated weightless, as did a few lumps of mud. But I had been expecting it, and it only took me 1,000 feet to recover.

We talked about this at some length and concluded that the oscillations had carried the tail-plane, which on the Barracuda was set high on the fin, out of the slipstream, or partly out of it, so that only the starboard half was still in it. The Barracuda's propeller, viewed from the cockpit, turned clockwise so that the slipstream on the port side would be slanted upwards. Normally there is a downthrust on the tail-plane to compensate for the fact that the centre of lift (pressure) of the wings is slightly behind the centre of gravity. The effect of destroying this downthrust would be just as if the tail had broken off, which is what it felt like. I believe that this violent bunt happened to a number of pilots while they were low over the sea.

A few Barracudas shed their wings during the dive or in the pullout. This was found to be due to the fact that one particular batch of aircraft had been fitted with mild steel wing locking bolts instead of high-tensile steel bolts. The mild steel bolts rapidly became worn and allowed the wings to develop a flutter during the dive which tore them off. How this blunder came about I don't know, but after all the Barracudas had been checked and the faulty wing locking bolts replaced that was the end of that problem.

Some pilots simply misjudged the pull out from the dive, but this also happened to Swordfish pilots. One of my friends rolled up to the wardroom mess at Crail one day, reeking of rum, after being rescued by the Anstruther lifeboat shortly after he had dived his Stringbag into the oggin. In conditions of poor visibility, with no horizon, this was not hard to do.

Some aircraft dived into the sea because of fuel contamination or due to misjudged deck landings but these causes were not exclusive to Barracudas, it was simply that when all the causes were added together this gave the Barracuda a rather bad name. One pilot I knew, who was an engineer, simply refused to fly them any more, as he did not see why he should be polished off by his own side when there were plenty of the enemy waiting to do it anyway. I don't think he was court-martialled, just sent home as a case of twitch. For these and some other reasons such as a poor performance, no front gun and dodgy hydraulics the Barracuda was not popular, but it was all many of us had, so we tried to enjoy it. It was a good dive-bomber and I think would have acquitted itself well in a torpedo attack had it ever been given the chance and used in one.

Eric 'Winkle' Brown: From Wings of the Weird and Wonderful

The next two extracts come from the book *Wings of the Weird and Wonderful* written by Captain Eric 'Winkle' Brown, who was Chief Test Pilot of the Aerodynamics Flight of the RAE Farnborough. Both are concerned with swept wings and the tailless layout, two factors which have a marked effect on stalling and spin recovery.

"The de Havilland DH 108 (Swallow) was a post-war research aircraft built to investigate the behaviour of swept wings and the tailless layout. It was one of a crop of Allied experimental aeroplanes that were inspired by German technology, and the resemblance of the DH Swallow, as it came to be known, to the Messerschmitt 163 was no coincidence.

Design work began in October 1945 to specification E 18/45; using the standard Vampire fuselage. The 43-degree swept wings were attached to the existing pick-up points and were of all wood construction with elevons fitted outboard of the split trailing edge flaps.

The RAE Farnborough had become involved in the design from the outset because much wind-tunnel testing was required to predict certain aspects of the flight behaviour. The RAE had warned that the aircraft might Dutch roll at low speeds or be likely to drop a wing severely at the stall and be difficult to recover from a spin. Thus the prototype had fixed slots extending inwards from the wing tip for a distance of 35 per cent span. I therefore knew of the existence of the Swallow before its first flight by the younger Geoffrey de Havilland on 15 May 1946. The prototype TG 283 first lifted off from the 3,500-yard emergency runway at RAF Woodbridge and made an uneventful 30-minute flight . . .

Simultaneously with the commencement of the slow-speed tests at RAE, Aero Department issued its Report Aero 2305 on Model Spinning Tests on an experimental tailless aircraft (DH 108 E 18/45). The report predicted that recovery from an accidental spin would take place only if the pilot took action immediately the spin started. Anti-spin parachutes streamed from the wingtips would provide a powerful aid to recovery. Recovery from an inverted spin was good, as the rudder was not blanked by the fuselage in the inverted spin attitude.

This information was to serve me well, and of course wing-tip anti-spin parachutes had been fitted on TG 283 from the outset on RAE advice. Now in addition a 100-foot trailing static was fitted for the stall tests to be undertaken. The device was rather like an 11-pound practice bomb with a perforated spike in the nose, and 100 feet of rubber tubing attaching it to the underside of the aircraft. In flight it was released from the cockpit and hung clear of all disturbed airflow, so that true airspeed reading was given on a wide-scale airspeed indicator available to the pilot and repeated in the automatic observer.

Getting into the Swallow needed external help as there was no retractable step like on the Vampire. The view of course was excellent and the cockpit closely resembled that of the Vampire. The brakes were very good, but during taxying there was a slight weathercocking tendency in a crosswind in spite of the tricycle undercarriage layout, and care had to be taken to ensure that the low swept-back wing tips were clear of any ground obstructions.

The Goblin 2 could be held up to full power on the brakes for take off, and with 1½ divisions of nose-up elevator trim I lifted the nose wheel off at 100 mph which required a fair pull force. I let the speed build up to this figure because as soon as ground effect was lost the aircraft pitched nose up and at a lower speed might self-stall. Just after unsticking the 108 was very sensitive to fore and aft control, and in a crosswind tended to drop the down-wind wing, and it needed a large lateral stick movement to raise it. No flap was used on take-off.

Climb was made at 190 mph, at 9,700 rpm, and was straightforward although the aircraft displayed longitudinal instability if the pilot took his hands off the stick.

Cruise at 220 mph at 15,000 feet at 8,700 rpm revealed poor stability round all three axes, and control harmony was also not very good, the rudder being too light and fore and aft control too heavy. The manoeuvring was restricted by a maximum permissible g limit of 2.4 because of strength considerations for the full-span wooden slots fitted to TG 283 before handover to Farnborough.

The real fun and games started with the stalling trials. Once speed was reduced below 105 mph the instability of the aircraft became apparent as it started a series of longitudinal oscillations accompanied by Dutch rolling in anything but smooth air.

At 87 mph with the nose well above the horizon the starboard wing started to drop slowly and gently, and if held up by opposite aileron then at 86 mph it snapped over almost to the vertical before one had time to react and push the stick forward. Any marked delay in taking recovery action resulted in the aircraft rolling right over onto its back and a lot of height could be lost in the ensuing steep dive. In consequence I never started stall tests below 10,000 feet.

The stall with trimmer flaps open occurred at 88½ mph with similar characteristics, but there was also a slight buffeting tremor felt on approaching the stall.

The stall with both drag and trimmer flaps open occurred at 83 mph—again with similar characteristics but there was more buffeting and the nose was less high above the horizon, although the stick was well back to produce the stall. The effect of lowering the undercarriage was negligible.

I have described the stall characteristics in detail because they almost caught me out and later resulted in a fatal crash to TG 283. In my case the incident came near the end of an extensive series of stalling test flights. I had lowered the trailing static at 15,000 feet and was carrying out a clean stall attempting to find if a combination of a small amount of opposite aileron and moderate rudder could delay the wing drop. When the stall came it was a very vicious wing drop to the inverted position and before I could centralise the rudder the aircraft was in a steep right-hand inverted spin. Fortunately, I had closely studied the RAE report of the wind-tunnel trials of the spinning characteristics of the DH 108 and so kept a cool head. I say this because the danger to a pilot in an inverted spin is disorientation. However, I had been applying left rudder at the stall, so I kicked on rudder with my right foot but found the somewhat slow rate of rotation was not stopping as quickly as I expected. I pushed harder and then realised the rudder was jammed, probably by the trailing static wound around it. However, the extra push force did the trick and as rotation ceased I eased the stick back and pulled very gently through the vertical for recovery at 3,000 feet. The trailing static remained wrapped around the tail for landing.

The landing was a rather tricky procedure in normal circumstances. Although the view during the approach was excellent in spite of the nose-up attitude of the aircraft, the powered approach attitude of the aircraft was very flat in order to keep the rate of descent within moderate limits, and also to prevent having to make a large change of attitude near the ground for touch-down, as such an increase in incidence would result in the tail end of the aircraft contacting the ground.

By trial and error I found the best method of landing was to lower the drag flaps at 150 mph on the cross-wind leg, and then when they reached 15 degrees to pull up the trimmer flaps to counteract the strong nose-down change of trim. Further trimming was necessary until full flap angle was reached with full nose-up elevator trim plus a slight pull force. Turn in on the final approach leg was made at a height of 500 feet and a speed of 140 mph, reducing this to 125 mph for the straight run in.

I kept the engine revs at about 6,000 and maintained this until I made a very slight check at 10 feet off the ground, then cut the throttle. The aircraft continued to sink after the check until it was about 2 feet off the ground, when a cushioning effect was experienced and it touched down gently on all three wheels at 120 mph.

A mere reduction of 5–10 mph in approach speed could result in the check becoming ineffective, so that the aircraft would sink through the ground cushion to make a heavy landing, or alternatively an early engine cut could set up a high rate of sink that would remain unaffected by any attempt to check attitude near the ground within the limits of backward stick movement one dare apply without fear of lowering the tail too far.

In spite of these rather sensitive landing characteristics, it was decided at RAE to conduct a series of dead-stick landings at the then deserted Blackbushe airfield, which was adjacent to Farnborough and had a runway adequate for the purpose.

My briefing was to keep the engine throttled right back from 500 feet and to progressively reduce approach speed over the series of landings. The test was made on 14 June 1949, and I got the approach speed down to 115 mph, but the hold-off to reduce the high rate of descent gave a large change of attitude so that the tail cone and wing-tip skids struck the runway first on touch-down at a recorded 103 mph. This jerked the aircraft violently onto its nose wheel and caused only minor damage, although the aircraft's accelerometer recorded $+ 10\frac{1}{2}$ g and $-4\frac{1}{2}$ g . . .

Stewart and I conducted a series of manoeuvre tests with the Swallow, but since the risk of stalling and spinning was high in such a programme, it was preceded by high-speed wind-tunnel tests to give us an idea of the likely g stall limits.

Except for take-off and landing VW 120 was being flown with tip slats locked shut. There was therefore a danger of ordinary tip stalling at low speed, and at high Mach numbers the earlier tip stall could be brought on by compressibility effects.

The g limitations due to Mach number were important above 20,000 feet. At $M= 0.88$ the maximum safe g at 20,000 feet was estimated 4.0 and at 35,000 feet was 2.0. For rapid manoeuvring it was estimated that 5 g could be obtained at all speeds above 380 mph, below 20,000 feet.

From a purely structural point of view VW 120 had a maximum allowable g of $6\frac{2}{3}$, which with a safety factor of 1.5 gave an ultimate stress limitation of 10 g.

I started the manoeuvre tests with an approach to the straight stall with flaps and undercarriage down, slats open. There was very little warning of the stall at 100 mph when either wing dropped accompanied by aileron buffet. Actually, intentional stalling of VW 120 was prohibited due to absence of wing-tip parachutes.

The next step was to investigate the g stalling characteristics of the slow-speed TG 283 in pullouts and turns. Owing to the structural limitation of 2.4 g on that aircraft the tests were necessarily limited to low speed g stalls.

In straight pullouts the aircraft had a marked tendency to self-stall and the right wing dropped between 80 and 110 degrees without any warning and a very steep dive ensued.

In turns there was again the marked self-stalling tendency before the aircraft flicked violently from a 60 degree turn in one direction to a 90 degree one in the opposite direction and finished up in a steep dive. Again there was no stall warning.

It was obvious from these tests that similar characteristics in VW 120 would be serious at high altitude owing to the rapid build-up of Mach number which would occur, and to the absence of air brakes to prevent the possibility of the aircraft being precipitated into a critical compressibility dive.

At this stage I left the RAE. I had always written single-line impressions of every aircraft I flew and the following appears alongside the DH 108 Swallows: 'A Killer. Nasty Stall. Vicious undamped longitudinal oscillation at speed in bumps.' These words were tragically truer than I imagined.

The final chapters of the DH 108 were written in the next eight months. Stewart Muller-Roland, recently promoted Squadron Leader, crashed to his death in VW 120 on 15 February 1950 at Birkhall, Buckinghamshire, in circumstances similar to those in which Geoffrey de Havilland lost his life.

His place as CO of Aero Flight was taken by 'Jumbo' Genders who was also promoted to Squadron Leader. He in turn crashed to his death in TG 283 on 1 May 1950, near Hartley Witney, Hants, when he spun into the ground while conducting stalling tests.

In retrospect one must ask if this ill-fated research aircraft was worth the cost in test pilots' lives. The answer must in my opinion be in the affirmative. Aviation was in the throes of breaking the sound barrier. It was as prestigious a goal then as going into space was later to be. Aeronautics was full of new innovations like the jet engine, reheat, rockets, sweepback, boundary layer control, power operated controls, the ejection seat and prone position piloting. Finding the correct configuration formula was the key to success. The DH 108 was a brave attempt to achieve the ultimate. It just missed by a hairsbreadth, but the formula had unknown risks. The Swallow was not without success—perhaps its greatest being the legacy of information it left—but the price it demanded will be held by many to have been too high.**

The second aircraft is the GAL/5C, a glider built to test some experimental theories.

**Often I have been asked which is the worst aircraft I have ever flown—well, this is it. I have had some exciting and indeed frightening moments with this tailless experimental glider, but I think for my flight observers they were mainly frightening.

General Aircraft Limited had a successful record of building military gliders during the war, such as the Hotspur and Hamilcar, and had been given contracts to build a series of experimental gliders incorporating all-wing designs. The GAL/56 had 28 degrees of sweep on its wings at the extremities of which were fins and rudders. It carried two crew sitting in tandem.

It arrived at the RAE in the spring of 1946, labelled as a problem child, which was certainly no exaggeration. Anyway, it became my assignment, and so the battle of wits with this capricious creature began for me on 1 May 1946.

It was a large, ungainly-looking aircraft with an undercarriage of substantial proportions and oversize wheels that did nothing to improve its appearance, which was further demeaned by the yellow and black striped paint scheme it carried on the underside of the wings, rather like a half-caste wasp—and it certainly had a sting . . .

The first stalling tests on the GAL/56 revealed very unusual characteristics, so much so that it was decided to have both wings fitted with wool tufts to show the airflow pattern, and full instrumentation and camera equipment recorded the results.

The first tests before this equipment was fitted were made at the normal weight and cg. A trailing static pitot was carried and the results recorded by auto-observer. A flight observer was also carried to take visual readings in case the auto-observer camera failed.

The first stall was made with an elevator trim setting of 1½ divisions tail-heavy. From 70 mph a nose-up pitching moment started showing itself and at 65 mph developed into a definite self-stalling tendency which rapidly increased in backward force and movement of the control wheel. The incidence rose to an alarming angle, so much so that the horizon was lost from view, and the feeling experienced by both the observer and myself was that of the possibility of the aircraft falling over on to its back.

During the nose-up pitching a distinct kick was felt on the port aileron at 64 mph, but the wings could still be held level with ease. When the stick was getting near the backstop and the airspeed had dropped to about 55 mph, and the impression was one of a tail-slide having developed or at least being imminent, the wheel was pushed hard forward until a force of 50–60 pounds was applied which seemed to bring it onto the forward stop, but in fact it was only about the mid-position and the stop was actually an aerodynamic one caused by the build-up in control force.

The aircraft's response to this rapid forward stick movement was very sluggish and then suddenly the nose dropped violently but squarely with very little negative g effect until level with the horizon, paused and then abruptly fell into a steep dive before control was regained.

The GAL/56 could be fitted either with a forward flap on the undersurface of the wing or a rear flap, and both were tried out for comparative effect. The forward flap gave a sharp nose-up change of trim for the first 10 degrees of movement, then there appeared to be very little further trim change for the next 50 degrees, whereas the rear flap gave a linear nose-down change of trim with increase in flap angle. With the rear flap fully down and its effect trimmed out at neutral cg there was not really sufficient backward stick movement left for a hold-off on landing at 70 mph and consequently the landing speed was raised by some 10–15 mph.

The all-up stall characteristics were identical with the forward flap fully lowered, but with the rear flap fitted the nose did not rise so steeply, and it eventually dropped in one phase instead of two. Rearward movement of the cg accentuated the steepness of the nose rise.

One impression I have firmly rooted in my mind is that the GAL/56 was undoubtedly the most difficult aircraft to land that I have ever experienced. After many hair-raising arrivals and one mild crash-landing, I finally evolved what seemed to be the answer to the violent ground effect attendant on every landing.

Although a normal approach was always made, if the normal hold-off was attempted it usually managed to coincide with the onset of the ground effect, and the subsequent nose-up pitch usually led to a display of the aircraft's peculiar stalling behaviour about 10 feet off the ground. The subsequent dive into the runway inevitably produced an enormous bounce from the very non-resilient undercarriage plus an instinctive pull back on the control wheel to start the sequence off again.

However, I found that by approaching a little fast (80 mph instead of 70 mph) and holding off very gently so that the aircraft was floating parallel with the ground, then clamping on the control wheel and holding it rigidly central, the aircraft took up a three-point attitude on its own from the ground effect and sat down squarely and firmly.

This technique had to be slightly modified with change in cg position. At forward cg the aircraft would not three-point but roll on the main wheels and then the control wheel had to be moved forward to maintain that attitude until speed had dropped very low, otherwise any premature attempt to lower the tail wheel to the ground would throw the aircraft into the air to start its antics.

At the aft cg the aircraft definitely had to be landed fast (about 85 mph) and after holding off parallel with the runway the control wheel had to be eased progressively forward and kept there to the end of the landing run, otherwise the accentuated self-stalling characteristics at aft cg tended to take charge when aided by ground effect. Moreover with the cg 88.5 inches aft of the datum the aircraft was out of forward elevator trim at 85 mph so a fair push force was needed to hold the control wheel steady as speed fell off, and the inclination was to think one was moving the wheel forward when in actual fact the push force was only holding it fixed.

The RAE tests finished on 28 August 1947,when I flew the GAL/56 to Lasham airfield where I handed over to Robert Kronfeld, the General Aircraft chief test pilot, who was going to repeat some of the tests for his own experience. Unfortunately he was caught out by the self-stalling characteristics some short time later and let the aircraft get into a spin from which it never recovered, and so one of the world's most experienced glider pilots crashed to his death in what was to be one long list of fatal accidents to tailless aircraft. In some ways, although saddened by this news it did not surprise me, for I had always had the instinctive feeling that the GAL/56 would one day win the eternal battle of wits with those who flew it.**

Eric 'Winkle' Brown: From Wings on My Sleeve

The next two items come from Captain Brown's book *Wings on My Sleeve*. The first dates from early 1948.

**An RAF machine in serious trouble was the new elementary trainer, the Percival Prentice. It had been exhibiting very dangerous spinning characteristics and had killed a number of students and instructors. After a few turns of a spin the aircraft suddenly flattened its attitude. This is the most dangerous type of spin, when the rudder, which is needed for recovery, is blanketed by the fuselage.

It would not recover with full application of rudder alone, but also required a two-handed, full-blooded push on the stick, hardly the thing you could expect an embryo pilot to do after a mere twenty hours or so in the air, and unlikely to inspire much confidence in the instructors either. We were eventually forced to change the face of the Prentice completely after a series of flights with different modifications running into double figures. I could have written a manual on spinning after that. I had great admiration for the boffins flying with me. Often we would do more than fifty spinning turns in one flight. A sick-making thing for a passenger.**

The second extract is from the account of a flight in 1952 while Captain Brown was flying in America.

**1 April 1952 was a day full of incident. Lieutenant-Colonel Marion Carl USMC had been doing a final series of check spins in the new Grumman Guardian. We had already spun this machine and successfully recovered, with the Guardian specially fitted with an ejection seat and a tail parachute. The tests were completed and the tail parachute removed, when Marion suddenly decided to spin it again to see if the loss of the tail parachute and its gear had altered the spinning characteristics. I was to fly the chase plane for him.

We climbed to 10,000 feet over Chesapeake Bay and I started to circle round him. He called 'All set', and went into a spin.

I circled him down. When he had reached 4,000 feet and was still spinning I got worried.

I called to him to jump as we passed 3,000 feet because he was obviously stabilised in his spin without enough recover height. But he continued spinning straight into the Bay with no sign of a bale-out.

As I circled the ring of the splash I saw a parachute canopy in the centre of it, floating on the water. Then Marion's head appeared and he gave a frantic wave. I radioed base to send a flying boat at once and stayed over him until it arrived some twenty minutes later.

He told me that he had tried to operate the ejector seat when I had called him, but when he pulled the face blind it ripped away in his hands and the seat failed to fire. He then tried the recommended method of getting out on the inside of the spin and found himself being forced back by the airflow. He finally got out on the other side and pulled his rip-cord. He felt his parachute open literally as his feet touched the water. He had fallen straight into the splash of his own aircraft, which is why I had never seen him hit the water.

The success of this bale-out provided factual proof of something which wind-tunnel tests had suggested at the same time—that the old method of getting out on the inside of a spin to avoid being hit by the tail was just a long-accepted fallacy.**

Charles 'Chuck' Yeager: from Yeager

The following item is one of the most gripping I have ever read. I present it for you without comment. It comes from General Charles 'Chuck' Yeager's book *Yeager*, and is his account of the fourth powered flight of the X-1A on 12 December 1953.

"Streaking up at 0.8 Mach to 40,000 feet, I fired the last chamber and was rewarded with that familiar kick in the butt. At 0.9 Mach we began bumping like a light airplane in turbulence; the buffeting meant I was about to cross threshold from subsonic to supersonic. We were flying the perfect flight.

Except for the blinding sun, it was bursting straight into my face, I could barely see my gauges, and when I took a quick look at my wing I saw I was climbing too steeply because the sun glaring off my helmet visor made it impossible to see my flight attitude indicator. Instead of a 45-degree climbing angle, I was going up at 55 degrees. By the time I levelled off I'd be a lot higher than the planned 70,000 foot ceiling on this flight. I lowered my nose going through 60,000 feet at 1.1 Mach, and by the time I reached the top of the arc and began to level off I could've shaken hands with Lord Jesus. Eighty thousand feet. A night-time sky with flickering stars at ten in the morning. Up there with only a wisp of atmosphere, steering an airplane was like driving on slick ice.

My Machmeter could register up to Mach 3. Nearing engine flame-out, I hit Mr Crossfield's Mach 2. I dropped my nose slightly to pick up more speed and watched the meter register 2.2 and then 2.3. I was accelerating at 31 mph per second approaching 1,650 mph, the fastest any pilot had yet flown, and the fastest that any straight-winged airplane would ever fly. In my headset I heard Ridley ask Kit Murray whether he yet had me in sight. Kit said, 'No—too small.'

The Machmeter showed 2.4 when the nose began to yaw left. I fed in right rudder, but it had no effect. My outside wing began to rise. I put in full aileron against it, but nothing happened. The thought smacked me: too high, too fast; Yeager. I might have added too late. Christ, we began going haywire. The wing kept coming up and I was powerless to keep from rolling over. And then we started going in four different directions at once. Careening all over the sky, snapping and rolling and spinning, in what pilots call going divergent on all three axes. I called it Hell.

I was crashing around in that cockpit, slamming violently from side to side, front to back, battered to the point where I was too stunned to think. Terrifying.

The thought flashed: I lost my tail. I've had it. G forces yanked me upwards with such force that my helmet cracked the canopy. Without seat straps I probably would've been blasted right through the glass. My pressure suit suddenly inflated with a loud hiss. I was gasping and my face plate fogged. Blinded, being pounded to death, I wondered where in the Sierras I was about to drill a hole.

We were spinning down through the sky like a frisbee. Desperate to see, I groped to the right of the instrument panel trying to find the rheostat switch to turn up the heat in my face plate. But then the ship snapped violently back on itself, slamming me against the control stick and somehow hooking my helmet onto it. As I struggled to get free I had glimpses of light and dark, light and dark, through the fogged visor. Sun, ground, sun, ground. Spinning down I had less than a minute left.

Through some sixth sense, I remembered that the stabiliser was set at 'leading edge down', and I could find that switch in the dark. Still fogged over, I reached for it and retrimmed it. Still groping, I found the rheostat and the heat flicked on. My face plate cleared and I saw more than I wanted to. I was spinning into the Sierras. Without even thinking, I set the controls with the spin. The ship flipped into a normal spin at 30,000 feet. I knew *how to get out of that!* I had spun every airplane imaginable, including the X-1. At 25,000 feet I popped out of the spin.

I radioed to Ridley. My voice was so breathless and desperate that I doubted he could understand me. 'Down to 25,000 feet over Tahachapis. I don't know whether or not I can get back.'

Jack replied, 'That's twenty-five Chuck?'

'I can't say much more. I gotta save myself.'

I heard a voice from the control van say, 'I don't know what's going on, but he's down from altitude.'

God, I didn't know what was going on either. I was so dazed and battered, I wondered if I could still fly. And I worried if the aeroplane could still carry me. 'I don't know if I've torn up this thing or not, but Christ . . .' Ridley couldn't understand, and when I repeated it I sobbed.

I barely remember the next moments. But then my head cleared and I was at 5,000 feet, lining up with the lakebed. I was gliding in from the other side of the Mojave, doing 270 mph and I started to believe I was going to make it. I got on the horn with Ridley.

'I think I can get back to base okay Jack. Boy I'm not going to do that again. Those [Bell] guys were so right [warning against going faster than 2.3 Mach]. You won't have to run a structural demonstration on this damned thing. If I hadda [ejection] seat you wouldn't see me sitting in here.' The lakebed filled my windshield and I put her down a little hard, with a thump and a cloud of dust, but no landing in my life was as sweet as that one. The flight data would later reveal that I had spun down 51,000 feet in fifty-one seconds. I survived on sheer instinct and pure luck.**"**

His wife, Glennis Yeager, commented as follows.

"I had no idea that Chuck had set a new speed record because when he walked in the door that afternoon my first thought was that he had been in a traffic accident. He was pale and very shaky. The way he carried himself I could tell he was hurting, and I wondered whether or not he had again broken his ribs. But then I saw his eyes: they were bloodshot, and I knew from past experience that happened from pulling heavy gs. So, whatever went wrong happened in the X-1A.

'Are you OK?' I asked.

'Yeah,' he said. 'They ran me by the hospital and nothing's broken. Just beat up some.' He complained that his neck was stiff and sore. 'I almost bought it today Hun,' he told me. I had never seen him so shaken.

I was already dressed in an evening gown because we were going to a formal banquet at the Army Navy Club in Los Angeles, where Chuck was to give a talk. In a moment of weakness I agreed to go, but I told him I thought we should cancel out.

'No, no, hell, no,' he said. He got home around four; by five he was dressed and we took off in our car for an hour and a half drive into LA. He drove of course. It was a posh dinner, although a little long and tedious, but he gave a nice talk. That man had been up since four to go off duck hunting. We didn't get home until two in the morning. Chuck was asleep before he hit the pillow.**"**

His commanding officer Major-General Albert G. Boyd makes the final comment.

"No pilot could listen to the tape of Yeager's last ride in the X-1A without getting goosebumps. I've played this tape for audiences and the impact was awesome. One moment, we're listening to a pilot in dire circumstances, battling for his life. In less than a minute he's back in control and cracking a joke about not having to run a structural demonstration on this airplane.

I don't know of another pilot who could've walked away from that one. Each airplane has its own stability limitations that at some point in speed and altitude registers zero on a stability curve. That apparently happened to Chuck at 80,000 feet, flying at 2.4 Mach. The X-1A began to tumble, pitch and roll out of control. The gyrations were so severe that there was an indentation on the canopy where he struck it with his head. He bent the control stick.

Chuck knew he was going to die. That is clear from his voice on the tape. He plunged 80,000 to 25,000 feet before somehow finding the way to save himself, and the moment that he did, he regained his composure. It's the most dramatic and impressive thing I've heard.**"**

Richard P. Hallion: Götterdammerung of the Bell X-2

Following Yeager's success with the Bell X-1 NACA decided to press ahead with attempts to reach Mach 3 with the X-2. The following is the account of the last flight of the X-2, which ended in disaster.

"No programme caused the NACA, especially the engineers of the High Speed Flight Station, more frustration and disappointment than the X-2. It highlighted the terrible effects of underestimating the technical complexities involved in developing a radical new aircraft. It also highlighted the dangers of succumbing to the pressure to set records in the guise of research. The X-2 programme was an unqualified failure, despite achieving both altitude and speed records. It failed to return any of the high-speed aerodynamic heating information anticipated from the programme. Two aircraft were built; both were destroyed with three fatalities.

The X-2 was the most exotic and complex of the early rocket-propelled research aircraft. Designed for supersonic tests of the swept-wing shape, the plane had an estimated performance in excess of Mach 3. The first plane designed to withstand the rigours of aerodynamic heating, its structure was fabricated from stainless steel and a nickel alloy. To be air launched and propelled by a two-chamber rocket engine, it would land on retractable landing skids. Bell had hoped to complete the first aircraft in 1948, but construction delays caused by the complex alloy structure and problems with its explosion-prone Curtiss-Wright 67,000-Newton (15,000-pound) rocket engine stretched the development programme by years . . .

On the advice of the NACA, the Air Force had bought a special computer, the Goodyear Electronic Digital Analyser, which would predict aircraft behaviour by extrapolation of results from test flights. This would give engineers and pilots some indication of what to expect as they flew higher and faster. NACA had designated Richard Day as the HSFS programme engineer for the X-2; he helped the new computer, providing equations and motions data. Day routinely briefed project pilot Pete Everest and, later in 1956 Iven Kincheloe and Mel Apt, Everest's replacements.

The simulations confirmed predictions from NACA wind-tunnel tests that the X-2 would have rapidly deteriorating directional and lateral (roll) stability near Mach 3. Aileron deflection (to roll the plane) could lead to an aerodynamic condition known as adverse yaw, followed by increasingly rapid rolling until the rolling motions reached 'critical roll velocity', the point where the plane would roll into inertial coupling and tumble. During 1956 as Pete Everest moved up in speed, NACA's Dick Day and Hubert 'Jake' Drake anxiously watched the directional stability curves, compared them to flight data, and urged the Air Force to move in smaller increments, not in great leaps of half a Mach number. In May Everest achieved Mach 2.53 making the X-2 the fastest aircraft in the world . . .

Following Everest's final flight, the Air Force momentarily lost interest in Mach 3 in favour of attaining the craft's maximum altitude. Test pilot Iven Kincheloe flew the plane to 33,470 metres, the first flight above 30,000 metres. At that altitude aerodynamic controls were useless. The X-2's behaviour in this region of low dynamic pressure ('low q' in engineer's shorthand) pointed to the need for reaction controls. Above 30,000 metres, still in a ballistic arc, the X-2 began a left bank which Kincheloe wisely did not attempt to correct, for fear of tumbling the airplane. He experienced less than 0.05 g for approximately 50 seconds, a foretaste of weightless space flight; popular science writers dubbed the pilot the 'First of the Spaceman'. In late August the Air Force had taken delivery of the X-2 and then extended its programme for an additional month (before the plane would be turned over to NACA), announcing the purpose as 'to obtain an incremental value of the high-speed performance of the X-2 airplane'. Into the cockpit stepped a new Air Force pilot, Captain Milburn G. Apt.

Though he had flown chase on many X-2 missions, Mel Apt had never flown a rocket-powered aeroplane. He was perhaps the most experienced pilot at Edwards on the phenomenon of inertial coupling, having flown many inertial coupling research flights in the F-100 fighter. Apt had received computer-based briefings on 29 July and 24 September, but the briefings had a flaw. The X-2 flights had accumulated useful data only up to Mach 2.4. Engineers extrapolated all data beyond that, and the predictions were dubious. One study, at a simulated Mach number of 3.2 at 21,000 metres, showed the aircraft 'diverging' (going out of control) during lateral (rolling) manoeuvres. Being extrapolations, none of these studies could be conclusive. On 27 September 1956 Mel Apt dropped away from the Superfortress mothership in the X-2 at 8.49 am. His flight plan called for 'the optimum maximum energy flight path', one certain, if successful, way to exceed Mach 3. In a post-flight question-and-answer session, a senior programme official said, Captain Apt was instructed to make no special effort to obtain maximum speed but rather to stay within previous limits and to concentrate on the best flying technique possible.' Clearly some confusion existed in the minds of mission planners. And there was the matter of experience; Apt had not even had the benefit of a glide flight in the X-2; his sole time in the cockpit was spent in several ground engine runs and posing for publicity photographs with Kincheloe. He had been cautioned to decelerate rapidly if he encountered stability difficulties and not to make rapid control movements above Mach 2.7.

As Apt climbed away after the launch, he followed a predetermined schedule matching the aeroplane's g loading versus altitude, based on code numbers radioed from ground-radar tracking. He reached high altitude, nosed over and dived past Mach 3, reaching Mach 3.2 (3,370 kph) at 20,000 metres. His rocket engine burned for another 10 seconds, longer than previously. The flight had been flawless, but now victory turned to ashes. Apt began an abrupt turn back for the lake. Perhaps he believed the X-2 was travelling slower than it was. Like all early X-series aircraft, the X-2 had lagging instrumentation. The cockpit camera film showed the Machmeter indicating Mach 3 for over 10 seconds. As the X-2 turned, it started a series of rapid rolls and the 'critical roll velocity', an engineering construct, now became a brutal reality. The X-2 coupled, tossing Mel Apt violently about the cockpit, knocking him unconscious. Apt slowly came to; tried to regain control, then jettisoned the craft's nose section in preparation to bale out. The shock of jettisoning the nose knocked him unconcious again, and before he could recover, the capsule plunged into the desert, killing him instantly. The rest of the X-2 spun into the desert 8 kilometres away. Barely three minutes after launch, Mel Apt had become the first pilot to reach Mach 3, and then died. Kincheloe's voice continued on the radio, 'Mel, can you read me, Mel?'

A valued pilot had died. A research aeroplane had crashed just as it might have begun justifying its development. A record had been set, but to little purpose. The accident illustrated the acute need for reliable cockpit instrumentation for high-speed flight research, and this eventually helped spawn the special gyro-stabilised inertial guidance system used on the X-15. Some tried to point to 'research accomplishments' of the X-2, citing limited heating data acquired from seared samples of temperature-sensitive paint—which rocket models could more easily have acquired. In reality, its research was nil. Groping for significance the Edwards historian asked one programme official, 'I imagine the X-2 programme contributed to aeronautical knowledge, didn't it?'

'More than ever before,' answered the official, 'we appreciate the requirement of providing the pilot with the information he needs to do his job, 'Back in Washington, the NACA staff fired off a series of messages to Walt Williams, fearful lest the High Speed Flight Station had condoned the flight. One from Dryden's deputy, got right to the point:

WHAT DOES OPTIMUM MAX ENERGY FLT PATH MEAN
PD SGND CROWLEY

The Air Force Flight Test Center issued its accident report in November 1956; it concluded that the fatal turn at peak velocity had led inevitably to coupled motion instability.**"**

W.A. 'Bill' Waterton: From The Quick and the Dead

In 1956 spinning was still not something to be taken for granted. Squadron Leader W.A. (Bill) Waterton, Gloster's chief test pilot was asked to do some tests on the Meteor Mark III. This extract comes from his book *The Quick and the Dead*.

"Some 220 of these early Meteors were produced before I joined the firm, but there was still work to be done on the Mark III. The Ministry of Supply were not satisfied with its spinning trials, and they had to be redone. One of their test pilots had lost his life on these trials, and it was curiously morbid to do a job that had killed another very competent pilot.

I found the Mark III a cumbersome 'plane to spin. She did not want to spin, but preferred merely to drop a wing and her nose. By using full rudder she could be forced onto her back, where she would rotate slowly before she put her nose down and went into sickeningly unsteady and drunken undulations. The stick tended to thrash about the cockpit and took a great deal of restraining. The 'plane shook and banged in protest, and the angle of spin was so steep that I was often convinced that her nose was beyond the vertical.

When recovery action was taken—full rudder in the opposite direction to the turning of the spin and stick forward—the nose seemed to drop even further into the dive and the speed of rotation increased. Then, without warning, the 'plane would stop dead like a frozen top. My head was snapped to the side of the cockpit, and in a horrible, stalled silence I could look straight down to earth. If the halt came when the 'plane was on its back and beyond the vertical, I would be thrown forward against my harness.

In this stalled condition things were tricky, for despite having my head treated like a shuttlecock, I had to centralise the rudder quickly—or the 'plane would start to spin in the opposite direction.

I could never persuade anyone from the Supply or Air Ministries to occupy the rear seat of a Mark VII two-seater during its spinning tests, and I frequently invited members of Gloster's design staff, just for the fun of hearing their excuses. Generally they did not conceal that they considered themselves too important to face such risks.

I generally started spinning at 20,000 feet, finishing at 10,000 feet. Further trials started at 40,000 feet. The trials called for two complete turns for a fighter, four for a trainer. We usually went well beyond this, and on one occasion one of our pilots achieved I think, sixteen turns.

The 'planes were fitted with a tail parachute for their first spinning trials. In emergency if other methods failed, the 'chute could be streamed to assist in getting the nose down and checking rotation. I never used it myself, although I had cause to complain of the position of the parachute's release switch. To begin with, on the Mark III it was near the floor on the right side of the cockpit, and I argued that it was ridiculous to have to take one's right hand from the vital stick in a time of emergency—a last resort before baling out—in order to grope for a switch. Glosters passed the buck. 'Boscombe approve of it where it is.'

'Boscombe have just lost a bloke,' I replied, 'and I want the switch on the left coaming just above my throttle. There it can be seen, and reached by a simple 6-inch movement of my not-so-important throttle hand.'

Glosters were adamant—the tail 'chute installations had taken months, and this would delay things still further. It was the old business: push, push, push, at the pilot's expense. I replied: 'All right, you can damned well get someone else to do it. I'm not, unless you put the switch where I want it.'

To which they came back: 'We've already had people fly with the switch in that position, so why shouldn't you?'

In the end, with ill grace, they gave way to me, and later the alterations became an official Boscombe requirement.

At the Central Fighter Establishment a flying man ran the show. He said what he wanted and got it. But in the industry the men who flew the 'planes seemingly came second to schedules, and the chief test pilot, at the end of the line, was a necessary nuisance who must not be allowed to interfere in the practicalities of commercial enterprise.**

Roland 'Bee' Beamont: Spinning the P 1A

The English Electric Lightning P 1B was Britain's first supersonic fighter. Its precursor the P 1A made its first flight in 1955. In 1956 spinning trials were done by Roland Beamont, English Electric's chief test pilot. This is his account, from *Aeroplane Monthly*, January 1992.

❝The first flight of the English Electric P 1 had taken place at Boscombe Down on 4 August 1955 and it had in the next two years achieved a high success rate test programme which had proved that the design philosophy (considered radical at the time) of 60-degree wing sweep with a low all-moving tail-plane and irreversible hydraulic-powered flying controls incorporating q and spring 'feel' was correct for this important breakthrough. The P 1 was in fact Britain's first aircraft with supersonic performance, and in the design phase this philosophy had been challenged strongly by some establishment aerodynamic experts on the grounds, they claimed, that the low tail-plane configuration relative to a 60-degree sweep 'shoulder' wing would result in unacceptable, possibly dangerous, pitch instability problems.

The English Electric design office under Teddy Petter had remained adamant, and their confidence had been rewarded by a contract for two development prototypes to AM specification F 23/49, accompanied by the reservation that a full-size low-speed semi-scale replica would be designed by the RAE and built, in a shorter time scale than the P 1 by Short and Harland. This research aircraft would have facilities for varying the wing sweep settings and the tail-plane position, in order 'to investigate the longitudinal stability of the English Electric proposal'.

The Short SB 5 in fact soon demonstrated (in 1953) that the low tail-plane configuration was eminently suitable, and eventually that the RAE's preferred high T-tail was unsatisfactory and potentially dangerous.

By 1956 the full flight envelope of the P 1 had been investigated to 675 knots IAS Mach 1.1 (level), and to M 1.4 in a shallow dive on the 'constant energy line'—the then new term for 'terminal velocity' where thrust equals drag and increasing dive angle only increases rate of height loss without significant increase in speed.

With some minor changes to power control gearings and control-runs and geometry, including improvement in static balancing of the flying control system to eliminate some undemanded control inputs which had resulted from thrust changes affecting the exceptionally low static friction in the control runs, the P 1 was regarded as a total success, pointing to similar success for its coming operational fighter development, the P 1B Lightning. But one corner of the flight envelope had not been fully explored—the high alpha regime beyond normal operating conditions.

At the high angle of attack associated with this new class of aircraft with highly swept or delta wings, a new overriding limitation had been reached—'ground angle'. The maximum usable angle-of-attack of the P 1 in the landing configuration was found to be limited not by lift coefficient or stability or control responsiveness problems on final approach, where these values were all precise and confidence-making; but in fact the minimum landing speed was dictated by the speed at which the tail bumper would touch the ground at the same time as the main wheels, and this occurred at about 14.5 degrees' incidence.

At typical landing weight on the P 1 this was about 140 knots IAS in a flared landing, but in a higher descent rate arrival this could be 10 knots higher and with the risk of minor tail end damage.

So, this being a finite limit that nothing could be done about, and as the landing run measured performance was to specification and satisfactory, further investigation of high alpha had been limited to stall-approaches in clean configuration which had demonstrated that the P 1 remained fully responsive and controllable down to at least 30 knots below the touch-down speed.

But now, at the end of the programme, we needed to look at the 1 g and accelerated stall again to pave the way for the Lightning.

In late 1956 WG 760 had been fitted with a new wing configuration, the 'cambered leading edge' modification, as the first stage towards improving cruise-drag for later and heavier Lightning developments; and it was with this wing that the stalling trials began. Before commencement an anti-spin parachute had been installed and, after some initial self-jettisoning failures in testing had been overcome, acceptable reliability was achieved in two consecutive air streams, and the first stalling tests began on 4 June 1958.

In the previous series I had taken the P 1 down to 120 knots at 20,000 feet in the clean configuration, with fully responsive controls and only mild buffet vibration, but with full up-elevator had not been able to prevent a descent rate of about 200 feet per minute.

On the flight on 4 June, this time with flap and undercarriage down, level flight was held down to 112 knots IAS (at almost full power to balance the high induced drag) with no other change resulting and with normal responses from small and cautious control displacements; but we were again at thrust-equals-drag at that point.

We had not yet found the stall, but for the next flight the Meteor (NF II) chase aircraft was set up with Don Knight, pilot, and John Whitaker with a cine camera. The schedule called for a slow-down at 20,000 feet, again to full power with almost full back stick thrust-equals-drag point, followed by a gradual reduction of power until either a full stall occurred or lack of elevator trim power allowed the nose to drop and IAS to increase—with the onboard instrumentation recording and the chase Meteor filming.

Getting Nowhere Fast

It was a fine, clear day as the small formation headed north over Blackpool away from the sunglare, and as before the P 1 nose-high at around 21 degrees AoA (no incidence gauge in those days!) reached thrust-equals-drag at 112 knots

IAS with the Meteor wallowing and struggling to keep in station up-sun behind for photography.

In my small but by now familiar cockpit everything seemed extremely normal except that at full throttle (max dry) with the nose pointing at the sky we were not going anywhere at all!

I eased the stick back to the aft stop and the ASI dropped through 110 knots, the descent rate increased and at 108 knots quite suddenly and very smoothly the P 1 rolled away to port.

There was no yaw or buffet, the nose was still high and I felt instinctively that this was an undemanded port roll from the ailerons or from some other configuration change like a flap asymmetry. But immediate right stick did not help, and as the roll to port continued past the inverted, the nose pitched down and yawed left, and I then came out of my stupor and realised that we were spinning!

Taking the planned corrective action I centred the stick progressively (I thought), then pushed on outspin (right) rudder, and by halfway round the second full turn I had started to ease the stick forward from neutral—but nothing happened!

Still with full outspin rudder and now with the stick on the forward stop, the P 1 set off into turn three. But this time the nose pitched down to over-the-vertical from the inverted position—at least it was responding to my forward stick and seemed to be about to enter an inverted spin!

Two things then began to register. This spin was not really responding to anything I could think of—and we were well below 15,000 feet on the fast unwinding altimeter, the minimum briefed height for spin recovery after which we were supposed to use the Martin-Baker option (ejector seat).

Even then I was reluctant to abandon this situation which I had a feeling (later justified) of being partly responsible for. But then the mind cleared and I remembered the only recently installed spin-'chute.

Centring the controls, I pulled the spin-'chute handle and almost immediately there was a jolt, the nose pitched further down and the rolling stopped, with the P 1 in a left-banked near-vertical dive. A glance at the ASI showed 120 knots and rising, and I resisted the strong temptation to pull out of the dive (and probably back into 'departure') while noting with interest the altimeter unwinding swiftly through 9,000 feet.

There would also be much lag in this reading, but there was still a margin to spare and so I delayed easing back on the stick until 160 knots and then recovered to level at 6,500 feet to find the engines still running and no further problems. I jettisoned the spin-'chute and returned to Warton.

Much was learnt from this event, not least that a long period of success in an experimental programme must never be allowed to lead to complacency in the planning of corner-point tests. For example we had apparently planned a potentially critical test point at 10,000 feet lower than our own safety criteria had suggested.

Then although I had absorbed the briefing on recommended recovery action, in the event instead of fully centering the ailerons, the instrumentation and the Meteor's cine camera film confirmed that I had held in 5 degrees of out-spin aileron throughout two and a half turns of the spin. Later P 1B intensive spinning programme revealed that with any out-spin aileron applied, the Lightning (and the P 1) would never recover from a spin!

This was a revealing episode, and it was finally decided that the full CA release spinning programme would be done in the P 1B Lightning beginning the following year, as the P 1 WG760, though relevant, was not sufficiently representative of the operational fighter for spinning tests to read across completely.

The subsequent Lightning spinning programme was massive, lasting more than six months and involving over 200 spins in all relevant configurations. This was completed by Warton's experienced test pilots and it established that in all circumstances and configurations the Lightning would in fact recover from a spin if the controls were released to neutral by the pilot—but at least 10,000 feet was needed for full recovery from an erect spin, and rather more from an inverted spin.

Nothing can be taken for granted in flight testing.**"**

Royal Air Force Manual: Stalling and Spinning

At this point I interrupt the chronicle of spins to include an extract from the *Royal Air Force Manual* of 1955, volume 2 (amended to 1958) on Aircraft Operation. In the section on basic flying is a chapter on stalling and spinning.

Read this with the thought that it is not an account of what happened to somebody else but what will happen to you when you take off and fly your aeroplane up to do it yourself. It is sufficient to cause a slight dryness of the mouth. You will be plummeting to earth, out of control, as you calmly apply these instructions.

"Stalling

Introduction
1.   An aircraft stalls when the smooth flow of the air over its wings changes to a turbulent flow and the lift decreases. As this may happen suddenly, a pilot must be able to recognise the approach of a stall and know the best recovery action required to prevent loss of control and minimise any loss of height.

Stalling Characteristics
2.   The stalling characteristics of an aircraft should be investigated at an early stage while becoming familiar with a new type of aircraft. Pilot's

Notes deal with stalling behaviour, but age and use may produce differences between individual aircraft of the same type.

3.　In general, stalling follows a common pattern. As speed is reduced, a warning of the impending stall is given in the form of buffeting which can vary from being fairly severe to almost imperceptible depending on the aircraft type and configuration. The buffet may start at some 5–15 knots before the stall, and usually increases in strength as the stall is approached. On some aircraft an artificial indicator of the approaching stall is provided. Several methods are used, for example, either the whole control column or an inset portion of the handgrip can be made to vibrate strongly at a pre-set speed close to the stall.

4.　On all aircraft, as speed is reduced the controls become less effective and larger movements are needed to correct or achieve a given displacement of the aircraft. On aircraft without power-operated controls, the feel of the controls becomes noticeably sloppy and their effectiveness decreases as the stall approaches. Just before the stall the aircraft may start sinking in spite of correcting movements of the control column.

5.　At the stall, either wing and/or the nose may drop suddenly and to a varying degree. With power on, the stalling speed is lower, the nose-up attitude of the aircraft at the stall is more pronounced, the sinking is less marked, and any wing-dropping tendency is aggravated; the lower speed is due to the vertical component of the upwards-inclined thrust line which provides an additional lifting force and so allows level flight at a lower speed. The greater the power used, the lower the stalling speed.

6.　On many types of aircraft, when the initial wing or nose drop occurs, the control column may not be fully back and any further backward movement of the control column in these circumstances may aggravate any wing-dropping tendency and tend to induce a spin. *In general, recovery should be made when the initial nose or wing drop occurs.*

7.　If an unintentional spin occurs when stalling with the flaps and under-carriage down, these must be raised immediately to ensure that they do not affect the recovery and to prevent damage, due to excessive speed in the dive following recovery.

Recovery from the Stall

8.　Recovery must be made as quickly and as decisively as possible with a minimum loss of height. *Recovery with a minimum loss of height necessitates the use of full power.*

9.　The recommended recovery action is to ease the control column forward far enough to unstall the wings, and to apply up to full power simultaneously as quickly as engine limitations permit. If the control column is moved too far forward additional height is lost. If sufficient thrust is available, it should only be necessary to move the control column forward slightly, as the thrust will be adequate to accelerate the aircraft to a higher speed and, as stated in para 5, the use of power reduces the stalling speed.

10.   If a wing drops, sufficient opposite rudder should be applied to prevent any further yaw and to raise the wing. This action should be taken simultaneously with the forward movement of the control column and increase of power. As the wings become unstalled the natural stability of the aircraft also causes a dropped wing to rise and this can be assisted by the use of the ailerons. *The aircraft must be eased gradually out of the dive following recovery*; any attempt to force a return to level flight will induce a g stall (para 15) and cause further loss of height.

Swept-wing Aircraft

11.   The general stalling characteristics of aircraft with swept-back leading edges may differ considerably from those of straight-wing types, and Pilot's Notes should always be studied carefully before practising stalling for the first time, otherwise difficulty may be experienced during recovery.

12.   As on any other aircraft, as the stall is approached on swept-wing types it is usual for stall warning buffeting to be felt, increasing in strength as the stall approaches, although the amount of buffet may, in some cases, be barely discernible.

13.   Before the stall, there may be a sudden nose-up change of trim, known as *pitch-up* or *tuck-in*, which occurs as the wing-tips stall. This is not usually strong but necessitates a push force or relaxation of the backward pull on the control column to maintain a set attitude. Unequal stalling of both tips may cause sundry rolling and yawing movements at the same time. When the stall spreads over the whole wing, the nose pitches down. However, during the time that the angle of attack has been increasing the drag has also increased to a high figure (ie the L/D ratio is very low) and this induces a very high rate of sink which may be sufficient to mask the development of the full stall. In this condition the aircraft descends very steeply in an almost level or slightly nose-down attitude with the control column well back. Very little encouragement is needed to make the aircraft spin and therefore the rudder and ailerons should be kept neutral. In practice stalling, there is nothing to be gained by reducing speed much below the point at which the stall warning buffet is encountered, and recovery should be made before the stall has reached its more advanced stages. Pilot's Notes advise on this point when the stalling characteristics include the aforementioned features to a marked degree.

14.   On all swept-wing types, therefore, it is most important to take recovery action as soon as the initial wing or nose drop occurs.

Stalling in Manoeuvres

15.   If an attempt is made to change the flight path in a pitching plane too quickly, eg by turning at too high a rate or by recovering from a dive

too sharply, a stall known variously as an accelerated or g stall, or less accurately as a high-speed stall, may occur. This last term is not altogether suitable since the speed may be only a few knots above the level flight stalling speed when the control column is moved back to apply the g.

16.   The manoeuvres described in para 15 involve accelerations in the pitching plane and result in an increased loading on the aircraft. Although the accelerated stall occurs at the same angle of attack as the normal stall, the IAS at which it occurs is roughly equivalent to the level flight stalling IAS times the square root of the load factor. For example, during a 60-degree banked turn (ie with a load factor of 2) an aircraft having a normal stalling IAS of 100 knots would stall at an IAS of 100 x 1.41 knots, ie 141 knots.

Stall Warning

17.   Warning of the approach of an accelerated stall is given by airframe buffeting which increases in intensity as the stalling angle is approached. The stick force and control effectiveness are proportional to the IAS at which the stall occurs, which may be any speed of which the aircraft is capable.

18.   At the lower speeds fractional amounts of g are sufficient to cause a stall. This applies particularly to aircraft with high wing-loadings. Steep approaches for landing should not normally be made on these aircraft, as the large backward movement of the control column required to round out for the landing may apply sufficient g to stall the aircraft at the low speed used on the approach.

19.   During dives and dive recoveries at low altitude, such as those used on air-to-ground armament practices, ample height must be allowed for recovery. Over-concentration on the aiming problem can result in insufficient height for normal recovery; and if in the subsequent attempt to recover excessive g is applied the aircraft will stall and possibly flick into a spin.; If the speed is high, even though the stalling angle may not be reached, the g threshold of the pilot and/or limitation of the aircraft may be exceeded.

Pitch-up in Manoeuvres

20.   Any pitch-up tendencies (para 13) possessed by a swept-wing aircraft are exaggerated when enough g is applied to stall the aircraft in a manoeuvre. The higher the g required to cause the stall, the stronger is the pitch-up and the resultant unavoidable increase in g before the motion can be checked by a forward movement of the control column. The increased g caused by pitch-up can be serious at high IAS and low altitude, since high g is needed to promote pitch-up under these conditions and any temporary overshoot might exceed the g limitations. However the g limitations placed on such aircraft take this possibility into account and, unless the g limitation is exceeded, pitch-up should

not occur on a correctly loaded aircraft, ie an aircraft having the cg within the specified limits. At the highest altitudes, although forming an operational weakness, pitch-up does not usually result in a serious g overshoot as both the initiating g and the resultant g are low as a result of the reduced indicated air speeds obtained at these altitudes.

21.   When the stall occurs in a turn, depending on which wing stalls and drops first, the aircraft tends to roll either into or out of the turn. During recovery from a dive, either wing may drop. In certain aircraft the wing drop is sudden and may be severe. If the control column is held back the aircraft may execute a series of flick rolls which, at high speed, cause severe overstress.

Recovery

22.   Recovery from any stage of an accelerated stall is made by moving the control column forward until the buffeting disappears.

Use of Ailerons

23.   Pilot's Notes state whether the ailerons are effective at and below the stall; in general, it can be taken that the ailerons on high-performance aircraft are always effective under these conditions. If the stall is accompanied by a wing drop, a small amount of rudder away from the dropping wing (port wing drop—starboard rudder) should be used to check any tendency for this roll to produce yaw and the downward progress of the dropping wing can be checked with aileron. However, even when the ailerons are still effective, a wing-dropping movement can often be arrested more positively and quickly by use of the rudder; in most aircraft only a small rudder movement is needed whereas a comparatively large amount of aileron is required. It should be noted, however, that on certain aircraft, aileron movements at the stall can, through aileron drag, induce sufficient adverse yaw to precipitate a spin. The effect of aileron at the stall should be investigated cautiously when stalling an aircraft for the first time; Pilot's Notes advise on the use of the ailerons under these conditions.

Spinning

Note: The following paragraphs are general remarks on spinning. Pilot's Notes should always be read before spinning an unfamiliar aircraft.

Introduction

The spin is not a normal manoeuvre: it is the result of yawing or rolling at the point of stall. As it is possible to enter a spin through mishandling the controls during aerobatics, steep turns and other quite normal manoeuvres, the pilot must be able to recognise a spin and recover promptly. This is done by practising spinning and spin recovery on suitable types of aircraft so that the pilot becomes accustomed to the sensation of spinning and quickens his assessment of the change of attitude and motion of the aircraft. The stick forces experienced during a spin may be high on some aircraft, necessitating the use of both hands to effect recovery; on other aircraft the forces may be so low that little or no effort is required to move the control column. In certain cases considerable snatching occurs on the control column and some strength is needed to hold the control column in the desired position.

During a rapid spin, or if a pilot is unaccustomed to spinning, considerable disorientation (giddiness) and mental confusion should be anticipated: instances have occurred when experienced pilots have been convinced about the direction of spin only to be proved wrong, and what appears to be correct recovery action in such cases only prolongs the spin. Thus, impressions gained during a spin should always be confirmed when possible by the instruments; this is particularly important with regard to the direction of spin which is indicated by the turn needle, deflection to the left indicating a spin left and vice versa. Often a conscious effort is required to transfer attention to the instruments.

Airmanship

Before practising spins, carry out the following checks:

(a) Ensure that the exercise is permitted and authorised and that the correct recovery action is known.

(b) Warn passenger or pupil when the exercise is about the begin.

(c) Ensure that sufficient height is available to complete recovery at not less than 3,000 feet above ground level (AGL) in elementary aircraft, or as otherwise stated for more advanced aircraft.

(d) Ensure that:
1. There are no loose articles in the cockpit.
2. Full rudder can be applied.
3. Undercarriage, flaps and air-brakes are retracted.
4. Gyro instruments are caged and all straps are tight and secure.
5. Immediately before starting the spin make sure that the area below the aircraft is clear of other aircraft and that there are no populated areas or aerodromes below.

Entry into Spin

When practising spinning, the throttle should be fully closed as the spin starts; entry is made by yawing the aircraft at the point of stall and maintaining the yaw and the high angle of attack, ie full rudder in the required direction and the stick held fully back. Out-spin aileron (aileron away from the intended direction of spin) may be needed to develop the spin, but Pilot's Notes will advise on this point. The commencing movements of the spin may be difficult to assess, and vary from a yawing of the nose around the horizon together with a small degree of roll, to rapid rolls involving an initial slow rate of yaw sometimes combined with varying rates of pitching. Some aircraft behave very erratically during the first few seconds of the spin and may even become temporarily inverted before settling down. If recovery is made during this period the attitude on the cessation of the spin is generally unpredictable.

Types of Spin

Spins may be divided into two main types. The first is the oscillatory spin in which the aircraft, perhaps after initial horizontal turns, will spin with varying rates of rotation, and changing nose positions (pitch attitudes) relative to the horizon. This may then develop into the second type of spin, which has a smooth and consistent motion in which there is less pitching but a faster rate of rotation.

Normal Spin Recovery

The standard spin recovery action is to apply full opposite rudder, holding the control column hard back and keeping the ailerons neutral (control column central), then, after a short pause, moving the control column progressively forward until the spin stops.

Keeping the ailerons neutral.   These actions are taken to stop the yawing motion and unstall the wings. On many aircraft there may be a momentary increase in the rate of rotation after recovery action has been taken. The moment rotation stops, the rudder and control column should be centralised; the rudder to prevent another spin in the direction of application, and the control column to prevent too steep a dive during recovery. As airspeed increases, the aircraft should be eased into level flight and power applied, care being taken to avoid a g stall. If the undercarriage and flaps are down on entering the spin they should be raised as soon as possible since they may delay, or even prevent, recovery. If an inadvertent spin occurs when carrying jettisonable wing loads—such as fuel tanks, bombs or rockets—these should be jettisoned as soon as possible to ensure a quick recovery. The attitude of the aircraft may at times have to be taken into consideration before taking recovery action; generally these occasions are when the aircraft is pointing steeply upwards during the incipient stage, or when full normal recovery action would obviously result in the aircraft passing through the inverted position and into an inverted spin. Only common sense and experience can guide the pilot in these circumstances and suggest to him when to wait until the nose falls below the horizon, or when he should hold the controls neutral until a more advantageous moment arises to apply full recovery action. In assessing the height available for recovery from spins, altimeter error should be considered.

When recovery action is taken it is not unusual for the spin to stop when the aircraft is inverted, particularly if recovery action is taken before the aircraft is settled in the spin. If this occurs it is best to ease the nose of the aircraft well below the horizon and allow the speed to increase before half-rolling.

Emergency Normal Spin Recovery Action

Emergency recovery action should only be taken after normal recovery action has proved ineffective; the seriousness of the situation must be assessed and the first consideration is one of height. If sufficient height is available the following actions should be taken after checking undercarriage and flaps—up; air-brakes—in; throttles—closed; and external stores jettisoned:

(a) Apply and maintain full rudder opposing the direction of turn, but see sub-para (c1).

(b) Ease the control column progressively forward and apply aileron as recommended in Pilot's Notes.

(c) If the aircraft does not respond try to change the stable character of the spin by:

    1. Applying full pro-spin control then repeating the recovery action.

    2. Opening and closing the throttle or using full throttle on the 'in-spin' engine (twin-engined aircraft).

    3. Inducing fore-and-aft rocking motion by moving the control column backwards and forwards. In single-engined propeller-driven aircraft action at sub-sub-paras 2 and 3 should be combined; when the control column is moved forwards the throttle should be opened and vice versa.

If the g increases noticeably re-examination of the instruments may show that the airspeed has increased and the aircraft may be in a spiral not a spin. Recovery action appropriate to a spiral should then be taken.

Effect of Aileron

Pilot's Notes indicate whether ailerons should be used in spin recovery, but it is important to realise that the use of ailerons may make all the difference between recovering more quickly and not recovering at all. The aid of powerful ailerons (as fitted on high-performance aircraft) to recover from a spin in one direction may suddenly reverse the direction of the spin. In general, the effect of ailerons on the spin depends on the weight distribution of the particular aircraft concerned, and this may alter completely during flight, eg as fuel or weapons are used. Since incorrect use of ailerons delays, or even prevents, recovery, ensure that the ailerons are neutral by visually checking the position of the control column, if necessary against a reference point in the cockpit. This applies particularly when the control column is cranked or the aircraft is very sensitive to the use of aileron. Aileron towards the direction of the spin is termed in-spin aileron; aileron away from the direction of the spin is termed out-spin aileron.

If an aircraft has most of its weight concentrated into a long fuselage and has proportionately light wings and a short span, then in-spin aileron assists recovery. The longer the fuselage in relation to the span and the greater the weight concentrated in the nose and tail, the greater is the beneficial effect of in-spin aileron during recovery.

If the aircraft has a short fuselage and a relatively heavy wing of large span, then out-spin aileron is most helpful. The carriage of wing-tip tanks would mean that an aircraft of the type described in the previous paragraph would be brought nearer to the short fuselage—large span type from the viewpoint of the use of aileron during spin recovery.

Ailerons should only be used for recovery when the normal method of recovery has no effect. All aircraft on which spinning is permitted recover if the normal action is taken. On the majority of aircraft, in-spin aileron has a beneficial effect. The natural tendency, however, is to apply out-spin aileron, and this must be guarded against.

Inverted Spinning

Intentional inverted spinning is prohibited except in aircraft specifically cleared for this manoeuvre by the Air Ministry.

In a normal spin the yawing and rolling motions are in the same direction but in an inverted spin they are in opposite directions. It is this factor which may make it difficult to decide whether a spin is normal or inverted, particularly when the normal spin in that type of aircraft is very steep and when the entry may have involved a series of confusingly rapid rolling and pitching movements. However, an inverted spin is less likely to occur than a normal spin because one of the requirements is that the control column should be forward of neutral when the aircraft is inverted or becoming inverted at low airspeed. The most common manoeuvres which can lead to inverted spins are a loop or half-roll off the top when the airspeed is too low at the top—the likelihood thus increases with altitude, and when a normal spin is stopped in the inverted position and an attempt is made to push the nose up to the horizon instead of allowing the speed to increase slightly, then half-rolling and easing the aircraft into level flight.

In an inverted spin, as with a normal spin, the direction is in the same way as the yaw which is indicated by the turn needle. In a flat inverted spin the amount of rolling motion is small but the yaw is very evident; in a steep inverted spin the yawing motion may be masked by the high rate of roll. It is a wise precaution, therefore, to always inspect the turn needle to confirm the direction of spin. In an inverted spin slight negative g may be present but this also may be so masked by the rate of roll as to be unrecognisable.

Inverted Spin Recovery

The standard recovery from an inverted spin is to apply full rudder in the opposite direction to the yaw and move the control column progressively backwards until the spin stops. It is essential that the ailerons are kept centralised throughout the procedure; this usually requires conscious effort particularly in aircraft with cranked sticks. Immediately the spin stops the controls should be centralised, and the speed allowed to increase slightly, then the aircraft should be gently half-rolled or eased out of the dive. Great care should be taken when easing out of the dive because a pilot's positive g threshold may be seriously reduced if negative g has been experienced during the inverted spin.

Often, when anti-spin rudder is applied, the yawing motion will stop, the aircraft will pitch through the vertical, pendulum fashion, and continue to spin but in the opposite direction. It is essential to watch for this pitch change and recognise that an inverted spin has been converted into a normal spin. Normal spin recovery action should then be taken.

Emergency Inverted Spin Recovery Action

The emergency actions for the normal spin recovery apply equally to the inverted spin except for the control column movement and the fore-and-aft rocking with changes in power. In an inverted spin the control column should be eased backwards and to create fore-and-aft rocking the throttle should be opened as the control column is moved backwards, the opposite to the normal spin case.

Steep Spins

In a steep spin it may be difficult to determine whether the spin is normal or inverted. A pilot should therefore always refer to the turn needle to establish the direction of spin. External references may enable the pilot to establish the direction of roll and if it is the same as the turn the spin is normal, if opposite the spin is inverted. If it is not possible to establish whether the spin is normal or inverted and sufficient height is available, the following recovery actions are recommended:

(a) Apply and maintain full rudder opposing the direction of turn.
(b) Take normal recovery action—stick fully forward, ailerons neutral, check ailerons neutral; if ineffective:
(c) Take emergency normal recovery action—stick fully forward, in-spin aileron; check aileron in same direction as turn needle; if ineffective:
(d) Take inverted recovery action—stick fully back, ailerons neutral, check ailerons neutral; if ineffective:
(e) Take emergency inverted recovery action—stick fully back, out-spin aileron, check aileron in opposite direction to turn needle; if ineffective:
(f) Attempt to change the stable character of the spin.

The aileron application at sub-paras (c) and (e) is usual and applies to most modern fighters and advanced trainers, but Pilot's Notes will advise for each type of aircraft. If the amount of height available is marginal the actions at sub-paras (b) (c) (d) and (e) should be held long enough to be effective normally. Pilot's Notes will advise on this point but the usual period is two turns. If none of the above actions are effective, the pilot should take his hands and feet off the controls and prepare to abandon aircraft.

Abandoning a Spinning Aircraft

If a pilot considers that his height is insufficient to recover from a spin the aircraft should be abandoned. Generally, in high-performance aircraft such as fighters and advanced trainers, if control has not been regained at 8,000 feet AGL the aircraft should be abandoned.**"**

That final piece of advice must always be kept in mind as the next extract shows.

Charles 'Chuck' Yeager: Going for Another Record

In 1963 General Charles 'Chuck' Yeager was engaged in some trials with the Lockheed Starfighter, an aircraft with a notorious reputation as a widow-maker. A formidable fighter aircraft, it required a high degree of skill to fly. Yeager's account of a flight in the F-104 is from his autobiography *Yeager*.

66Lockheed's Starfighter, the F-104 was the first Mach 2 fighter aircraft, and the first to break the sound barrier in a climb. I had flight tested it for the Air Force back in 1954. The aeroplane had a bad pitch-up problem. Flying it at a 30-degree angle of attack, its short, thin wings blanketed its T-shaped tail, causing the nose to suddenly rise dramatically. The next thing a pilot knew he was in a flat spin towards earth, pushing the throttle forward as far as it would go, high engine rpms being the only way to recover a 104 out of a flat spin.

The special rocket-powered 104s we had at the space school had the same pitch-up problem. Lockheed delivered three of them to us in 1963 for use in high-altitude, zero g training. Before our students began flying them, I decided to establish some operating parameters to learn at what altitude the aerodynamic pitch-up forces would be greater than the amount of thrust in the hydrogen-peroxide rockets installed on the nose. We had two 250-pound thrusters to train for manoeuvring in zero g conditions. We thought we would encounter pitch-up somewhere around 95,000 feet. And while I was at it, I wanted to establish an altitude record in the rocket version of the 104. I flew it on the morning of 12 December 1963 and had the airplane up to 108,000 feet. It had gone beautifully, and I was scheduled for a second flight in the afternoon. Mom was waiting for us, and Glennis drove her over to base operations. We had a quick lunch; I was still wearing my bulky pressure suit because once you get sweaty and take it off, you can't get it back on. Then they took off, and so did I.

I climbed to 35,000 feet, about 100 miles from Edwards at the foot end of the San Joaquin Valley near Fraser Peak, and headed for Rogers Dry Lake at 37,000 feet in the afterburner. I was travelling at better than Mach 2 when I fired the 6,000-pound thrust rocket in my tail that burned a mixture of hydrogen peroxide and jet fuel. By then I was climbing at a steep 70-degree angle, whistling through 60,000 feet, and the afterburner flamed out, oxygen starved in the thin atmosphere. That was expected. Later, I planned to go into a shallow dive to allow the engine blades to windmill in the rush of air, working up the necessary revolutions enabling re-ignition in the lower air, at about 40,000 feet. So I shut down the engine and let the rocket carry me over the top. I had to watch my tailpipe temperature, because at my steep climbing angle it would over-temp even though I was on idle.

I went over the top at 104,000 feet, and as the airplane completed its arc, it fell over. But as the angle of attack reached 28 degrees, the nose pitched up. That had happened in the morning flight as well. I used the small rocket thrusters on the nose to push it down. I had no problem then. This time, the damned thrusters had no effect. I kept those peroxide ports open, using all my peroxide trying to get that nose down, but I couldn't. My nose stuck high, and the damned airplane finally fell off flat and went into a spin.

I was spinning down like a record on a turntable, and because I couldn't get into a shallow dive and drive air through the engine turbine, my rpms were falling off drastically. I had no hydraulic pressure because that operated off the engine, which had wound down to a point where it stopped and locked at about 40,000 feet. I was feeling kind of hopeless about this ride. The data recorder would later indicate that the airplane made fourteen flat spins from 104,000 until impact on the desert floor. I stayed with it through thirteen of those spins before I punched out. I hated losing an expensive airplane, but I couldn't think of anything else to do.**"**

Derek Piggott: Spinning in Gliders

A glider has a greater wing span relative to its size than most powered aircraft. It is usually lighter, flies more slowly and often near to stalling point. It is more likely to be accidentally stalled than a powered aircraft especially on approach to a landing or in a turn near to the ground, or after a winch-cable break during take-off. Although most gliders carry an airspeed indicator, with no engine the rustle of the glider through the air usually helps indicate to the pilot how fast it is flying. When everything goes quiet the pilot is alerted!

Some of the features of spinning a glider are discussed in this extract from *Gliding*, 1972 by Derek Piggott.

"Incipient Spins

Sometimes when the glider stalls, one wing may drop. More height is lost than in a straight stall, and there is a possibility of a spin developing if the correct recovery action is not taken. A stall with wing dropping is known as an incipient spin because it is really the first stage of the entry into a spin.

If the wing drops during the stall, apply opposite rudder and then ease forward on the stick to unstall the glider. Immediately the noise of the airflow indicates that normal flying speed has been regained, bring the wings level with the ailerons so that the loss of height is minimised. If the correct action is taken promptly, only a small angle of bank will be reached and little additional height will be lost. A steep angle of bank will probably result in 200 or 300 feet being lost and this would be very critical near the ground.

If a glider is stalled while it is turning, it will usually drop the inner wing. The stalling speed is higher than normal so that, particularly in very steep turns, recovery may be immediate if the backward pressure on the stick is relaxed.

This is because at the higher speed, good control is regained the moment that the wings are unstalled.

Particular care must be taken when turning below 500 feet. A safe margin of speed (considering the angle of bank) must be maintained throughout any turn. Because of turbulent conditions and the 'wind gradient' effect near the ground, the recovery from a stall during the final turn on approach may take several times as much height as the recovery from a practice stall. This fact alone accounts for approach accidents in the past costing hundreds of pounds for repairs, quite apart from the risk of injury in this type of accident.

Such accidents would be avoided by increasing speed for the approach at 300–400 feet instead of waiting until the last possible moment. This avoids the possibility of arriving in a position close to the ground at a low speed with the final turn and approach still to be made. When this occurs it is difficult to find sufficient height either to increase the speed or to make a correctly banked turn. In windy or gusty conditions this type of approach results in an accident sooner or later.

Most gliders are unlikely to go into a fully developed spin but, near the ground, an incipient spin is certainly as dangerous and far more likely to occur.

Spinning

A spin will develop if the controls are misused while the glider is stalled. The wings must be stalled and the glider must be yawed to make it spin. The prevention of a spin is, therefore, merely a matter of avoiding the stall and checking immediately any tendency for the glider to drop a wing and yaw should an unintentional stall occur.

The entry into a fully developed spin is in two stages. At first the glider drops the wing and falls into a slow spiral. Then after about three quarters of a turn, if the glider or aircraft is one which will spin fully and no corrective action is taken, the rate of spin increases rapidly until the spin is fully developed. The motion is then automatic and will continue until recovery action is taken.

Recovery from the incipient stage is easy and immediate if opposite rudder is applied and the stick moved forward sufficiently to unstall the wings.

The full spin takes much longer to stop, and the recovery action is more critical if a quick recovery is required. The order in which the controls are moved becomes important because there may be interference between elevators and the rudder in the spin which will reduce their effectiveness.

The correct method from a fully developed spin must be learnt by heart: full opposite rudder – slight pause; stick steadily forward until the spin stops; centralize the rudder and recover to cruising flight. (Note: In most gliders recovery is immediate as soon as the stick is released).

Intentional spinning should not be carried out below 1,000 feet although incipient spins in which prompt recovery is made can be safely carried out down to about 700 feet in some types of gliders.

It is most probable that your instructor will just demonstrate to you one turn

General Charles 'Chuck' Yeager, standing beside *Glamorous Glennis* the Bell X-1 in which he made the first supersonic flight and in which he subsequently spun out of control and recovered.
(National Air and Space Museum, Smithsonian Institution)

The Bell X-1. The aircraft in which General Charles 'Chuck' Yeager broke the sound barrier.
(Aeroplane Monthly)

(*Above*) The General Aircraft GAL/56, described by Captain Eric 'Winkle' Brown as 'The worst aircraft I ever flew' spun in killing its test pilot Robert Kronfeld. (*Aeroplane Monthly*)

(*Left*) Captain Eric 'Winkle' Brown CBE DSC AFC MA FRAeS RN Commanding Officer of the Aerodynamics Flight at Farnborough. (*Brown's Collection*)

(*Below*) The de Havilland Swallow DH108. Flown by John Derry, it exceeded Mach one, but all three prototypes crashed killing their pilots, Geoffrey de Havilland, Squadron Leader J. S. R. Muller-Rowland and Squadron Leader George Genders. (*Aeroplane Monthly*)

Wing Commander Roland 'Bee' Beamont CBE DSO* DFC* DL FRAeS RAF in the cockpit of an English Electric Lightning F6 at Warton in 1964. *(Beamont Collection)*

The English Electric P1A taking off on its first flight (cambered leading edge) with Wing Commander Roland Beamont at the controls on 15 February 1957. Note tail bumper closer to the ground than main wheels. *(The Aeroplane)*

The P1A spinning.
1.
112 kts, 20,000 feet.
(All photographs from the Beamont Collection and photographed by John Whitaker)

2.
108 kts, rolling left.

3.
Right stick.

4.
Spinning.

5.
Pitching down.

6.
Yawing left.

7.
Yawing left – pitching up and rolling left.

8.
End of first turn – continuing spin, rolling left into turn two. 90 kts, 18,000 feet, having lost 2,000 feet in first turn.

Lockheed F-104A Starfighter, modified in 1963 with a 6,000lb thrust Rocketdyne AR-2 rocket engine, two-foot wing-tip extensions, enlarged vertical surfaces of the F104G and hydrogen peroxide control thrusters at nose, tail and wing-tips. *(Frank B. Mormillo)*

A Wasp 229 B3 Hang Glider, which I spun into the ground in 1974. I broke my wrist. Erik piloting. *(Author's Collection)*

The Piper Tomahawk. This aircraft came under suspicion following a spinning accident. After investigation it was found to be safe so long as modified pilot's notes regarding spin recovery were obeyed. *(Flight International)*

The Grob Twin Astir sailplane taking off. A two-seat tandem glider typical of the sort of sailplane used to teach spinning and spin recovery. *(Philip Hadley)*

A Boeing 737. *(Aeroplane Monthly)*

The CFM Metal-Fax Streak Shadow is a good example of stall/spin resistant aircraft. During flight testing for the UK Civil Aviation Authority the CFM Shadow clearly demonstrated that there was no 'defined' stall. It was also found that the aircraft could not be forced to spin. This is achieved with a 'dropped leading edge D section camber line towards the tips'. *(CFM Metal-Fax)*

of a full spin and will spend much more time on the incipient stage which is much more important. Prompt action in the incipient stage will always prevent a full spin, and a safe airspeed will prevent any possibility of either.

Later on you will receive more training in full spins so that you will become more experienced in making quick recoveries. At first you may find the sensations of spinning disturbing, and this may affect your ability to move the controls correctly to recover. Further practice will overcome this, and as you get more experience you will probably find that you gain confidence through the knowledge that you can control the machine in a steep attitude.

Auto-rotation and Spinning.

If a wing drops when the aircraft is stalled or nearly stalled, the downward movement of the wing results in a change of the direction of the relative airflow. The angle of attack of the down-going wing will be increased and this may cause it to become stalled, or more seriously stalled than the other wing. The reduction in the lift developed by the dropping wing will help to make it drop farther. The rising wing will have a reduced angle of attack and be almost or completely unstalled and will be developing much more lift than the one which is falling. The result of these differences in lift is an unstable rolling movement which is known as auto-rotation (see diagram [Figure 5]). If no other factors were involved, the aircraft would continue to roll until the wings

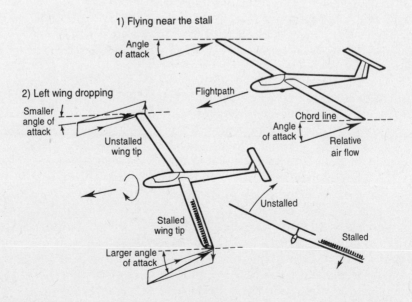

Figure 5. The effect of one wing dropping at the stall. The glider becomes unstable and starts auto-rotation. In normal flight the increase in angle of attack of a dropping wing results in more lift and stops the movement.

were unstalled. This horizontal spinning manoeuvre is known as a flick roll. However, the effect of the force of gravity acting on the aircraft, together with the nose-down pitching movement at the stall, causes the auto-rotation to change from a horizontal rolling motion to a steep diving one.

The uneven stalling of the wings which causes the auto-rotation also results in the wings developing unequal drag. The badly stalled wing has much more drag than the other one. This causes a yawning movement towards the dropping wing which pulls the aircraft into a steep spiral descent which is the first stage of a spin. In most modern gliders, this yawing effect is insufficient for a full spin to develop. Additional yaw caused by applying the rudder or creating a large amount of aileron drag by using a large movement of the aileron may cause a spin to develop.

Whenever the aircraft is stalled and one wing drops, auto-rotation will begin. This is an incipient spin. It is sufficient for only one wing to be stalled to start an incipient spin. If the rate of yaw is sufficient to maintain the spiral and the wings remain stalled, the incipient spin will develop into a full spin. The angle of attack of both wings becomes much greater and the rate of rotation increases. The angle of attack of the wings in a fully developed spin is usually 30–40 degrees so that it is much more difficult to unstall them once the spin has developed. Some gliders spin erratically, some steeply, fast or slow. However, most gliders need to be held into a spin or they will recover by themselves.

The spinning characteristics of all modern British gliders are tested during trials, and using the standard method of recovery the glider must stop spinning within one turn, and it must be possible to recover to level flight within 300 feet of initiating recovery action. Most gliders are very loath to spin beyond the incipient stage, and will recover if the controls are centralised or released. The correct recovery action is, of course, much more rapid and certain in its effect.

It is not unknown for individual aircraft to have slightly different spinning characteristics. Recovery action should be taken immediately if there is any tendency for the nose to rise progressively during a prolonged spin. Recovery from a flat spin is slow and unpredictable. It is wise to wear a parachute and to have sufficient height to use it if you intend to make prolonged spins. (There is seldom any reason to do this unless you are testing a new type of glider.)

If the centre of gravity is too far aft, it will be easier to put the glider into a spin and much more difficult to make it recover. In effect the extra power of the elevator will enable the wings to be stalled to a greater angle and the spin will become flatter. However, when it comes to the recovery, the elevator will have to overcome the tail heaviness and, therefore, the recovery will be more difficult. In some gliders, the position of the centre of gravity is critical and on no account should the glider be flown with too light a pilot or it may be impossible to recover from a spin. The placard in the cockpit states the minimum load which may be carried. Usually this is 120 pounds for a solo glider.

A large yawing force provided by a powerful rudder or a large amount of aileron drag will speed up rotation and this will tend to flatten out the spin.

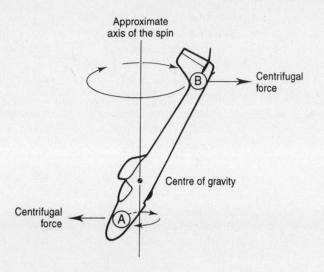

Figure 6. Spinning. If the glider is considered as though its weight was concentrated at A and B, the effect of an increase in yaw becomes clear.

Any flattening effect will increase the angle of attack of the wing and make the recovery more difficult. The diagram [Figure 6] shows why an increase in the rate of yaw flattens the spin. As the rotation increases, the centrifugal force produces a nose-up moment which prevents the nose from dropping and unstalling the wings. Conversely, during recovery, any reduction in the rate of yaw will help to allow the nose to drop which will help to unstall the wings.

The effect of having the spoilers or air-brakes out during the spin will vary with each design of glider. Usually they help recovery and prevent an excessive speed being reached in the dive. Air-brakes should always be opened immediately after a spin has stopped if the glider is in cloud.

Unlike a steep diving turn, or spiral dive as it is generally known, the speed remains low in a spin. This is the most distinctive feature when recognising a spin from the instruments.

Sometimes the elevator is unable to keep the wing stalled beyond the incipient stage of the spin. In this case, as the nose and wing drops, the wing will unstall and the speed will increase with the glider in a spiral dive. The glider is no longer spinning and is not stalled. Recovery to level flight can be made using all three controls normally.

Prompt action is the key to making a rapid recovery from an incipient spin and this is largely a matter of keeping in practice.

The opposite rudder is used to check the tendency for the glider to yaw towards the dropping wing. Unstalling the wing will eliminate any possibility of auto-rotation and prevent a spin. The wings must be brought level quickly if the minimum of height is to be lost and, since by then the wings are unstalled, the ailerons should be used for that purpose. The rudder will not pick up the

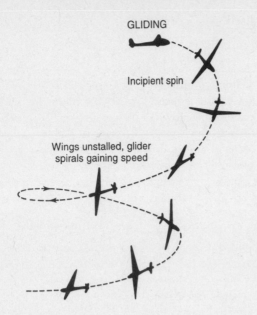

GLIDING

Incipient spin

Wings unstalled, glider
spirals gaining speed

Figure 7. Recovery – reduce the bank,
then raise the nose. The recovery from
a spiral dive.

wing at this stage as the glider is side-slipping steeply and the weather-cocking action of the fuselage overpowers the effect of the rudder. Note also that the rudder is not used to raise the dropped wing in the recovery action. It merely checks the yawing tendency slightly.

It is very important not to attempt to raise the wing with the aileron while the wing is stalled. The increase in the effective angle of attack of the wing when the aileron is lowered will tend to stall the wing more and help the auto-rotation. The aileron drag will also help the yawing and at the very least, this will delay the recovery and cause precious height to be lost. The correct use of the controls at this time is not instinctive, and plenty of practice is needed if the right action is to be taken in an emergency. Prompt action can always prevent a spin from developing, even if the corrective action is applied after the wing has dropped.

The recovery from a fully developed spin is important, but it should be remembered that only gross mismanagement of the controls and very slow reactions on the part of the pilot will make the average glider go beyond the incipient stage.

The order of the control movements is important. It is arranged to minimise any possible blanketing effects of the tail-plane and elevator on the rudder. The amount of forward movement on the stick required to stop the spin varies with the aircraft and the stage of the spin. It is best to think of the forward movement as being a steady progressive movement continuing until the spinning stops. In most gliders, the spin may stop after only a small forward movement. However, in some gliders and many powered aircraft, no apparent change will occur until several turns after the stick has been moved fully forward. the ailerons should always be centralised. The corrective action takes effect as follows.

1. *Full opposite rudder*. This tends to slow the rate of spin which results in a nose-down pitching movement helping to unstall the wings. As the rate of spin is reduced, the auto-rotation is also reduced because the wings become more equally stalled. The pause is to allow the rudder a moment to take effect before taking any further action.
2. *Stick steadily forward*. This pitches the nose down and unstalls the wings. Immediately the wings become unstalled, the auto-rotation must cease, and the spin has stopped, leaving the glider in a dive. The rate of spin may actually increase just before it stops and this or any other change are signs that the spin is stopping. The speed-up in the rate of spin is caused by the governor effect of the mass of the aircraft while it spins. When the spin steepens, the radius of the spin is reduced and the intertia in the governor effect speeds up the rotation.
3. *Centralise the rudder*. Since the spin has stopped, the rudder is no longer required. The aircraft is in a steep dive or diving turn and the controls should be used normally to bring the glider back to level flight. If necessary air-brakes should be opened fully to prevent the speed from becoming excessive.

Note that the pause after applying the full opposite rudder is not intended to be a pause until the spin stops. In some types of aircraft the spin will not stop until the stick has been moved forward to unstall the wings. In others, the spin may stop immediately the opposite rudder is applied and the rudder must be centralised promptly or a spin in the opposite direction may occur.

Care must be taken not to pull out of the dive too sharply or a high-speed stall may occur and more height will be lost.

No mention has been made of any action to be taken if the glider does not seem to be recovering from a spin after the correct recovery action has been taken. Any other action may only hinder the recovery and it cannot be too strongly emphasised that on no account should the full opposite rudder be relaxed until the spin has stopped. Provided that the glider is correctly loaded and is undamaged the normal recovery action will be effective.

The Effect of Ailerons

The position of the ailerons can have a marked effect on the characteristics of the full spin and recovery, but it varies with the type of glider. Usually in modern machines, aileron applied in the direction of the spin (known as 'in-spin' aileron) increases the rate of rotation and delays the recovery slightly. 'Out-spin' aileron then helps to stop the spin and tends to turn it into a yawing, spiral dive, with some older designs the aileron has little effect except to help a full spin to be achieved when the full 'out-spin' aileron is applied.

These effects may vary slightly with different loading and the ailerons should always be centralised at the start of the spin-recovery action.

It is interesting to recall the effect of aileron during the incipient spin. Then, any attempt to stop the dropping wing almost always results in the wing falling further. It should also be noticed that a rapid movement of the ailerons near the stall can roll the glider so quickly that the dropping wing-tip stalls in spite of that aileron being up at the time. *This can easily occur during a slow winch launch if the 'too slow' signal is given too enthusiastically.*

Inverted Spins

Unintentional inverted spins in gliders are almost impossible because of their inherent stability. If the glider is stalled while it is upside down, it will fall away to one side by dropping the nose or one wing with no tendency to spin upside down. It may possibly fall into a normal spin, in which case a normal spin recovery should be made.**

Darrol Stinton: Anatomy of Spinning

Even in 1972 spinning is still a topic of hot controversy. Darrol Stinton, writing in *Flight International* in March 1972, makes the following observations, with some new jargon, to explain what is happening.

**Statistically, more accidents happen at low speed than in any other phase of flight. The main danger lies in the stall; not so much the symmetrical, straight stall as the asymmetric stall, where an aeroplane is skidding and one wing is stalled more than the other, which can cause auto-rotation and a spin.

Stalling and spinning are more the everyday concern of light aircraft owners and pilots than their professional brethren. Most aeroplanes can be made to stall and spin, and large aeroplanes can be every bit as dangerous as small aeroplanes, but their flight profiles are so well scheduled, and their pilots should be so well trained, that they should never get anywhere near to stalling and spinning in the course of their normal lives. Having said that, stalling is, nevertheless, a major factor in large aeroplane accidents, so pilots of large aeroplanes could profit by reading on.

Unlike large aeroplanes, which, though strong, are floppy beasts, small aeroplanes have more specific stiffness. Their greater specific stiffness (more stiffness per pound structure weight) and greater liveliness in response to control enable them to be tumbled around where large aeroplanes rarely go. In such corners the aerodynamic tricks up the sleeve of an aeroplane can often be more than the average pilot wants to handle.

Stalling is a case in point, but as this is 1972 perhaps the stall should be redefined. Old concepts which blame wing-flow separation *per se* no longer apply consistently in the Concorde era where lift is generated by separate flows. the important point is that stalls are caused by uncontrolled, often asymmetric, separation of wing flow.

The French describe the stall as *decrocher*, the point at which an aeroplane 'unhooks'. It is not quite that simple, however, because a modern aeroplane may not unhook (or 'g-break') cleanly; it may merely waggle downwards at a steeper angle of descent than before, in a degraded state of control. Therefore we shall take the term *stall* to mean that the aeroplane has reached a large enough angle of attack to have suffered partial (or complete) loss of control. This does not imply that all, or much, lift has been lost.

British Civil Airworthiness Requirements define very carefully the rate of approach to the stall, because the speed at which lift is insufficient for controlled flight varies with the rate at which the stall is approached. A fast approach, in which the aeroplane is rotating rapidly about its cg usually results in a much lower stalling speed than that obtained by going gently into the stall at around 1 knot per second (or 1 mph/sec, near enough). Low stalling speeds make it possible to schedule low approach and take-off safety speeds and hence short fields for take-off and landing – obviously desirable features.

Most British Civil Airworthiness Requirements are based on stalling speeds in differing configurations such as gear and flaps retracted or gear down and flap down. While low stalling speeds are a boon for the salesman who wants to sell short-field operations, they can make problems for the designer trying to provide enough stability and control. He has to cope with a mixture of performance-power requirements, out-of-balance control and other moments, and sheer physical inertia about various axes.

Who wants to stall anyway? Modern light aeroplanes with nose-wheel gear and car-type brakes can get into and out of quite small fields. The trend, set long ago in the USA, is towards machines which, though small, feel like something much bigger. Pilots become drivers using perhaps 30 pounds/g with a wife and two children on board, by means of a spectacle control wheel instead of a stick, and herein lies a danger. Deliberate stalls rarely cause accidents; most pilots of light aeroplanes have no inclination to stall. The killer stall is the one that creeps up unawares, catching the chap who, not wanting to stall anyway, is out of practice when he does. That is one reason why the Air Registration Board makes an issue of stall-handling requirements.

As long as the approach speed is low enough to cope with, say, a 2,000-foot field, then all that is needed (it might be argued) is enough elevator control power to rotate such an aeroplane into the right attitude for take-off and landing. Aeroplanes of this kind belong to the class of flying automobiles. They tend to be docile and gutless and the lowest speed obtainable is elevator – not stall-limited. They cannot penetrate into a stall, because the cg is usually well forward and the control deflection available does not generate enough power in pitch.

But as the modern light aviator says, 'Who cares?' Perhaps he is right. He cannot afford to fly frequently. He does not want to be bitten when he does.

He wants to fly in straight lines from point to point, navaid to navaid. He does not want to upset the stomach of his passenger. And, anyway, there is a specialised club for those few enthusiasts who want an aeroplane to respond like a young horse.

Modern light aeroplanes are designed for the people who want to fly for the same purpose as they drive along the motorways. They are not designed for stalling — although they will stall if forced far enough nose-up — and that requires use of some power. Because such aeroplanes cannot penetrate the stall they are reluctant to spin. But just as almost any aeroplane can be coaxed to stall, so too can it be induced to spin, if you poke a stick in its ear at the right moment.

Spinning is a complicated and long-winded subject in which it is hard to generalise without saying too much or too little. Perhaps the first point to be made is that no two aeroplanes spin exactly alike, even though they may be of the same type. Furthermore, the characteristics of a spin are determined by the interaction of aerodynamic properties (size, disposition and relative proportions of aerodynamic surfaces) and dynamics (in which the aeroplane has to be considered as a family of juxtaposed masses, to be set in motion and stopped by use of the control surfaces).

It is the author's view that spins are not really in the same class as other aerobatic manoeuvres, and should not be defined as such. Accidental spins are simply the worse things that happen when an aeroplane bolts and runs away with the pilot. The design of an aeroplane should be such that the pilot can either recover from a fully developed spin, when the aeroplane is doing exactly what it wants to do to him, or at least have sufficient lateral and directional command to maintain control in the asymmetric pre-spin stall and to regain control in the incipient spin.

A spin consists of rotation about a vertical axis during which an aeroplane describes a helical path which may be anything between steep and flat. Furthermore, the wings may be anywhere from reasonably level to banked markedly into a spin. The shallower the angle of bank into the spin, the greater the slip out of the spin. Spinning is auto-rotation, caused by an asymmetric stall, and must not be confused with a spiral dive.

The difference between a spin and a spiral dive is that a spin has a low indicated airspeed; the slip and turn indicators are in opposition, turn being in the direction of rotation and slip (or skid) outwards. The spinning motion may be erratic in the early stages. The spiral dive on the other hand, has a higher, increasing, indicated airspeed and the slip indicator is more nearly central, with turn still shown in the direction of rotation. Spiral dives tend to be much smoother although buffeting may occur as speed builds up with full up elevator.

The figures [Figures 8 — 10] shows the set of conditions to induce a spin. Some aeroplanes may also need a downward deflection of the aileron on the side to which a spin is required (starboard down for spin to starboard) to force

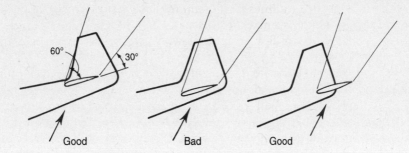

Figure 8. The influence of tailplane position on rudder blanking is seen in Figure 8. A minimum of 30 per cent of the rudder area should not be shielded.

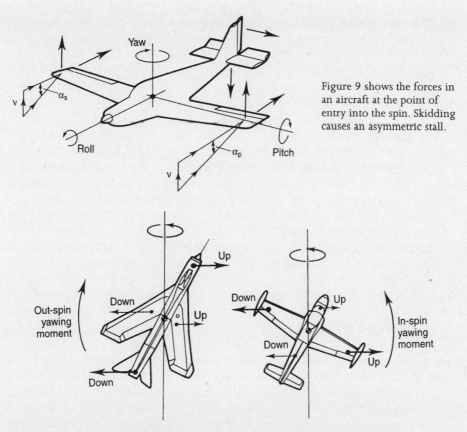

Figure 9 shows the forces in an aircraft at the point of entry into the spin. Skidding causes an asymmetric stall.

Figure 10. The effect of the distribution of mass between the fuselage and wings is demonstrated in Figure 10. This shows the extremes of in-spin and out-spin inertia.

that wing to stall. Once in a spin to starboard, higher lift on the port wing rolls the aeroplane to starboard. Higher drag on the starboard wing yaws the aeroplane to starboard causing increasing slip to port, which increases roll to starboard. The motion is self-generating.

Side-slip, or skid, is an important ingredient in the spinning. Any slip or skid during a straight stall can make the best of wings spin-prone – if one can make the angle of attack large enough to reach far enough down the reverse slope of the lift curve with the downward wing.

A spin has three phases: incipient, developed and recovery. But before enlarging on those three phases, let us consider preparations for spinning.

Spins should never be treated triflingly, but it is just as bad to have such a fear of them that one never practises spinning in the right kind of aeroplanes. ie. an aeroplane cleared for spinning on a British Certificate of Airworthiness.

Always check that the centre of gravity is within limits. The further forward the cg, the longer the moment arm of the tail surfaces and the greater their effectiveness in recovery. One may find, however, that with the cg well forward the aeroplane is reluctant to spin and may prefer a spiral dive. If that is the case, watch the airspeed like a hawk, because the design manoeuvre speed must not be exceeded with controls deflected for spinning.

Never spin deliberately unless you are in practice.
Never spin deliberately with power on.
Never spin deliberately with slippery-soled shoes.
Never spin deliberately with rudder pedals improperly adjusted.

(All of which the author found out for himself the hard way when very young.) It is imprudent, if not downright foolish, to spin without a parachute, for every aeroplane has its sense of humour, no matter how sedate and coy it seems. If you have a parachute and are determined to spin, make a decision height for baling out and stick to it. It could take you 2,000 feet–3,000 feet to get clear. Decide which way you are going to spin and which way you will bale out. It is best to hop overboard on the outside of the spin: better (though less likely) to be hit by the tail than to be caught by the propeller, which is a possibility when leaving on the inside.

If you have no parachute, then give yourself enough height to attempt to force a flat spin; if the aeroplane refuses to come out, you are more likely to be able to walk away from a flat spin.

Finally make sure that the ground is clear beneath before spinning. A colleague in the same RAFVR unit, many years ago, spun in flat on his works football pitch. He walked away, but the Tiger Moth burst into flames behind him. The match was cancelled and his mates wouldn't talk to him for weeks.

The incipient phase of a spin is meant here to include behaviour that is not truly auto-rotational in an established sense. At one extreme the aeroplane may be teetering on the verge of a spin. At the other, it may well be spinning but not yet steady in its full, natural, auto-rotational motion. This phase may last for up to five or six turns, though most light aeroplanes are spinning steadily by the fourth turn. It is the author's experience that most spinnable light aeroplanes seem to recover quicker in the unsteady, incipient phase than when spinning steadily, but that is not to say that unsteady spins are less dangerous than developed spins. It is likely that most spinning accidents are caused by inadvertent stalls in the initial climb, or approach, phases when too near to the ground for the spin to have developed, or for recovery action to have been effective.

The developed spin is steady and, more often than not, everything is smooth and quiet. The inertias and aerodynamics have had time to adjust themselves into a mutually dependent equilibrium. One may find the spin tending to flatten with increased rate of rotation. Under such conditions pilots are most prone to disorientation, and they are likely to make wrong actions. One of the most important things that can be said is that before attempting to recover, wait if you can. A five-second wait may seem an age, but it may be vital to gather scattered wits.

To recover from a spin the pilot needs to generate out-spin yaw (ie in-spin slip or skid). This may involve complications, especially where an aeroplane is long in relation to its span and has a large fuselage/wing moment of inertia, like high-performance jets. Light aeroplanes in general, however, do not have such features, so their conventional, erect, spin recovery consists of the following drill: throttle closed; centralise the ailerons; full rudder (out-spin) opposite to the direction of spin, to generate out-spin yaw; after *a pause* (repeat *pause*), stick fully forward and hold it there until the aeroplane unstalls; centralise the rudder when the spin stops. Finally recover from the ensuing dive. The need to pause before pushing the stick forward cannot be emphasised too strongly. When an aeroplane is wound up as a system of rotating masses, aerodynamic control surfaces need time to bite.

Always remember that, if you have the height, you can afford to spend five seconds looking around to sort out exactly what you intend to do. If the aeroplane fails to recover, then your next actions depend upon height and whether or not you have a parachute. If you have both then things are relatively simple.

It could pay you, if you have not recovered and have not reached the height at which you have decided to leave the aeroplane, to tease it a bit. Try the effect of power, try reversed-control recovery (stick forward before rudder applied), and try aileron into spin as well as out. It might just be possible to make the spin unsteady enough to force out-spin yaw and hence recovery. Remember if you try these things to *wait* after each control movement, to see if the control will bite.

If all else fails and you cannot bale out, then try a flat spin. Put all the controls pro-spin, ie in-spin rudder, stick hard back, out-spin aileron. You could try a burst of power to force the machine to a steeper angle of attack (flatter attitude) thus often increasing the rate of rotation.

With the process of spinning more or less exhausted, let us consider what can be done to an aeroplane to make it better able to recover from spins.

Any aeroplane that is certificated for aerobatics (as defined by BCARs) must be able to recover from spins. For that reason many aerobatic aeroplanes have additions (like fuselage strakes) that mark them as once having had problems in spin recovery.

The first important aerodynamic anti-spin feature is the arrangement of vertical and horizontal tail surfaces which must be such that something like one third of the rudder is out of the wake of the horizontal tail.

Secondly, remedies in the tail area are devices like strakes or additional dorsal and ventral surfaces. These are used to generate favourable anti-spin vortices which increase rudder control and/or tail damping (thus slowing down the rate of rotation about the spin axis).

A third set of devices that inhibit, or prevent, tendencies to spin includes washout, where the incidence of the wing-tip is less than that of the root; wings with little or no taper (the broader the tip the larger the angle of attack that can be reached before the tip stalls): slats and slots; changes of wing section and/or camber at wing-tips; sharpening the nose of the wing aerofoil sections inboard, often by the addition of simple bits and pieces of angle which force the wing roots to stall, first reducing the chances of auto-rotation; reduced elevator travel, to prevent biting deeply enough into the stall; and forward positioning of the centre of gravity to reduce the pitching effectiveness of the elevator.

The stalling and spinning picture is an unsatisfactory one, because the modern design tendency is to inhibit or merely to reduce the ability of the average pilot to make an aeroplane stall or spin. It would be dangerous for pilots to assume they are safer, because such aeroplanes can in fact stall and spin if given the right conditions. One has only to look at a number of modern aeroplanes, and the remedies that have been introduced to enable them to recover from spins, to realise that the problem is still around. If an aeroplane can be made to bite deeply enough into the stall it can almost certainly be forced (or coaxed) to spin, given the right amount of yaw. It is possible that we are now far too flabby in our attitude to stalling and spinning. We are breeding a generation of pilots who can be caught out too easily when an aeroplane takes it into its head to bolt with them on board.

Light aeroplanes that will spin, given the right conditions, should, ideally, be able to recover from fully developed spins. But certification authorities have settled for less by demanding enough lateral and directional control to recover from any incipient spin. The author's view, for what it is worth, is that one should go for the ideal state of affairs, regardless of how loudly designers and salesmen may disagree. In all of this, training is a most vital ingredient in making light aviation safer. Good instructors with authoritative voices, and who know stalling and spinning backwards, are the only ones worth their salt, and we need stallable, spinnable aeroplanes for such training. The author's view again is that aeroplanes for training should be certificated as such; to be fully aerobatic and able to come out of the worst fully developed spin. Nothing less will do.

The author wishes to thank the Air Registration Board for permission to present views that do not necessarily reflect those of the board. **"**

'Aerodynamicist': Article from Flight International

Following the article by Darrol Stinton, *Flight International* published the following comments by an aerodynamicist on 23 March 1972.

"The auto-rotational property of a wing at post-stall incidence is the primary cause of spinning, but this does not necessarily result in a spin. The damping moments provided by the fuselage and fin oppose the propelling moments from the wings, with the result that for a given combination of control settings there is a single value of equilibrium rate of rotation at each angle of attack. A spin can occur, however, only if equilibrium of pitching moments (aerodynamic and inertial) can be sustained, as illustrated in the figure [Figure 11]. This is true for all aeroplanes, irrespective of inertia distribution. If equilibrium of pitching moments cannot be obtained simultaneously, either an oscillatory spin or self-recovery will occur.

If the wings are tilted the picture changes as follows: with the inner wing tilted down, side-slip towards the inner wing produces an anti-spin (damping) moment, due to dihedral effect. There is now a component of nose-up pitch rate (if you have difficulty in visualising this, consider the extreme case of 90-degree bank and it is all pitch rate). The nose-up pitch rate combines with roll to generate an inertial yawing moment. Whether this is a propelling or a damping moment depends on whether the moment of intertia in roll (A) is greater than in pitch (B) or vice versa. This can best be seen by isolating the motion in roll and pitch, as shown in the [Figure 10 on page 137]. The two aircraft (a Lightning and a Jet Provost) show the extremes of the possible proportions of fuselage inertia and wing inertia in order to show clearly the resultant in-spin or out-spin yawing moment.

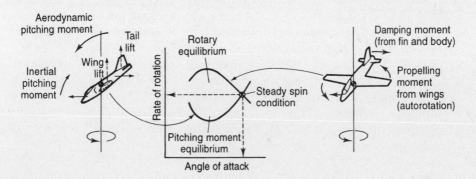

Figure 11. Only one equilibrium condition can lead to a steady spin, shown at the intersection of the curves in Figure 11. If total equilibrium is not achieved an oscillatory spin will result.

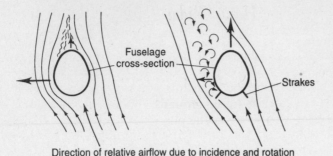

Figure 12. The effect of the addition of strakes to the Jet Provost lower nose was to reduce the fuselage damping during a spin.

The effect of wing tilt (rate of pitch) can therefore be summarised as follows:

	Mass in fuselage dominant A<B	Mass in wings dominant A>B
Inner wing down	Damping	Propelling
Outer wing down	Propelling	Damping

Aeroplanes with the mass spread mainly along the wings tend to spin more readily, requiring only a small amount of in-spin wing tilt. They are generally more difficult to recover because out-spin rudder increases and the resulting inertial yawing moment opposes the direct effect of the rudder. It is therefore more important to apply down elevator to resist the nose-up pitch rate and assist recovery on such aeroplanes.

Aeroplanes with mass spread mainly along the fuselage tend to be easier to recover. Modern combat aeroplanes, however, with high structural density, have very high rotational energy even at quite slow rates, so the controls take a longer time to have effect. Added to this, the rate of descent is high, due to high wing loading, so the height loss on recovery can be large, even from a docile spin.

Aeroplanes can be un-spinnable if the rotary damping is great enough or the nose-down pitching moment at high incidence is large enough, but it is very rare to find an aeroplane that will not spin with some combination of control settings, even though it may not respond to the conventional entry technique.

The Lightning spins fairly slowly because its fin remains unblanketed by wing and tail-plane wakes and the fuselage cross-section (circular at the nose, changing to egg-shaped) is good for damping.

The Jet Provost Mk 5 had a bit too much rotary damping, so the spin tended to go oscillatory. This was the reason for the nose strakes which act as spoilers at high incidence, reducing body damping, giving nose-up pitch, hence a slightly faster, much smoother spin. [Figure 12].**

D.L.Hadley: Hang Glider Spin

If after the last item your brain is spinning the next is a little less demanding. It is about something that happened to me in 1974. It was scarcely a major event but it does highlight an occurrence which is not uncommon amongst aircraft flying slowly, especially close to the ground, and has also more than once affected even very large aircraft when the pilot has flown unknowingly into wind shear.

I was flying a Rogallo hang glider, which is little more than cloth wings, controlled in flight by the pilot shifting his weight, and flying during take-off and landing at about walking speed. If stalled a hang glider may spin. Although some hang gliders have aerodynamic control surfaces, most do not and in the absence of control surfaces recovery depends upon the ability of the pilot to dive in order to increase speed.

Weight shift may prove insufficient in a stall when the pilot is falling at the same speed as the glider, and therefore weightless, although some alteration of the location of his mass, and drag, may be beneficial.

However, because a hang glider flies so slowly, prompt action when it stalls, by pulling the nose of the machine down, may enable it to pick up speed rapidly and avoid a spin. Once in a dive the wings, unless stiffened by batons, may collapse and destroy lift and without some form of built-in reflex at the trailing edge may not resume the aerofoil shape required to produce lift before the glider hits the ground. Otto Lilienthal was fatally injured when his hang glider stalled but modern hang gliders usually recover easily. Lilienthal's glider, as a matter of fact, had cloth wings stiffened with wooden rods. He was unable to recover from the stall before crashing.

The Steyning Bowl is a depression in the high ground to the west side of the village of Steying in Sussex. It is actually horseshoe-shaped, open to the south-east. It is about ½ mile across and, from the rim of the bowl to the floor, about 150 feet. The sides are sufficiently steep so that when the wind strikes them it creates enough lift to sustain a hang glider in flight. With a south-east wind soaring is good, but a south-east wind is not often blowing and the prevailing wind is south-west. This is not so good as the wind blowing over the south-west rim of the bowl forms a rotor which causes turbulence and gusting in the floor of the bowl and this makes landing a hang glider hazardous.

In 1974 during my eighth flight in a hang glider I took off from the north-east rim of the bowl into a south-west wind of about 15 knots. My previous seven flights represented a total flying time of 65 seconds. One learned to fly a hang glider in very short stages. I was flying a Wasp 229 B 3 Rogallo-type hang glider. This was considered about the best hang glider available in Britain at the time and was flown by all the top pilots. The take-off was good and I glided down the hill quite smoothly. Arriving near the bottom after about 20 seconds of flight I was just about to flare out to make my landing when suddenly the glider stopped flying. I was about 15 feet off the ground when this happened. I knew that I had stalled but had no idea why so I pulled the nose down a little to try to gain speed and regain control but it was no use. The right wing dropped and the glider dived into the ground, hitting nose and control bar at the same time. The impact broke my right wrist and bent the right upright of the A-frame.

At the time I did not understand what had happened. Despite my very short experience of flying a hang glider I was in fact an aircraft pilot with several hundred hours in conventional aircraft. I had not stalled because I had been flying too slowly; moreover, I tried at once to increase speed to recover from the stall but to no avail, the glider did not respond.

The explanation only came to me much later. Dr Paul McCready Junior, the American aviator, pointed out in an article I came across in a magazine about a year after this had happened that since a hang glider had a stalling speed of about 6 or 8 knots it is unsafe to land, or fly for that matter, when the wind is gusting by that amount or more. A glider flying at 8 knots into a wind of 15 knots which suddenly drops to 5 knots will immediately lose all flying speed and stall. This is especially liable to happen when descending through a wind gradient or wind shear. The wind at 100 feet above ground level may be 15 knots and only 5 knots or less at the surface. If it is gusting as well, then even though the pilot increases speed – say to 20 knots – to allow for the gradient a sudden lull will cause the glider to stall.

I know now that this is what happened to me. Descending into the turbulent air in the floor of Steyning Bowl, caused by the wind curling over the south-west rim, I simply flew into a patch of dead air at about 15 feet up and spun in. Yes, it was a true spin, a stall and right wing drop with the glider turning and entering a spin to the right. Pulling down the nose would have regained control had I had enough height. As it was it would have been better to do nothing. The glider would have behaved something like a parachute—I think.

Part 4

To Spin or Not to Spin

In 1978 I came across a letter by M.G. McDonnell, from the London School of Flying, published in *Flight International*, 19 August. Spinning in 1978 was still very much in people's minds but this letter introduced a new thought.

❝From the London School of Flying, Elstree Aerodrome.

Over the years *Flight* has contained many excellent articles on the art of spinning. For some time now I have wondered about the value of teaching spinning and spin recovery in the PPL (Private Pilot's Licence) syllabus, and discussions with various of my colleagues lead me to believe that I am not alone.

The UK is one of very few countries (I understand the number is four or five) to insist on spin recovery as part of PPL training. While all the other countries could be wrong, one is inclined to wonder why so many reputable aviation authorities throughout the world have reached this decision. Perhaps it is we who are wrong.

The aircraft which we fly now – and especially those in which we train for PPLs – simply do not want to spin. We have all spent many hours of our training time trying to make our aircraft enter a spin, and then hold it in. If modern light aircraft are so difficult to spin, and so reluctant to stay in a spin, is there much point in teaching the recovery?

Stall-recovery teaching concentrates to a great extent on spin avoidance, and in the normal operation of a serviceable aircraft a spin cannot occur without a preceding stall. It is my contention that this preventive training is far more effective than recovery training.

We often read of accidents which result from *intentional* spinning, but never of any resulting from *unintentional* spins from which a recovery could have been made. (From this I exclude accidents due to structural failure, control malfunction, lack of recovery height and IMC) we do not teach spin recovery on instruments. This may lead us to assume that, because spin recovery is taught, our pilots all recover from their unintentional spins. Perhaps a check of accidents in those countries which do not teach spin recovery would show that pilots simply do not enter unintentional spins in normal operations.

Once away from the training environment, a PPL-holder is unlikely to practise spin recovery, and the contention is that in the event of an actual inadvertent spin his previous training would be useless. To the best of my knowledge, no flight-training operator permits solo spinning during the PPL course, and the exercise is seldom covered afterwards.

One other significant factor is the fact that many students live in dread of their spinning detail, and once it is over they vow never to do it again. Some have even given up flying because of it. Others find it enjoyable and are tempted to try it themselves.

Having queried the value of teaching spin recovery, I believe that there are some situations in which such training is desirable. The first lesson of an aerobatic course concentrates on recovery from unusual attitudes and situations. Amongst these is included spin recovery. No one would dispute the value of this training, and it must be retained as part of the aerobatic course. The IMC Rating also includes a section on unusual attitude recovery, again as a preventive measure. This is useful training and should be retained.

There are probably aircraft on the British Register which will spin at the twitch of an aileron, so to speak, and will stay happily spinning until adequate recovery action is taken. These must however be few and far between, and are surely known to the Airworthiness Requirements Board. Perhaps such aircraft should be brought into group C, and spinning included in their training and testing schedules.

The aim of this letter is to get as many of us as possible to reconsider the value of spin-recovery training as part of the PPL syllabus. This means not only qualified flying instructors but also examiners, the AOPA panel of examiners and the CAA. Would any interested parties, especially QFIs and CFIs, please write to me with their views. If there is enough informed opinion against spinning, perhaps it could be removed from the syllabus. If most people are for spinning, I will keep quiet and get on with it.**

Ray Di Mascio: Response to M.G. McDonnell

I do not know how many replies M.G. McDonnell received but a month later the following letter appeared in Flight International from Ray Di Mascio of Dublin.

**M.G. McDonnell is in part right when he says that many modern trainers are very stable and require a lot of effort to spin intentionally. This is true. But without checking any statistics, I can call to mind four crashes – three of them fatal – which were directly attributable to unintentional spins.

I believe that too much importance is attached to intentional spin entry and recovery. Apart from mishandling during aerobatics, there are three situations in which a spin can be encountered very quickly and quite unintentionally.

1. On a 'drag-it-in' approach, ie having gone low on the approach into a short field with full flap and high power setting. If the aircraft reaches a high angle of attack, it will invariably spin. The required yaw will result from the high power setting and the fact that the ball is not central.
2. On the overshoot. The aircraft is flared too high, the stall warning blows, and so an overshoot is initiated. The application of full power – if allowed

– will cause the nose to pitch up and yaw. Again a spin will follow.
3.   Loss of an engine on a twin below V-MCA at a high power setting.

I firmly believe that more instruction should be given on the recognition of the factors that cause the spin and how to prevent their development. I have found that the demonstration at a safe height of incipient spins caused by either 1 or 2 have proved to have better instructional value than the usual intentional entry technique.**

The mention of a stall-warning device is an indication of the passage of time, and the fact that the thought of spinning is still very much in the average pilot's mind.

Harry W. Hawthorne: The Controversy Continues

A week later another letter appeared. From Harry W. Hawthorne of Berkshire, it appears to reflect the more traditional view of spinning.

**I would like to reply to M.G. McDonnell's 19 August letter on spinning. Although over the past decade aircraft have been built with the spin out of them and various authorities have dropped the requirement for demonstration of full recovery, I am sure that syllabuses will one day include the spin again.

In North America it is becoming common practice for many pilots to take an aerobatics course so as to improve their confidence and recognition of unusual attitudes. The recognition of attitudes such as the stall, side-slip and spin should all be taught, with the instruments included. Throughout the demonstration of a spin the instructor should be pointing out the readings of the turn and bank, altitude and airspeed indicators. I realise that many pilots refrain from practising the spin, but once taught you'll never forget.

In June 1965 I was eastbound at 5,000 feet from Oshawa to Hamilton over Toronto Island. I was levelled off in my 1946 Fleet Canuck, with my regular flying buddy occupying the right seat. We noticed a DC-8 crossing the lake shore inbound for Toronto at about 5,500 feet and directly across our flight path. We both commented on how great it was to be up with the big guys and said no more until we found ourselves in an inverted spin and wondering what the hell had hit us. It was decided afterwards that we must have executed a high-speed stall in the wing-tip vortices of the DC-8. This incident occurred just after I received my PPL, for which I had to demonstrate the art of spin recovery. What would my chances of survival have been without any spin training?

As a CFI instructor since 1970 I have trained many people and worked with quite a few instructors, and the general consensus of opinion has been for the inclusion of the spin in training. Mr McDonnell said that one rarely hears about accidents resulting from unintentional spins. I suggest that he reads more than Flight: unintentional low-level spins are in fact not too uncommon. And as for the students who quit the course after a spin demonstration I suggest that an improved initial indoctrination would solve this problem.

One of the three major US aircraft manufacturers has just produced a civil trainer which spins like a top. Many of the clubs and schools in the UK have had a demonstration of this particular aircraft by now, and all of them have been interested in its ability to spin. Send me a student and I'll send you back a spinning pilot who likes it.

Under the right conditions any aircraft will spin unintentionally. Why take the chance and not be trained or prepared for recovery action?**

Flight International: UK Tomahawks Re-cleared for spinning

Three years passed and another little snippet appeared to re-kindle the embers of controversy (Flight International 21 February 1981).

**As reported briefly in World News last week, the UK's Civil Aviation Authority has lifted its restriction on deliberate spins in Piper Tomahawks and given the aircraft a clean bill of health, subject to a flight manual amendment.

Following the fatal accident last May, several unreported incidents involving protracted spin recoveries on Tomahawks came to light. Analysis of pilot reports and interviews showed that various methods of spin entry had been used, and that some pilots were not precisely following the manufacturer's recommended recovery technique. Piper and the CAA then carried out joint flight tests to explore Tomahawk spin characteristics, and especially its ability to recover if incorrect control inputs [mishandling the controls this used to be called, only the language has changed – Ed] were used. CAA test pilots later flew each of the aircraft involved in the delayed recovery incidents. The aircraft's spin characteristics have now been declared satisfactory, no modifications are called for and the flight manual revision is the only change.

The Tomahawk was the first of America's 'new-generation' trainers to come on the market, and the full text of the spinning amendment is reproduced below. Main points about it seem to be these:

- While training spin entries are often made on other light aircraft by making control inputs several knots before the stall (and sometimes with power) in order to get a positive entry, this is not recommended on the Tomahawk for the reasons given.
- In 'standard' spin recovery technique there is a brief pause after the application of full rudder, before moving the control column forward. In conventional tailed aircraft the main reason for this is to avoid the possibility of shielding the rudder by the elevator, but in the Tomahawk making this pause can delay recovery. [The Tomahawk has the elevators set at the top of the fin and rudder – Ed]
- The instruction to 'move the control wheel fully forward' might seem extreme to a lot of pilots used to spinning modern light aircraft, but the

manual does later state that in most cases spin recovery will occur before the control wheel reaches the fully forward position.

- The immediate effect of applying normal recovery actions may be an appreciably steeper nose attitude and higher rate of rotation, but the anti-spin control inputs must still be held until the spin stops.

One lesson, and perhaps the most important, to come out of all this is the real value of incident reporting. If the previous spinning incidents had been reported and investigated, two pilots might be alive today.

Here is the major part of the amendment to the Tomahawk Operating Handbook, prepared by the CAA and Piper.

A one-turn spin, properly executed, will require 1,000–1,500 feet to complete and a six-turn spin will require 2,500–3,000 feet to complete. The aeroplane should be trimmed power off at approximately 75 knots before entering the stall prior to spinning. This trim airspeed assists in achieving a good balance between airspeed and g loads in the recovery dive.

Spin entry. The spin should be entered from a power-off glide by reducing speed at about 1 knot per second until the aeroplane stalls. Apply full aft control wheel and full rudder in the desired spin direction. This control configuration with the throttle closed should be held throughout the spin. The ailerons must remain neutral throughout the spin and recovery, since aileron application may alter the spin characteristics to the degree that the spin is broken prematurely or that the recovery is delayed.

Spin recovery. 1. Apply and maintain full rudder opposite the direction of rotation.
2. As the rudder hits the stop, rapidly move the control wheel full forward and be ready to relax the forward pressure as the stall is broken.
3. As rotation stops, centralise the rudder and smoothly recover from the dive.

Normal recoveries may take up to one and a half turns when proper technique is used. Improper technique can increase the turns to recover and the resulting altitude loss.

Further Advice on Spinning

Spin entry. Application of full aft control wheel and full rudder before the aeroplane stalls is not recommended, as it results in large changes in pitch attitude during entry and the first turn of the spin. Consequently the initial two or three turns of the spin can be more oscillatory than when the spin is entered at the stall.

Spin recovery. The recommended procedure has been designed to minimise turns and height-loss during recovery. If basic or standard recovery procedure is employed (during which a pause of about one second – equivalent to about one half turn of the spin – is introduced between the rudder reaching the stop and moving the control column forward) spin recovery will be achieved with equal certainty. However, the time taken for recovery will be delayed by the length of pause, with corresponding increase in height loss.

In all spin recoveries the control column (wheel) should be moved forward briskly, continuing to the full forward position if necessary. This is vitally important, because the steep spin attitude may inhibit pilots from moving the control column (wheel) forward positively. The immediate effect of applying normal recovery controls may be an appreciable steepening of the nose attitude and an increase in the rate of spin rotation. This characteristic indicates that the aircraft is recovering from the spin and it is essential to maintain full anti-spin rudder and to continue to move the control wheel forward and maintain it fully forward until the spin stops. The aeroplane will recover from any point in a spin in not more than one and a half additional turns after correct application of controls.

Mishandling Recovery. The aeroplane will recover from mishandled spin entries or recoveries provided the recommended spin-recovery procedure is followed. Improper application of recovery controls can increase the number of turns to recover and the resulting altitude loss. Delay of more than about one and a half turns before moving the control wheel forward may result in the aircraft suddenly entering a very fast, steep spin mode which may disorientate a pilot. Recovery will be achieved by briskly moving the control wheel fully forward and holding it there while maintaining full recovery rudder. If such a spin mode is encountered, the increased rate of rotation may result in the recovery taking more turns than usual after the control wheel has been moved fully forward.

In certain cases the steep, fast spin mode can develop into a spiral dive in which the rapid rotation continues, but indicated airspeed increases slowly. It is important to recognise this condition. The aircraft is no longer auto-rotating in a spin and the pilot must be ready to centralise the rudder so as to ensure that airspeed does not exceed 103 knots (VA) with full rudder applied.

Dive Out. In most cases, spin recovery will occur before the control wheel reaches the fully forward position. The aircraft pitches nose down quickly when the elevator takes effect and, depending on the control wheel position, it may be necessary to move the control wheel partially back almost immediately to avoid an unnecessarily steep nose-down attitude, possibly negative g forces and excessive loss of altitude.

Because the aircraft recovers from a spin in quite a steep nose-down attitude, speed builds up quickly in the dive-out. The rudder should be centralised as soon as the spin stops. Delay in centralising the rudder may result in yaw and 'fish-tailing'. If the rudder is not centralised, it will be possible to exceed the maximum manoeuvre speed (VA) of 103 knots with the surface fully deflected.**

John Stanley Owen: To Spin or Not to Spin

Another two years passed, then once again controversy reared its head. I came across an article written by John Stanley Owen in the *International Journal of Aviation Safety*, 1983. It started with a brief statement of the reason why he had written the article.

❝The investigation into the spinning accident to Tomahawk PA 38G-BGGH in May 1980 (Aircraft Accident Report No 11/81) raised a number of points that are relevant to this controversial instructional sequence and drew attention to differing spin-training requirements throughout the world.

Spinning accidents still occur at random intervals in both civil and military aviation; they also occur during dual or solo instructional flying exercises, that are aimed at preventing this type of accident, despite the accepted standards of excellence in flying instruction, the efforts of flight-safety authorities and a wealth of experience which has been dearly bought throughout the history of powered flight.

It is none-the-less encouraging to see that one of the Safety Recommendations contained in the AIB (Accident Investigation Board) report generated, or perhaps revived, a constructive dialogue between the UK Regulatory Body and the flying instructor fraternity on the subject of spin-training requirements for a private pilot's licence.

The Argument

The art of flying instruction is as old as flying itself and a remarkable degree of standardisation has been achieved in most matters relating to instructional flying and aircraft handling techniques. However, there still remains an important area of contention between flying instructors; should *ab-initio* civil pilot trainees be taught (or exposed to) the fully developed spin, the incipient spin or, for that matter, any spin whatsoever unless they are aspiring aerobatic pilots?

It is beyond argument that realistic training in spinning and recovery from spins initiated from various attitudes and flight manoeuvres is a sensible training requirement for aerobatic proficiency. What is arguable, however, is whether spin training serves any useful purpose at all in the basic training syllabus for civil pilots. Many regulatory authorities think not.

There is a number of arguments to support either viewpoint but perhaps the most powerful argument for the retention of spin training in the UK is the *status quo* which has existed since the end of the Second World War. CAA research has discovered that an attempt was made in 1938 to require an applicant for an 'A' licence to complete entry and recovery from left- and right-hand spins. For reasons which cannot now be established, the proposal was deferred indefinitely only a month after the NOTAM was published. The existing UK requirement, for a demonstration of competence either during test or training, was introduced immediately following the end of the Second World War.

In Favour of Spinning
The main reasons advanced by protagonists of spin training are:

1.   It is essential that a student pilot should recognise the onset of a spin and to be able to recover.
2.   Spinning gives the student confidence in dealing with the worst situation of loss of control.
3.   Spinning is an effective method of training a student to cope with the effects of disorientation.
4.   Training in full spins and recovery is reassuring because it is possible to enter a full spin whilst practising incipient spins or aerobatic manoeuvres.

There are probably other arguments for spin training but it is thought that a number of protagonists, who are also highly competent pilots and instructors with a background of military flight instruction, are influenced by their service experience during which they flew aircraft to the limits of their performance and taught others to do likewise. In this respect it should, none-the-less, be mentioned that the Royal Air Force do not, nowadays, introduce spin training into the syllabus until the student has progressed beyond first solo stage and is being taught aerobatics (after about eighteen hours). This concept evolved from many years of experience and continued review of training methods and operational requirements by the 'guardians' of RAF flying and instructional standards, the Central Flying School.

Against Spin Training
1.   The argument that a student should be trained to recognise and be able to recover from a spin is countered by the assertion that if a student inadvertently enters a stall/spin situation whilst on a first solo flight, it is unlikely that a safe recovery would be effected should it occur at or below circuit height. It is also unlikely that prompt recovery action would be taken, having got into a stall/spin situation through ineptitude, inattention, confusion or panic.
2.   With regard to the second point in the protagonists' arguments, whilst not disputing the vital need for spin training as a prerequisite to aerobatic training, the wisdom of introducing spinning before the first solo stage is indeed arguable. In the case of a nervous student, and most are apprehensive of spinning, it might adversely affect their confidence and prove counter-productive, an important factor to be borne in mind by a flying school struggling to make ends meet! Also in the case of a nervous student, it might generate an unpredictable response such as 'freezing'.
3.   Spin training as practised in the UK and perhaps many other countries (with the exception of the USA) bears little relation to real situations, often encountered early in one's flying career. It is suggested that more emphasis

should be given to the importance of maintaining balanced flight in critical situations; to quote two examples:

(a) the low airspeed climb-out at full power with insufficient rudder applied: and

(b) the final turn on the approach to land – where an attempt to tighten the turn or increase the rate by injudicious use of rudder can lead the unwary into allowing a stall/spin to develop.

There is moreover a tendency to concentrate on the normal entry into a spin from nose-up level flight at idling power with a recovery which amounts to an exercise in 'changing feet on the rudder pedals' (together with the rest of the 'standard' spin-recovery actions). This was convincingly demonstrated by a Central Flying School examiner during an instructor check flight. (Tomahawk Report).

4. Studies have indicated that most aircraft in general aviation are not so likely to be involved in stall/spin accidents – modern types contributed about 20 per cent to stall/spin accidents in the UK during the past twenty years. With this in mind it is suggested, with a few exceptions, that if spin training is necessary it should only apply to those who train on the few remaining types that stem from pre-Second World War design. Some countries also take the view that if spin training is required for, say, an aerobatic rating, the aircraft concerned should also be cleared for aerobatics. In the UK on the other hand, a flying instructor is allowed to teach spinning without being qualified to instruct in aerobatics. It is also interesting to note that in some countries, Sweden and Switzerland for example, spin training is considered to be sufficiently dangerous as to warrant the wearing of parachutes as a regulatory requirement.

5. The most convincing argument against spin training is seen in the USA General Aviation Safety Record following its discontinuance in 1949 as a training requirement for an airman's certificate. In the following thirty-one-year period, the proportion of stall/spin fatal accidents to all fatal accidents in the USA fell from 49 per cent to less than 13 per cent. This is attributed to training methods which concentrate realistically on stall avoidance as opposed to spin avoidance, it being recognised that a spin is an aggravated stall. It is also felt that half a million active private pilots in the USA represent a valid sample on which to base the foregoing statistical analysis for a thirty-one-year period. However, it should also be noted that regardless of the apparent effectiveness of the measures taken by the CAB in 1949 there was also an on-going debate between flying instructors and the licensing authority on the question of spin training and its possible re-introduction. This culminated in a congressional hearing in the House of Representatives in 1980 on the subject of spin-recovery training. The FAA position and the GA Safety Record were presented by Mr Bernard Geier, Chief of General Aviation and Commercial Division, who is also an experienced military and civil flight instructor and flight examiner. As a result of the hearing the reintroduction of spin training is considered unlikely in the USA in the foreseeable future.

Proposed Changes in UK PPL Requirements – Spin Training.

Since the handling characteristics of aircraft certified for intentional spins are carefully evaluated prior to certification or validation of existing certification by Airworthiness Authority test pilots, it is tempting to conclude that ensuing accidents during deliberate spinning exercises are unlikely to be due to faulty design or lethal handling characteristics, but are more likely to be caused by human shortcoming, inadequate training or a lack of awareness of the circumstances that generate a spin or a full understanding of spin recovery techniques.

Following publication of the Tomahawk accident report, the CAA encouraged a meaningful debate with flying instructors on the need to include spin-training as a licensing requirement for private pilots. There was, not unnaturally, some opposition to change but the consensus favoured the proposals put forward by the CAA Flight Crew Licensing Directorate. The intended changes will delete spinning as a training requirement for a PPL but theoretical training will include emphasis on awareness of the dangers of the inadvertent stall during manoeuvres in a state of unbalanced flight. Students will be left in no doubt that any departure of the slip indicator is an indication of danger. Changes in airborne instruction during the pre-solo stage will include basic stalling awareness and recovery, the less obvious types of stall progressing to the methods of stall/spin avoidance as applied to straight forward stalls and the insidious stall/spin entry. An Aeronautical Information Circular (AIC) is due to be published this month explaining the changes in PPL requirements.

The changes relate only to the training of pilots to the standard appropriate to qualifying for a PPL; applicants for an Assistant Instructor's Rating will be trained to instruct in both full spin-recovery techniques and stall/spin avoidance as previously described.

By these measures it is hoped to minimise the chances of a stall/spin accident; only time will show the effectiveness of such a departure from traditional thinking but it is none-the-less felt that the proposed measures are a positive step in the right direction.**"**

John Stanley Owen is an experienced flight instructor/examiner and an experienced air safety investigator with 8,000 hours to his credit, 5,000 of them as a flying instructor. Two points occurred to me as I read the article. (*See note on page 165*)

1.   During Parke's Dive he lost control during a gliding turn below circuit height (usually 1,000 feet), one of the two critical situations described by Owen. However, although knowing nothing about spin recovery techniques and with only a few hours of flying experience, he managed by good luck to recover.

2.   The owner of a private pilot's licence is entitled to carry passengers. I would not wish to be a passenger in an aircraft being flown by a pilot who had not been trained in spin recovery.

General Aviation Safety Committee: To Spin or Not to Spin

I also wrote to the General Aviation Safety Committee seeking their views and received the following reply from the secretary, John C. Ward.

"Thank you for your letter regarding the spinning article published by AOPA in the summer edition of their magazine *Light Aviation* [also by the *International Journal of Aviation Safety*. Ed].

In fact I know John Stanley Owen well (he sent me on my first solo in a Meteor) and, despite his experience as an AIB accident investigator, I would have no hesitation in challenging his views on aviation if I did not agree with them. In fact, however, I found nothing in his article with which I did not agree and, indeed, what he says is very much in line with the views of this committee as expressed in the article we published in the summer 1982 edition of the Committee's *Flight Safety Bulletin*, a copy of which is enclosed. [see below]

Personally I believe that it is not so much a matter of whether or not a pilot is subjected to two or three spins during the training for PPL so much as how and when he should be taught to recover from a spin in any type of aircraft. There is a world of difference between an intentional and an unintentional spin and RAF trials at Boscombe Down have shown that a great deal of training and practice is necessary to ensure quick recognition of and recovery from an unintentional spin, certainly far more training and practice than it would be possible to include in the PPL syllabus. But I do not believe that that means he should never learn how to get into and out of a spin. I think he must go through that procedure if he is going to be a flying instructor and attempt aerobatics and, as I understand it, that is exactly what is now proposed. [A second letter to me in February 1997 told me that he had not changed his views.]**"**

This is the article referred to in the letter.

"In the spring of 1982 issue of this *Bulletin* (No 1/82) we drew attention to the AIB report on the fatal accident to Piper Tomahawk G-BGGH at Kidlington, Oxfordshire on 27 May 1980, which stated that this accident was caused by failure to recover from a deliberately induced spin during a dual instructional flight. We pointed out that the report also recommended that the need for spin training for basic PPL licensing requirements in the UK should be critically reviewed and we quoted some statistics for spinning accidents in the UK over a twenty-year period 1960–79. These showed that, of 2,241 accidents suffered by aircraft of less than 2,300kg MTWA spinning was a factor in sixty-one accidents and thirty-one of these were fatal. Six of the accidents, including three of the fatal ones, occurred as a result of intentional spins.

In view of the AIB recommendations, we thought that a close look at the accident statistics might be justified especially with regard to the height above ground at which the spin was entered. We thought that any pilot probably did not stand much chance of recovery from a spin that was entered when the aircraft was at a height below about 500 feet above ground level but that, if he was really switched on regarding spin-recovery techniques which, of course, is the object of spinning training, he should stand a reasonable chance of recovery if the spin was entered above 500 feet and he certainly should recover if above 2,000 feet. The table below is the result.

Spin height	Intentional		Unintentional	
	Fatal	Total	Fatal	Total
Below 500 feet agl	0	0	10	26
Between 501 feet and 2,000 feet agl	1	1	13	17
Above 2,000 feet agl	2	5	0	1
Unknown, but probably above 2,000 feet agl	0	0	5	11
Total	3	6	28	55

We would suggest that this analysis indicates two things. First that a significant proportion of accidents are the result of entering a spin at a height from which recovery is unlikely to say the least and, second, some 10 per cent of spin-related accidents are as a result of an intentional spin with the proportion of fatal to total accidents virtually identical regardless of whether or not the spin was entered intentionally. It is further suggested that the main conclusion to be drawn from this is that we might do far better during training to put much greater emphasis on spin prevention than on spin recovery and, indeed, abandon spin training altogether for the student pilot although it probably would be necessary to retain it for instructor training and for any pilot contemplating doing aerobatics. Indeed it might be argued that time spent in subjecting the student with only thirty or so flying hours to the confusing business of carrying out two or three fully developed spins would be more adequately spent in practising 'slow flight'. The fact that 10 per cent of the spin-related accidents, half of them fatal, occurred as a result of intentional spins would seem to reinforce this view.

Perhaps a valid comparison is with the situation, which developed in respect of accidents during asymmetric training on multi-engined aircraft, when it was the practice actually to shut down one engine. It didn't take many accidents during such training flights with one stopped before the 'zero thrust' concept below 3,000 feet was introduced, so maybe it will not be long before spin-recovery training is limited to the incipient stage and much more emphasis is put on teaching pilots to fly carefully, accurately and safely close to the stall.

Incidentally, further analysis of the spin-related accidents showed great variation in pilot qualifications and experience. With regard to intentional spins, all pilots were PPL holders whose experience varied from 726 hours to over 5,000 hours total. Of the unintentional spins, four involved student pilots, forty-two involved PPL-holders whose experience ranged from fifty hours to

3,417 hours and eight involved professional pilots, one with more than 10,500 hours experience!

Another interesting fact is that Tiger Moth aircraft were involved in twenty of the sixty-one spin-related accidents, the next most 'popular' spin accident types being the Auster and Stampe, with four accidents each. The Chipmunk, often regarded as one of the few light aircraft that will spin properly, featured in only three accidents although two of them were the result of intentional spins, and the only aircraft with a score of two were the Cessna 150 and the Andreasson BA 4B, so perhaps the CAA was right when it decided recently to prohibit spinning in any Tiger Moth aircraft not fitted with anti-spin strakes because even this measure does not appear to have eliminated the problem with this aircraft type!**

Following these articles it seems that the evil and awesome reputation of the spin has not diminished over the years. But, like the giant whirlpool at sea or the tornado over land, is a spin a fatal spiral, of the pilot's own devising, which must be avoided because it cannot be tamed? Is it a dragon? Should the intrepid pilot fight the dragon or steer clear of its lair?

Well, I do not think I can be sure to give the correct answer but my instincts tell me to fight the dragon. During my first spin I was terrified. This fear was soon replaced by a healthy respect, largely brought about by learning how to recover from a spin if I ever got into one accidentally. For a pupil this may well happen and in my view it is better to know what it is like and what to do about it (even if it doesn't always work) as well as how to avoid it before going solo. Any pilot who wishes to be considered competent must know how to try to recover from a spin and I believe not be afraid to spin deliberately from time to time, even if it is a little more risky. A person learning to ride a horse can never be quite sure that they will not fall.

D.L. Hadley. The Pupil's Point of View

At this point I felt compelled to join in the controversy and give one pupil's point of view. I wrote the following letter to the *International Journal of Aviation Safety*, which had published the article written by John Stanley Owen.

**I am an ex-service pilot with very few flying hours compared to John Stanley Owen and no experience in instructing, so I am nervous about crossing swords with him. However, I feel in my bones that it is important to learn how to recover from spins, so I will try to put my point of view.

Ab-initio civil pilots should be taught (or exposed to) spins because, although frightening to begin with, a pilot should become accustomed to the sensation, and usually does so quite quickly. There is also the fear of the unknown to be overcome, and a pilot so trained would, I think, stand a better chance of recovering from an accidental stall or dropping a wing.

The Royal Air Force probably postponed spin training until later in the course (after eighteen hours) for several reasons connected with the change of basic trainer from Tiger Moth to Jet Provost.

If a student inadvertently enters a stall or a spin while on his first solo I agree that the chance of recovery may be small, but he should have a chance to try; training would lead to a more effective reaction.

A nervous student will become less nervous after a demonstration – say three spins – and he should not be holding the controls for the first two. If he freezes no harm is done. Careful explanation should prevent this. Will a student who is nervous before a demonstration spin be perpetually nervous if he never spins?

I do not think that the argument that the students may be frightened away from a school 'struggling to make ends meet' is a valid argument.

I agree that maintaining balanced flight is of the greatest importance, but a pilot can still blunder into a spin [see the letter from Harry Hawthorne on pages 147 and 148 – Ed.]

The result of the steady improvement in aircraft design is that some schools may not have an aircraft which is suitable to use to teach spinning. This is a real problem but perhaps arrangements could be made for a student to go for an hour of spin training elsewhere.

I cannot dispute the figures of a fall of fatal accidents from 48 per cent to 13 per cent and I agree that the teaching of stall avoidance as opposed to spin avoidance is correct. Nevertheless, I would like to know how to get out of the worst position I could be in, before going solo.

I agree that inadequate training and lack of awareness or a full understanding of spin recovery techniques are the likeliest causes of accidents in spin-recovery training, but I do not think that theoretical training can replace the actual sensation.

It may be that the measures proposed by the CAA for PPL training will minimise the chance of accidents from stalls and spins at that stage of training and possibly later, but if such pilots should one day accidentally spin, theory may not be enough to get them out of trouble.

I am willing to concede that because modern aircraft do not normally spin, a case against teaching spin recovery can be made out. But I would want to know what this terrible thing is that I am being protected from learning about.**"**

I had already had my answer I suppose in John Ward's letter to me (page 155), and for a while things went quiet, which as anyone who flies knows is usually an ominous sign.

Dave Martin: Going for a Spin? Call Gene Beggs First

No more chit-chat on the subject of spinning crossed my horizon for a couple of years, then in 1986 I came across another piece on the subject by Dave Martin, writing in *Private Pilot* in February 1986.

"Aerobatic pilot Gene Beggs is a crusader. His crusade is all about spinning in airplanes; spin training, spin-recovery techniques, spin myths and reality.

Like many other flight instructors, Gene Beggs of Midland, Texas, has thought seriously for a long time about two famous killers in general aviation: weather and spins. Beggs became interested in aerobatics in the 1970s, then zeroed in on spin accidents after a close friend of his was killed in a spin in 1981. He also noticed that other experienced aerobatic pilots were failing to recover from spins.

An article in the November 1981 issue of *Sport Aerobatics* magazine caught Gene's attention, and life has not been the same since. Author Eric Mueller, a Swiss aerobatic pilot, described a simple spin-recovery technique which he said works for all types of spins. The method:

1. Cut throttle.
2. Take your hand off the stick:
3. Kick on full opposite rudder until the spin stops.
4. Neutralise rudder and pull out of dive.

Don't stop reading here though. The method does not work for all types of spins in all airplanes. Certain spins in the Cessna 150 and 152, for example, are resistant to the hands-off method.

Beggs doubted the method would work in the most popular American aerobatic planes, the Pitts Special and the Christen Eagle. A Pitts owner himself, Beggs went out and tried the technique. In Beggs's Pitts S-1S, the new technique worked at least as well as conventional spin-recovery methods for every type of spin: normal upright or inverted, cross-controlled flat, accelerated spins, and upright or inverted full-power flat spins.

At this point, Beggs was a 12,000-hour ATP-rated flight instructor with seven years of aerobatic competition behind him. He had won the US Intermediate Competition in 1978 and was US Advanced Champion in 1979. 'I thought I knew all about spins,' Gene noted, 'but I was wrong.'

He began collecting stories of pilots who had experienced spin problems – and lived to tell about them. An amazing number of pilots didn't know how they managed to recover, but Beggs noted a recurrent theme, the spinning stopped when the pilot gave up on stick deflections, pulled the power back and let go of the stick (often to start the bale-out procedure).

Beggs tried the Mueller method on numerous aircraft, including the Christen Eagle. With a few exceptions, he found the new recovery method worked in every one of them. The exceptions include the Beech T-34C (A and B Models have not been tried), which will recover only slowly using the new method. As noted above, another exception is the Cessna 150 and 152 (normal and aerobat models). Right spins will recover with the Beggs – Mueller method. But left spins entered with power on or with in-spin aileron – and allowed to develop to two turns or more – will not recover using the hands-off method. The normal push-the-yoke-forward technique will break these spins.

The third plane tested which has an unrecoverable mode using the new method is the North American T-6. In this airplane it is a right spin entered with power on or with in-spin aileron and more than two turns that will not come out using the power-off-then-hands-off method. Again the normal stick-forward recovery will work.

Beggs contends that these few exceptions do not indicate a deficiency in the new recovery method but rather a design deficiency in the airplane. He thinks that these three planes lack sufficient tail-damping force, a combination of aft vertical area, moment arm, rudder area and deflection.

'My main concern initially was for people who flew the Pitts or the Christen,' he said. After talking and flying with a lot of aerobatic pilots, Gene Beggs designed a course in spin instruction for pilots who want to spin safely. What causes experienced aerobatic pilots to kill themselves spinning? 'Confusion and panic,' Beggs answers without hesitation. 'Pitts and Eagles want to fall out of a vertical manoeuvre into an inverted spin to the left,' he said. 'Pilots are mistaking an inverted spin to the left for an upright spin to the right,' he continued. If the pilot looks up (at the ground, because the plane is inverted), the perception will be an upright spin in the wrong direction! The solution? Look forward over the cowl to determine spin direction. (More on this later).

The combination of a single recovery technique and his course on spins should eliminate the problems among aerobatic pilots he thinks.

More recently Beggs has enlarged his target. 'What we need now is a general aviation course for those who want to keep from spinning,' he said. He envisions a thorough stall course, but he continues to condone spin training for all pilots, especially during flight instruction.

Gene Beggs would like to see the FAA take two steps towards spin education. First he wants the government to fund a study to determine how all of the popular general aviation aircraft respond to the Beggs – Mueller spin-recovery method. (Beggs has already tested a number of general aviation planes, including, most recently, the Piper Tomahawk.)

Second, he would like the FAA to list the Beggs – Mueller method as the normal spin-recovery technique, unless tests determine the system will not work on a specific airplane. 'We need to de-stigmatise spinning and spin training,' he said.

Having recently completed a basic aerobatic course myself, I travelled to Midland, Texas, to let Gene Beggs 'de-stigmatise' me. After reading one of his articles on the new recovery technique, I'd tried it with my instructor in a Bellanca Decathlon and found the new method to be faster than the normal stick-forward recovery for an upright spin.

Gene Beggs's office is decorated with his aerobatic trophies and he showed me some of the letters from pilots who have taken his two-year-old spin course. 'Many of these pilots were non-believers when they came here,' he said. 'There's a lot of resistance, but not from anyone who has taken the course.' One letter was from George Meyers III of Denver FAA office. Meyers was involved in the certification of the Pitts S-2B and S-1T. 'The inverted spin instruction was the best aviation training [I have] ever received' Meyers's letter says.

Beggs's one-hundredth advanced spin course student (Bill Flaherty of Foster City, California) was one hop away from graduation during my visit. The course consists of five flights of about one hour each and it costs (in 1986) $895 in Beggs's Pitts S-2B.

My single flight with Gene seemed to skip the preliminary stuff. After a climb to 8,000 feet – during which I managed to lose altitude in what was supposed to be a steep-level turn – I demonstrated a normal upright spin entry and recovery, using the Beggs – Mueller method.

Satisfied that I had memorised the four-step recovery, Beggs pulled out the stops. He entered an inverted, flat, full-power spin and said softly into the intercom 'You've got it!'

I'd never spun inverted flat before. Looking over the cowl revealed a blur, but the direction of rotation was obvious – and that was something of a surprise to me. Time to retard the throttle, let go the stick, boot full opposite rudder. The spinning stopped in just over half a turn and I pulled out of the dive. Amazing!

Gene then demonstrated the 'normal' stick-back recovery for this same inverted flat spin and it took the same three quarters of a turn to recover.

The accelerated spin was next. After a normal spin entry, Gene eased the stick forward slowly – and the spin rotation rate seemed to double instead of slow down. This response to nearly normal recovery technique would really scare an unsuspecting pilot. In planes on which it has been tried, the Beggs – Mueller technique avoids the problem.

Cross-control spins, often resulting in high-rate flat spins, were demonstrated next. The new recovery method worked for all of them.

One of the big advantages of the new recovery method is that it is almost fool-proof. With the hand off the stick, the plane will not enter a spin in the opposite direction, even if full rudder is left in too long. (Some surviving pilots have reversed a spin five times trying to break a spin.)

The bottom line is that the Beggs – Mueller emergency spin-recovery technique works better than any other method on most aircraft on which it has been tried. At this point Gene Beggs would no doubt appreciate your noting the caveat 'on which it has been tried'. Your particular airplane might be one, like the T-34C or the Cessna 150 or 152, which does not recover quickly using this method!

In an era of ridiculous liability judgements, Gene is sticking his neck out to promote a 'radical' change in procedures. He has made a point not to endorse other instructors to teach 'his' method. But the word is getting out and an increasing number of aerobatic pilots have adopted the Beggs – Mueller technique for emergency (that is, inadvertent spin recovery).

It should be noted that airshow and aerobatic competition spins must stop on a precise heading, and 'normal' techniques are usually better at that than the new technique.

Here is another warning. Don't try the Beggs – Mueller or any other spin-recovery technique if your airplane is placarded against spins or if you have not had spin training. Even if you and your airplane meet both conditions, be advised that you may be placing yourself in the category of experimental test pilot to try any new flying technique such as this. Most of us are neither trained nor paid to be experimental test pilots.

Despite all the caution and disclaimers which seem to be necessary today, the Gene Beggs – Mueller emergency spinning recovery technique already may be saving the lives of general aviation pilots and passengers.**"**

Maurie Bradney. From Basic Gliding Knowledge

In 1986–7, while on a visit to South Australia, I took some gliding lessons at the Waikerie Gliding Club. I had not spun an aircraft for over thirty years, but as spinning was required before going solo I did three spins with my instructor in a Grob Twin Astir sailplane. We used the standard spin-recovery method which, despite the lapse of time, came to me quite naturally. Two points seem worthy of comment. I had not been in a sailplane before and I expected it to behave in a more leisurely way than a powered aircraft. It did not. It snapped into a spin as smartly as any aircraft I have flown. During my first spin I pushed the stick forward a bit too briskly and the glider, although it came out of its spin with no hesitation, went into a dive which was steeper than necessary, and picked up a lot of speed. This was of no consequence except that a glider may build up speed very rapidly in a dive and can exceed the velocity never to be exceeded (VNE) unless care is taken. In the last two spins I pushed the stick forward more slowly and recovered with no trouble and without risking the destruction of the glider.

The following are the notes on stalling and spinning prepared by Maurie Bradney and used by the club to instruct their pupils. They are clear and concise and contain one warning which I have not seen elsewhere, which is that when checking below before going into a spin not to fly in a circle as another glider pilot may think that your glider is simply thermalling and join what he believes is the up-going air just beneath you.

"The smooth air-flow over the wing can be upset by trying to fly at too great an angle of attack. This is usually achieved by flying too slowly, but can be brought on by a very abrupt pull-up, or very steeply banked turn. It *always occurs* when the wing is at its *critical* or *stalling angle*.

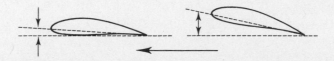

For the same weight, the sailplane in straight flight will always stall at the same speed, hence we can have a stalling speed. However, this speed will be increased by:

1.   Increasing the weight.
2.   Increasing the load factor.

In order to moderate the stalling characteristics, most sailplanes have a small amount of twist, or washout, built into the wing. This places the tip at a lesser angle than the wing root. The critical angle is reached first by the inner portion of the wing so that only a portion of the wing stalls.

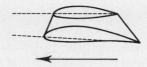

This allows the tip portion of the wing to remain unstalled and also keeps the ailerons functioning effectively. Coarse aileron use at, or near, the stall can induce the side where the aileron goes down to stall and cause the wing to drop sharply to that side.

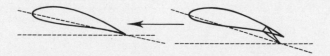

Flaps reduce stalling speeds and usually alter the stalling angle as well. Airbrakes and spoilers increase stalling speeds but have no effect on the angle.

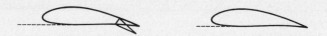

Aircraft are balanced such that when the wing stalls, the nose pitches down. Contrary to what we would at first imagine, holding the stick back to raise the nose does not effect a recovery, as this continues to keep the wing at the critical angle, and therefore it remains stalled.

Although the aircraft goes into a steep descent, as long as the wing is held at a high angle of attack (by keeping the stick back) it has high drag, hence no great speed is achieved.

To effect a recovery the angle must be reduced. To do this the stick must be moved forward. Immediately on doing this the sailplane will accelerate and normal control will be restored very rapidly.

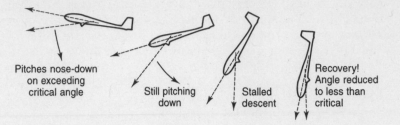

Pitches nose-down
on exceeding
critical angle

Still pitching
down

Stalled
descent

Recovery!
Angle reduced
to less than
critical

Spinning is a stalled manoeuvre, where one wing has stalled before the other and the aircraft tries to yaw and roll towards that wing. All sailplanes will recover using the standard technique:

1.   Apply full rudder opposite to the direction of turn.
2.   Ease the stick *forward* until the spinning stops.
3.   Centralise rudder.
4.   Level wings.
5.   Recover (carefully) from the resultant dive.

Note that the spinning *will not stop on the application of rudder*. It is the forward movement of the stick that unstalls the wing, which stops the spinning.

In most sailplanes the sequence occurs quite rapidly. The actions can be carried out at about the speed it takes to say them.

Modern aircraft have very docile stall and spin characteristics and can be recovered from any stage of the following:

a slow pre-stall
a stall
a stall with wing drop
a stall with commencement of spin (incipient spin)
a full spin – more than one complete turn

When thermalling, the efficient speeds to use are often within 5 knots of the stall speed. Gusts can cause a temporary variation well in excess of this. Thus it is not unusual to inadvertently stall. Training is needed to recognise the situation and be able to recover with minimum loss of height.

Most sailplanes have warning signs of an impending stall. It becomes quiet; often there is a turbulent feel from the controls and they become excessively slow in response.

The alert pilot should acquaint himself with each type's warning features, and be able to take the correct action if necessary.

Stalling and spinning result in a rapid loss of height. In order to prevent them occurring when low, it is normal practice to always use a speed with a good margin above the stall when near the ground. This is known as 'safe speed near the ground'. It is calculated as 1.5 times the stalling speed. The recommended circuit speed for each type is usually at this speed or slightly faster.

Before any stalling, spinning or aerobatic manoeuvres that result in a rapid loss of height are attempted, a pre-aerobatic check is necessary. Where these are planned pre-flight, most of the check can be done while still on aero-tow.

A suitable check is:

	A	AIRBRAKES located and locked (you might need to open them in the manoeuvre);
	F.	FLAPS set as required for specific situation – normally zero;
	T.	TRIM set – normal position for stalls or spins;
3 Hs H.	H.	HEIGHT available for planned sequence;
		HARNESS tight;
		HATCHES secure (close slide windows);
3 Ls L..	L.	LOOSE OBJECTS secure (check sailplane pockets, etc)
		LOCALITY – not over town, or circuit entry area, etc.
	L.	LOOKOUT – clear around and below.

To check this, using about 50-degree bank so a clear view below is obtained, make a 180-degree turn one way, followed by a 90-degree turn the other.
Do not use a 360-degree turn as other sailplanes may think you are thermalling and move in underneath.**

NOTE
I received a letter from John Stanley Owen on 28 February 1997, from which I quote two extracts.

1. 'Without belabouring the point, I would like to emphasise that both the article under consideration, and the AIB report No 17/81 of which I was also the author were, regardless of my instructional experience, totally neutral as to my own views about the pros and cons of the need to include spinning instruction prior to first solo. One of the Safety Recommendations contained in the AIB Report was that: "The need for spin training for basic PPL requirements in the UK should be critically reviewed." This Recommendation had to be made in the light of statistical evidence of stall/spin accidents on a world-wide scale which came to light during my investigation into the Tomahawk accident in 1980 and the marked improvement in the USA safety record when greater emphasis was placed on stall avoidance during ab-initio training.'
2. 'I would not like to be flown on a non-aerobatic flight by any licensed pilot who would allow a condition or situation to deteriorate to a point where spin recovery would be necessary.'

Part 5.

Into the Nineties

A.C. Kermode: From Mechanics of Flight

At this point I consulted one of the standard text books, Mechanics of Flight by A.C. Kermode. I did not expect to find anything very different, but it puts the subject into a nutshell.

"A spin is an interesting manoeuvre, if only for the reason that at one time there stood to its discredit a large portion of all aeroplane accidents that had ever occurred. It differs from other manoeuvres in the fact that the wings are 'stalled' – ie are beyond the critical angle of attack – and this accounts for the lack of control which the pilot experiences over the movements of the aeroplane while spinning. It is, in fact, a form of 'auto-rotation' which means that there is a natural tendency for the aeroplane to rotate of its own accord. In a spin the aeroplane follows a steep spiral path, but the attitude while spinning may vary from the almost horizontal position of the 'flat' spin to the almost vertical position of the 'spinning nosedive'. In other words the spin, like a gliding turn or steep spiral, is composed of varying degrees of yaw, pitch and roll. The amount of pitch depends on how much the wings are banked from the horizontal. In general, the airspeed during a spin is comparatively low, and the rate of descent is also low. Any device, such as slots, which tend to prevent stalling, will also tend to minimise the danger of the accidental spin and may even make it impossible to carry out deliberately. The area and disposition of the fin, rudder, and tail-plane exert considerable influence on the susceptibilities of the aeroplane to spinning.

Many of the terrors of the spin were banished once it was known just what it was. We then realised that in order to get out of a spin we must get it out of the stalled state by putting the nose down, and we must stop it rotating by applying 'opposite rudder'. In practice the latter is usually done first, because it is found that the elevators are not fully effective until the rotation is stopped. The further back the centre of gravity, and the more masses that are distributed along the length of the fuselage, the flatter and faster does the spin tend to become and the more difficult it is to recover. This flattening of the spin is due to the centrifugal forces that act on the masses at various parts of the aircraft. A spin is no longer a useful combat manoeuvre, nor is it really a pleasant form of aerobatics, but since it is liable to occur accidentally, pilots are taught how to recover from it."

Miles McCallum: The Deadliest Myth

The next extract comes from the magazine 'Flyer'. Written by Miles McCallum in March 1991 and it goes into somewhat more technical detail.

"Most of us regard the limits of the flight envelope as test pilot territory. That is certainly true of three sides of the envelope: in their territory lie structural deformation, control surface or flying surface flutter and structural failure. You exceed them at your peril and you'll need a large measure of luck to tell the tale.

However, two sides of the envelope lie within the structural limits of the aircraft, and involve altered control characteristics (sometimes leading to loss of control). We enter the edge of this zone every time we fly and should be proficient and knowledgeable about it as a matter of self-preservation: I'm talking of course about the stall.

Wings produce lift by accelerating air over the top surface, and, because it effectively spreads out, the pressure drops. The pressure difference between the top and bottom of the wing provides the lifting force. The amount of lift is determined by the speed of the air and the angle of the wing in relation to it. Getting slightly technical, for each angle of attack ($\propto$) there is a particular coefficient of lift (cl) for a specific aerofoil section, and lift is cl multiplied by airspeed. That's a simplification of what really happens but it will suffice.

As $\propto$ rises, so does cl to a point called cl max where the wing is producing as much lift as it can (see figure 13). This is the stall point of the wing. If you increase $\propto$ beyond that figure, the cl drops off – very sharply for some aerofoil sections, more gradually for others. What effectively happens is that air travelling over the top surface cannot maintain the contour of the skin and breaks away and becomes turbulent (see figure 14). This process starts at quite a low angle of attack and the stalled portion moves forward and expands as $\propto$

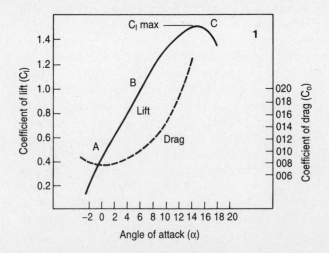

Figure 13

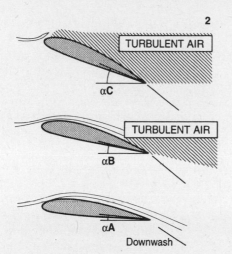

Figure 14. The relationship between angle of attack, drag and lift (above) illustrates that the stall and the maximum lift of the wing are close neighbours on the curve. Note that it is the angle of attack that matters and not attitude. (Below) How the wing stalls. As the angle of attack increases, air above the wing becomes turbulent and, at the critical angle of attack, destroys the airflow over the wing . . . and with it lift.

increases. Around cl max, this process accelerates and, with wings that have a sharp stall, the last few degrees might increase the area of turbulence from just the back half of the wing to nearly all of it.

Since the amount of lift is not just ∝ dependent, but is also a function of airspeed, the actual amount can vary enormously – enough to accelerate an aircraft upwards (or sideways) to a loading of 6g or more. But for convenience's sake all aircraft manufacturers publish a minimum speed figure where cl max is obtainable in level erect flight – the stall speed of the aircraft at 1g. If you reach cl max at a higher speed you will experience an 'accelerated' stall at more than 1g. The flipside is, of course, that as the angle of attack increases, so does the induced drag. Which is just as well, as it provides the brakes that slow you down as you flare to land. The important thing to grasp is that the stall is produced by exceeding a specific angle of attack and the attitude of the aircraft has nothing to do with it: it can happen inverted, or pointing straight down and at any airspeed from about half the published stall speed at 1g to VNE (Velocity Never to be Exceeded).

The manner in which a particular aircraft stalls is largely determined by the manufacturer. Aerofoil characteristics play a major part, as does the geometry of the wing; a rectangular wing, say that of a Cherokee 140, tends to stall at the root first and the stalled area then moves forwards and outwards. This provides a measure of stability as the tips are the last to stall, and there is less of a tendency to roll off when it all lets go.

Slab wings are not very efficient compared to tapered wings when it comes to drag, but a tapered wing tends to stall nearer the tip and has a tendency to drop a wing: to counter this the manufacturer has a variety of tricks, including changing aerofoil section, making it thicker or twisting the wing so that the tips are at a reduced angle of attack compared to the root, which has the same effect of making sure that the tips stall last. All of this good work can easily be overcome by inaccurate flying.

With the exception of a handful of exotic military prototypes the centre of lift of a wing is always arranged to be behind the centre of gravity of the aircraft: the horizontal stabiliser (tailplane) provides a counter-balancing downward force to this nose-down moment and to a greater or lesser degree is positively stable — that is to say it tends to return to a particular state if disturbed. How stable it is depends on the down-force being provided by the tail. If you move the centre of gravity (cg) back (closer to the centre of lift) less force is needed and the elevator will become more sensitive — in extreme cases to a point where it may be hard to control the aircraft.

As the aircraft nears a stall, the turbulent air coming off the stalled roots hits the elevators, causing rapid fluctuations in pressure over the surface. This is felt as buffet and many aircraft have small triangular stall strips fitted to the leading edge to produce this effect and warn the pilot. If the tip stalls first or the stabiliser is clear of turbulent air, you will get no such convenient warning. However, as long as the stabiliser is still flying, that is to say producing a downward force, the nose will not drop even with the wing pretty well fully stalled: the aircraft will mush and the only clear indication of your plight will be rapid altitude loss.

When an aircraft does have a break (that is to say drops its nose) it does so because the tail stops flying and stops producing a downward force. It is actually the moment of the lift that puts the nose down and at very forward cg conditions the pitch change rate can be quite rapid, giving the illusion of an abrupt loss of lift. In its gentler forms it is a desirable characteristic, as it produces the required corrective action to unstall the wing, reduce $\propto$ and increase speed.

Everyone is familiar with adverse yaw with aileron inputs which is an aspect of roll-yaw coupling. Depending on the type, a change in one will induce a change in the other to a greater or lesser degree. A stalled wing is much less stable in roll because very small changes in $\propto$ or airspeed will produce large changes in lift — and if it is unbalanced it will induce a roll to the aircraft.

Yawing the aircraft at cl max a small amount will have a dramatic effect, both because the outside wing moves faster producing more lift and the inside wing slows and experiences an increase in $\propto$ due to change in relative wind, reducing the lift.

You can get roll rates that are much more dramatic than full aileron application at three times the airspeed. To make matters worse, the reduction in drag to the outside wing reinforces the yaw, further aggravating the situation and unless the wing is unstalled it will lead very quickly to a spin. Eventually the pro-yaw and pro-roll forces become balanced by other forces (drag, centripetal force) and the aircraft settles into a reasonably stable condition.

All of this can be the result of mis-rigging, or more usually, of pilot input, however unintentional. Not that it's all bad: if the aircraft already has a degree of roll input (it stalls in a turn) and the aircraft is in a slipping turn — not enough rudder, or to put it another way, outside rudder — it will roll upright as the wings stall. A curious phenomenon of slipping turns is that the fuselage is producing quite a lot of lift and that helps make the stall much more gentle requiring less input to correct the situation. Quite often you will find the stalling speed of an aircraft at 1g is lower in a slip than wings level. In a skidding turn the converse is true: the fuselage produces considerably more drag making it easy to enter a deeper stall with excellent pro-spin conditions.

This is the standard base turn to finals killer: overshooting the centre line and reluctant to steepen the bank because of ground proximity, bottom rudder is added to quicken the turn, this has the effect of pushing the nose down so more up elevator is added to bring it up. Snap. Instant spin.

Most people who are fortunate enough to survive such an accident never realise that they did a spin entry into the ground; the most common description is one of sudden disorientation – and anyone who has experienced an under-the-bottom spin entry will tell you that the roll rate on entry is astonishing, sometimes enough to roll the aircraft 360 degrees before settling into a spin.

Other factors can have a similar effect: in a slow steep turn, banging a lot of recovery aileron can have the effect of increasing $\propto$ on the low wing (because the aileron is deflected downwards), stalling it and rolling the aircraft into the turn. Even if there aren't enough pro-spin forces to help continue the process to a full-blown spin, you will definitely be out of control and nothing more than a passenger for a period of time. This is the main reason you should centralise the ailerons during a spin or stall recovery. In an extreme case – a flat spin or one where repeated anti-spin controls have no effect, into-spin aileron may help by providing an anti-spin shift in drag. The outside wing with the aileron down (increased $\propto$) has an increase in drag to help slow it.

Unless an aircraft has a specific endorsement for spinning, no one knows quite how it will react. The FAA requirement as regards spinning for normal-category aircraft is that it recovers from a one-turn spin in one additional turn. That, quite frankly, is at the wrong end of horrible recovery characteristics. Most spins don't become fully developed for at least three turns and an inexperienced (in spinning not hours) pilot may not recognise the situation for what it is for more than one turn, by which time things are beyond recovery with normal anti-spin controls – rudder and elevator. If you get into this sort of situation, anything is worth a try, you will be in territory that test pilots seldom venture into.

The first thing to do in a proper spin recovery is to pull the power. High power settings tend to flatten spins (more yaw, less roll), making them harder to recover from. Then centralise the ailerons for the reasons outlined earlier, and next apply fully opposite rudder. If you're unclear about the direction of the spin, perhaps because the ground appears just as a blur, the only reliable indication is the turn needle which always leans into the spin. (Indicates left for a left spin.) The slip ball is unreliable and will give different indications depending on its position in relation to the centre line of the panel. If you use elevator first, you may aggravate the situation by either tightening the spin due to pitch-roll coupling, or possibly flick the aircraft into an inverted spin. If you have any doubts whether the spin is erect or inverted, full pro-spin controls (rudder into spin, full back elevator) will always put the aircraft into a normal spin from where normal techniques will work. Hopefully, after full opposite rudder, you will unstall the aircraft by applying down elevator – some aircraft need nothing more than releasing back pressure whereas others require the elevators to be banged down hard on the stops. Some aircraft need full rudder for recovery and won't play ball if they don't get what they need.

If the recovery takes more than two turns, it might not happen and you should go back to full pro-spin controls before banging maximum anti-spin controls in sequence. Some aircraft speed up the spin rate at the initiation of recovery, but this is normal and nothing to worry about. There is no substitute for knowing what's required for the aircraft you are spinning.

By comparison, recovery from straightforward stalls is simple: centre the ailerons, pick up the low wing with rudder and reduce the angle of attack with down elevator. Most inadvertent stalls need nothing more than releasing back pressure. The danger here is not allowing sufficient time to allow airspeed to build up for a proper recovery and hauling back initiating a high-g stall. High-g stalls tend to be deeper because of improved elevator effectiveness (it takes less elevator to reach cl max) and more prone to a fast flick into a spin. Even a balanced low-speed stall (around 1g) won't necessarily be friendly. Rolling into gliding (ie descending) turns – a condition that usually occurs fairly close to the ground – a stall will usually cause the aircraft to roll into the turn. This is because the low wing has a greater angle of attack induced by the descending action of the wing, stalling it first or more completely.

The problem here is usually flying at a slightly too slow approach speed – you may be flying only a few knots more slowly than usual, but the coefficient of drag is much higher than normal. By the same token, if you have the same pitch attitude, the greater rate of descent will produce a higher $\propto$ and more drag. This can bleed off speed much faster than you are accustomed to and you may not notice the approaching danger. A small amount of skid will exacerbate the situation dramatically whereas a little top rudder to produce a mild slip will make all the difference. The amount of extra drag from a five-knot reduction can be considerable; flying the same descent path, an approach slightly slower requires a considerable amount of power.

The rule of thumb for approach speeds (V ref) is 1.3 Vs (Vs is velocity at stall) and this in most cases puts it very close to best rate of climb speeds – where total drag is at its lowest. It allows sufficient elevator power for quite a large window of flare and gives a reasonable amount of time for drag to take effect if you slow the aircraft down.

Below this figure is a region of transferred command – pitch controls airspeed and power controls descent rate. Or to put it another way pitch controls drag and power controls flight path. This is the mode we go into in preparation for landing. Another aspect of V ref is that it requires loading the wing to a factor of nearly 2g before it will stall and this is a convenient threshold that most people are uncomfortable with and will be very aware of.

Further down the line, a common problem with some pilots is the fear that they will stall over the runway if they hold off for as long as possible to drop the nose in. Any tail-dragger pilot will tell you that this is patent nonsense.

Because a stall is not a sharp-edged phenomenon, the first symptom is just a higher sink rate and you would have to be very high to allow enough time for reduced elevator authority at such low speeds to deepen the stall sufficiently to drop the nose.

In addition, at altitudes below one wing span to the ground, the downwash from the back of the wing is flattened slightly, changing the airflow over the top of the wing: as much lift is produced, but the wing is fooled into thinking it's at a lower angle of attack and induced drag is lessened. The stalling speed of an aircraft at 1g is lower in ground effect than in the air. Tail-draggers are usually landed in a three-point attitude very close to cl max and with some, such as the Citabria, it's possible to plant the tail wheel with the mains well clear of the ground.

Tail-draggers that are not three-pointed but wheel-landed (in a level attitude just on the mains) are done so to retain a measure of control authority; with the tail down the rudder may be blanked by the fuselage, for instance, the tail wheel might not have enough power to contain swings until the speed drops below a certain figure.

There are occasional dangers even with take-offs: as you fly into ground effect the aircraft tends to pitch down slightly (due to the change in downwash). Flying out of ground effect the opposite happens: the nose pitches up slightly.

You probably never notice it as you transition out of ground effect rapidly in a normal departure. But aircraft flying out of hot, humid or high-density altitude conditions may have a very small margin of speed as they lift off an insufficient runway. Instead of keeping the nose down and taking advantage of the reduced drag to accelerate to Vx or Vy the pilot pitches up to normal climb attitude and flies out of ground effect.

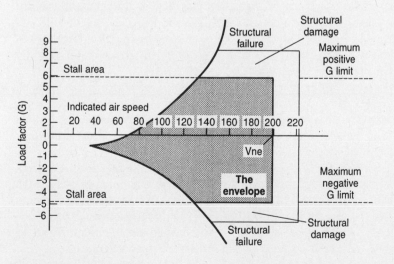

Figure 15. HOW THE ENVELOPE LOOKS: within the envelope, flight is stable. Outside, the effects range from simple stall to structural failure depending on, g loading and airspeed.

The nose pitches up further and just a small increase in $\propto$ increases the drag considerably and the aircraft settles into the ground in a semi-stalled condition. An indication of the reduction in drag at very low levels can be seen by the speed increase: you may get as much as 10 knots above normal max level speed and it's for this reason that racing aircraft used to fly as close to the ground as possible, not because the pilots were after the buzz.

The trend these days is to teach the student pilots stall recognition and avoidance and to dispense with spins: this has a tendency to link stalls with attitude. A few under-the-bottom spin entries with the nose below the horizon will eliminate that idea. On top of that, the minimum requirements to retain your licence here mean that most people don't stall an aircraft intentionally once they have got their licence; as the symptoms can be quite subtle in the early stages, they lose their feel for what's going on.

The American system of biennial flight reviews goes quite a long way to correcting this as you are obliged to perform several stalls during the course of it. If you do get the urge to explore the edges of the envelope (figure 15), take an experienced instructor with you at least for the first time. Stalls and spins aren't the bogiemen you might have once perceived them as and they're a lot more fun than boring holes through the sky.**

I found that to be hard reading but there is a lot of good sense in it, and much that is missed in other articles.

Mike Cuming: Don't Pull the Stick, Push It

By 1991 stalling and spinning were both still well up amongst the causes of what might be termed 'going in'. In particular glider pilots were well to the fore in this activity. This article by Mike Cuming from *Sailplane and Gliding*, of April/May 1991 plugs the theme.

**Stalling

The more we pull back on the stick, the more work we are asking the wings to do, and there comes a point at which we are asking the wings for more than they can deliver – the stall. In fact, pulling back on the stick increases the angle at which the air meets the wings (the 'angle of attack') and the stalled condition occurs when the angle of attack (AoA) of the glider exceeds a certain value. The airflow will then break away from one wing or the other or both.

Because of this, the wings' reduced lift-producing capacity will no longer fully support the weight of the glider, which must therefore begin to descend faster. The nose of the glider may or may not drop during the stall (depending largely on how vigorously the stall has approached) and also a wing may or may not drop.

Stalling is in itself a benign flight condition but it seems often to be a major contributory factor in flying accidents. Such accidents appear generally to involve lack of perception of the stall, rather than lack of knowledge of the correct recovery. Sometimes the pilot's attention is diverted at a critical moment, on other occasions the pilot simply does not 'see' the stall symptoms, or ignores them for reasons of his own. It seems plain that the traditional stall/spin training does not cause enough alarm bells to go off in the pilot's head as a stall is approached.

Theoretical Aspects of the Stall

The slower we fly, the higher the AoA required to support the glider, so stalling is often associated with flying too slowly. However, it is quite possible to stall at almost any speed, for example by demanding too much lift from the wings (ie by pulling g) or even by being caught in a violent gust. The moment the AoA reaches the stalling angle, the glider has begun to stall; and the more the AoA exceeds the stalling angle, the greater the extent to which the stall spreads.

When an area of stalled flow occurs, the lift of that area drops markedly (sometimes dramatically) and the drag rises sharply. In general also there will be a pitching moment change but – for a whole aircraft – the sense of this will depend upon the aircraft configuration. Good design is to arrange matters as a whole such that a glider will pitch nose down as the wings stall.

Note that it is rare for the whole wing (or wings) to become stalled. On a

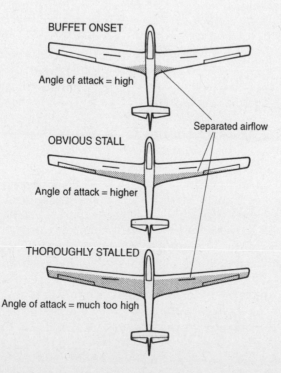

BUFFET ONSET

Angle of attack = high

Separated airflow

OBVIOUS STALL

Angle of attack = higher

THOROUGHLY STALLED

Angle of attack = much too high

Figure 16

typical glider wing – designed to stall in a smooth and progressive manner – the stalled or 'separated' flow first begins on the upper surface at the trailing edge near the wing root, and then spreads forwards and outwards as AoA increases further. The diagram [figure 16] illustrates this.

In its most minor form, a small area of stalled airflow is merely inefficient, owing to the higher local drag. There is of course also that irritating buffeting and possibly a distracting flickering on the ASI or vario if the stalled air streams past the static pressure holes. But handling and performance are scarcely affected by a little bit of buffet, so a wing such as this is in fact a good choice for a trainer – offering plenty of natural stall warnings and with no sudden or severe penalties.

Ignoring the warning and allowing the AoA to increase still further will enable the stalled area to spread; the buffeting will worsen and soon there will be a perceptible loss of performance (just look at the vario!). Eventually, the stalled area will include the wing-tip and aileron control will be diminished or even lost altogether.

The foregoing description applies to a 'safe' design, using a predictable aerofoil section and plenty of washout (ie wing twist such that the tip is at a lower AoA than the root). Unfortunately such a wing will never win the Nationals and wings which are designed for performance above all else will inevitably have to give up some docility. The designer is guided in his choice of characteristics by the airworthiness requirements, which prescribe minimum acceptable handling conditions and – in particular – lay down minimum allowable degrees of stall warning.

For example, a thinner wing will have less drag than a thick one – but its sharper front may just give rise to a widespread stall originating suddenly from the leading edge. This would have the same sort of effect as activating a spoiler! Alternatively, washout could be abandoned in order to improve the glide angle at higher speeds – but this may lead to the stall first appearing at the tip, with little warning and possibly with immediate loss of aileron control.

The fitting of flaps will have a profound effect on stall characteristics and in very broad terms, lowering the flaps will worsen the stall/spin handling while negative (cruising) flap settings will improve handling. The stall speeds will of course also be affected (lower flaps, lower stall speed).

Other factors which also have a big impact include wing condition. Dirt, rain or bugs will all tend to promote early stalling, increase stall speeds (often 5–10 knots), worsen handling and disguise natural stall warnings. Then there's elevator power; a small elevator, or one with a restricted deflection, will possibly not be powerful enough to hold the glider in a sustained stall. Conversely, a large powerful elevator – or possibly one with damaged stops, and a consequent abnormally large deflection – will offer all sorts of exciting possibilities.

Centre of gravity (cg) location is extremely important in determining stall characteristics. As well as having a huge effect on the elevator effectiveness, it will also markedly affect the glider's willingness to drop the nose – or a wing, aft cg (=low cockpit weights, or high placard figure) gives sprightly stalls.

Wing sealing, and also the dreaded Reynolds Number, have a lot to do with stalls at very low speeds (ie walking speed, which is just when you get a wing drop during take-off or landing ground run) and this is because a low-grade sealing job or a low Reynolds Number will reduce stalling angle. So you stall sooner.

There are thus lots of theoretical aspects to stalling, which is one of the reasons why stall awareness is so complex to teach and to learn. There is, however, only one important point regarding stall avoidance/recovery: reduce the AoA = stop pulling the stick.

Spinning

This condition occurs when the aircraft is partially (or wholly) stalled and a rotation develops. Any stall – whether in level flight, turning or during aerobatics – is potentially a spin and indeed the term 'incipient' spin has been used for years to describe the period of time while the glider decides whether just to stall or to develop into a full-blooded spin.

In fact the incipient spin concept is not particularly helpful, suggesting as it does the existence of three separate phases of spin entry (stall, incipient and full) and therefore three sorts of exit. In truth there are only two ways out of a spin: either moving the stick forward (the normal stall recovery) which always works for stalls and so-called incipient spins, and almost always works even in well-developed spins; or the 'classic' spin recovery, which we teach because some gliders won't come out of a spin very quickly without it.

Theoretical Aspects of the Spin

In a straight stall, both wings begin to stall evenly and progressively but what if one wing is a little dirtier, or has some surface damage? What if just a little rudder – or aileron – is being applied so that the 'straight' stall is in fact slightly asymmetric.

In this case one wing will tend to drop sooner than the other; the dropping wing will undergo a further increase in AoA owing to the very fact of dropping – and this will stall it further and cause it to stall even more. A vicious circle. Pun! Meanwhile, the upgoing wing will have enjoyed a slightly reduced AoA which may even be just enough to unstall it and restore some of its lift. Thus – for one wing at least and possibly for both – the very fact of a wing drop will tend to induce a further wing drop. The paddle action of the wings as the glider rotates will stop the roll from accelerating indefinitely, however, and soon a steady continuous roll rate will develop.

Meanwhile the down-going wing – being excessively stalled – is producing excessive quantities of drag while the other wing is producing much less, and this causes a marked yaw towards the down-going wing; a yaw which continues so long as the wing goes on dropping. Admittedly the weather-cock stability afforded by the fin/rudder will tend to keep this in check. Thus the drag produces yaw which causes roll, and the roll produces more roll and also more yaw. The system continues to 'drive' itself – at the expense of height, which is lost rapidly as the glider descends vertically.

Once the glider has begun its vertical spin, several other factors come into play. Already we know that there are aerodynamic 'damping' contributions from the wings and tail side area as they effectively flail round like paddles. Also there is the bob-weight effect of the weight of the various components, which variously helps or hinders – depending on the glider design and cg position.

If matters are left unchecked, a semi-stable condition may develop in which all the aerodynamic, gravitational and bob-weight forces cancel out and the spin becomes 'steady'. Commonly the glider will make slow up and down pitching motions (at least during the first few turns) and this of course – like the famous ice-skater's trick of spreading the arms in and out – will quickly affect the speed of rotation and hence all other forces.

Learn a Sequence of Control Movements

If a glider pitches down far enough, or if the rotation slows down enough, then the recovery will begin automatically; indeed this is the case with all modern gliders. Certainly there are very few gliders that will remain even in a provoked spin for more than a few turns. On the other hand the glider may settle permanently into the spin! Since we don't necessarily know what the glider will do, it is therefore essential to learn a sequence of control movements that will reduce the rotation, unstall the glider and hence recover – with minimum height loss.

Such a sequence must plainly work for every type of glider and indeed it is a requirement for Cs of A that the glider type has been shown to recover quickly and reliably, even from spins in the worst possible combinations of cg and configuration.

It should never be forgotten that even though the nose may be a very long way down (almost vertically in some cases) – the glider is still very definitely stalled during a spin and so the nose will have to be lowered even further, albeit only momentarily, to recover. Such a callous control movement requires nerve and experience or, in the absence of these, *training*. Lots of it. The pilots who 'spin in' are those who, at the critical moment, cannot bring themselves to push the stick forward, indeed, since most gliders will spin only with the stick on the back stop, we can say with some certainty that such pilots could not even bring themselves to stop pulling! Hence my title.

Cg position has a lot to do with spin characteristics since it effectively changes the moment arm of several of the forces involved. The further aft the cg the less 'laterally' stable the glider will be (ie keener to drop a wing or spin, and more reluctant to recover). By 'lateral' stability I mean the glider's response to the coupled effects of yaw and roll. Further, an aft cg location will effectively increase the power of the elevator (this time reducing the 'longitudinal' stability, ie the stability in pitch) and thus the pilot's ability to hold a sustained spin.

Conversely (and this is often the case with say, K 13s) the combination of a plump student and a fat instructor may move the c of g forward to the point where the elevator lacks the power to hold the AoA up, the nose drops after only half a turn – even with full back stick – and the spin recovers all by itself. This does not mean that the glider won't spin!

Air density and temperature (and, between them, our old friend Reynolds Number) affect stability too. As we go higher the tail becomes smaller in aerodynamic terms, and a glider that won't spin readily at sea level will often spin nicely on a wave flight at 20,000 feet. The Pegasus is a good example of this and so is the K 21.

Undercarriage, flap and air-brake settings all affect spin characteristics too. A large undercarriage with big doors will have a marked effect on the weathercock stability (just try side-slipping gear-up and gear-down) and if the wheel is forward of the cg (ie the glider sits on a tail-wheel or skid when on the ground) then this will aggravate any spinning tendency. Air-brakes usually have a stabilising effect, and may well cause pitching motions – sometimes good, sometimes bad.

Flaps merit a whole chapter on their own in this respect! Each glider type has such unique flap effects that it is difficult to generalise without drivelling, but in general lowering the flaps (thermic or landing) will substantially encourage wing drops and spins and raising the flaps (cruising setting) will tend to avert them. The best example is the ASW–20 which will not normally spin at all with neutral or negative flap, spins very nicely indeed with thermic flap, and spins like a top with gear down and landing flap. The ASW–20 is a lovely glider but many owners who have never spun their machines in the final turn configuration will be willing to bet money that their glider will not spin. Suckers!

Designers Err on the Side of caution

Notice that we haven't even talked about the primary control effects yet. All the foregoing remarks apply to gliders which are spinning with stick and rudder neutral – at least in principle. In practice, glider designers err on the side of caution, and it is commonly necessary to provoke and sustain a spin by the use (deliberate or otherwise) of full pro-spin rudder and full up elevator. Although we normally fly 'safe' gliders like this, and we all know that they will recover in a flash as soon as the pro-spin control inputs are even reduced, there are still some gliders – especially older types, and often open-class machines of large span – which genuinely do require the 'classic' recovery in order to get out of a spin quickly or indeed (very infrequently) to recover at all.

With this fact in mind we teach the 'classic' recovery as well: the theory is simple. Full opposite rudder tends to reduce the rotation, and hence reduce the difference between the inner and outer wing in terms of both lift and drag; and moving the stick forward will eventually unstall the glider.

What about the ailerons? Much depends here upon the nature of the wing design and hence its stall characteristics. If the tip is stalled and the aileron isn't working then trying to use the aileron will generate *less* lift (and *more* drag) – not more lift like it is supposed to! On the other hand the aileron may still be working after a fashion and this control might quite possibly be useful in a spin. All we can teach is that the effect of the ailerons is unpredictable during a spin; therefore leave them central and use the controls which *are* working.

Most pilots – and many instructors – will never have thought about all these factors; nor will they have made genuinely sustained spins, even though they may make brave claims in the bar. And it is a certainty that hardly anyone has even noticed the aileron position while spinning, let alone deliberately experimented with it, for this is the province of the test pilot, is it not? Do consider steeling yourself for a 'serious' look at spinning. Any glider with C of A is guaranteed to recover from a five-turn spin within one turn, even at aft cg and in the worst possible configuration, it says so in JAR–22. A word of advice though – don't *begin* your experimenting with a five-turn spin at aft cg; work up to it.

The only remaining major factor that you will (either consciously or unconsciously) have encountered as a matter of course while spinning is what one knows as the 'rates' – pitch rate, roll rate, yaw rate. In short, the more briskly (faster rate) you pull into a spin, the deeper into a spin you will get. This will magnify the aerodynamic forces especially and the ensuing manoeuvre will be sharper. This is most often demonstrated when trying to spin off a turn; merely inching the stick towards the back stop is often not quite enough to prevent a nose-drop and auto-recovery. As a pilot you will intuitively find that a sharp backward movement is needed. This gives you the pitch rate you require for your manoeuvre.

The really good pilots are those who have learnt – through experience, intuition or (more usually) through training – which stick positions and which stick rates are needed to get the results they want.

Stall Reinforcement Exercises

Most of the points I have made are well illustrated by so-called 'stall reinforcement exercises' which have been part of the standard BGA instructing patter for several years. This seems a good opportunity to remind everyone that these marvellous exercises exist and indeed seem to be a first-class way of learning the very skills and experience to which I have alluded.

The purpose of these teaching points is to explore some of the more advanced aspects of stalling, to ensure that the pilot can recognise and react to a stall even in complex circumstances, and to explode any myths that he or she may have picked up – possibly from other instructors!

In particular, the exercises teach the pilot to move the stick forwards under loss of control circumstances, and to pull up with care when pull-ups are needed. They also accustom the pilot to unusual bodily sensations and aircraft attitudes, and disassociate weightlessness (or reduced g) with stalling.

Here are the exercises in a nutshell.

The 'Spot the Difference' or 'Hump-back-bridge' Stall Exercise

This is a stall with a marked nose-drop followed immediately by a push-over from the same attitude and is designed to show that weightlessness proves nothing. Instructors fake the exercise by diving first. In real life you may unexpectedly encounter reduced or even negative g at any time. But in what circumstances? Gusts, aerobatics, pull-up/push-over manoeuvres, cable breaks, bumping the map while map folding or peeing and of course – sometimes – stalls!

The Changing Effect of the Rudder

The purpose of this exercise is for the student to see how the effect of the rudder changes from producing yaw to producing primarily roll instead as the stall is approached. More importantly, he will learn the habit of moving the stick forward if a wing drops. Experienced pilots have done this hundreds of times while thermalling of course!

The Changing Effect of the Ailerons

All sorts of vague expressions like 'the ailerons become sloppy' spring to mind here, but all that is sloppy is the exercise itself. There is no point in trying to teach 'the ailerons become less effective' if in fact they do not! Virtually all training gliders enjoy excellent aileron control not just at the stall but well beyond it, so it is usually nonsense to prattle on about effectiveness. Stick forces – and displacement – do of course vary as the stall is approached, while on the other hand the ailerons usually become very heavy as speed increases.

The Changing Effect of Elevator

Every pilot should know what happens to the effectiveness of the elevator at the stall. The correct answer is of course that 'up' elevator ceases to function. 'Down' elevator remains reliable and is indeed the recovery action. The whole point of this exercise is to reinforce the student's memory of this simple but vital point, which remains valid even if the nose is apparently a long way down. •

Stall in Accelerated Flight or Stall off a Stall Recovery

This exercise proves that we can stall at almost any speed, and also that – while we need to recover from inadvertent stalls with minimum height loss – it is still possible to stall again even during a stall recovery, through pulling back too hard on the stick.

Stall in a Turn

This exercise demonstrates that stalling speed is not a universal constant and does in fact increase during turns and other manoeuvres.

Picking up the Wing with Rudder, or Spin Left off Wing Drop to Right

Although the rudder will pick up wing, we can easily make matters worse rather than better in this way – and of course it doesn't address the primary problem, namely that the glider is stalled because the stick is too far back.

Spin off a Tight Thermal Turn

The glider can enter a spin quite abruptly if you abuse the controls enough even at an incredible 55 knots — which just shows that the way you handle the controls is more important than the speed you are flying at. Or in other words, speed alone is no insurance against a stall or spin.

Spin off a Shallow Over-ruddered Turn

The nose doesn't have to be above the horizon at all (and hardly above the normal attitude) but if you over-ruddered the turn and then try to hold the bank constant with aileron you will soon get a stall with a wing drop — leading possibly to a spin.

Spiral Dive

There is a manoeuvre which looks rather like a spin but is quite different; that is the spiral dive. In a spin we are stalled and the airspeed is low, also we do not often get pressed into the seat very hard by g force. In a spiral dive we are not stalled; the speed is rising and we usually can feel the g since we are turning tightly. The recovery from a spiral dive is simply to level the wings gently — but probably quite firmly — with aileron then pull up from the dive.

Epilogue

What if your home club can only offer winch launches to 1,000 feet? Well, apart from asking the BGA for advice on better winches, cables or weak links you can in fact do all these exercises without using much height and 1,000 feet will just suffice for any of them.

Any instructor trained during the last few years will definitely know all these exercises, and hopefully most of the longer-established instructors will have been brought up to date by their CFIs (who are upgraded regularly with masses of bumph from the BGA instructors' committee). I hope you have fun.**"**

Mike Cumming, as a tail piece, adds the following:

From which of these attitudes is the glider LEAST likely to spin, either deliberately or inadvertently?

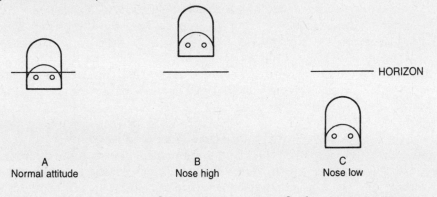

| A | B | C |
| Normal attitude | Nose high | Nose low |

The answer is B. 90 per cent of pilots get it wrong! If, after thinking about it, you cannot see why this should be so ask your flying instructor to explain.

Derek Piggott: Stalling or Low G

In May 1991, stalling and spinning were still hot topics, especially for glider pilots who spend much more time flying near to stalling speeds and attitudes than the pilots of powered aircraft. This article from *Sailplane and Glider* reviews the subject of low g.

❝We are all aware of the sensation of a lift as it starts to descend or a car going over a hump-back bridge. On the ground it only lasts a fraction of a second but it can last longer and be more severe when we are flying.

Since we live under the influence of normal gravity, ie at 1g, for virtually all our lives, this feeling of anything less is unusual and if unexpected it can be alarming. Many associate the feeling of reduced gravity or low g with nightmare dreams of falling.

The majority of us acclimatise to these sensations after a few flights but those who are particularly sensitive often develop a total abhorrence of stalling and pitching manoeuvres and may become a danger to themselves and others if they fail to overcome their inhibitions.

Early Flights

It is a help if the instructor mentions the sensation of reduced g on a first flight and links it with the pitching movement so the student realises it is quite normal. At first almost every normal beginner is unsure what is happening when they get unexpected sensations. They are worried about the reduced g sensation and the feeling of slipping as the aircraft is banked over into an under-ruddered turn.

Almost everyone dislikes these sensations which normally remain for a few flights and then gradually disappear. They occur because the beginner is unable to interpret what is happening in time to connect it with his sensations or his control movements.

After a little more experience he learns to recognise what is happening to the aircraft and an alarm signal is no longer sent to the brain. For example, after a short time, as the stick is moved forward, he sees the glider's nose moving down and his brain expects the sensation and understands what is happening.

These unpleasant sensations often come as a complete surprise to the layman. It helps if they are warned that this is quite normal on early flights, particularly when starting to use the controls. But it is a great mistake to introduce stalling or any pronounced nose-down pitching movements in the very early stages as this may make them more sensitive.

Turbulence

If there is reduced g because of flying through turbulence, there is often no change of attitude and therefore no visual sign of what is causing the sensation. This is more alarming for the beginner who just gets a horrible sinking feeling and the impression the aircraft is falling out of control. So it helps to make the first flights in smooth weather with a clear horizon and avoid unnecessary pitching movements.

Because of the connection between sensations and vision, the sensations are greatly amplified if the visibility is poor or if looking in the cockpit so there is no visual reference to help recognise the exact movements of the aircraft.

Even experienced pilots get very disturbing sensations if taken into cloud without the help of instruments. Try being blindfolded for a few minutes in a two-seater while the other pilot makes a few well-banked circles then straightens up. Besides a vivid impression of a turn in the other direction, you will feel the effects of reduced g as you stop turning – something you are quite unaware of in normal flight. Even in clear air this slight reduction of loading is noticed by the absolute beginner.

To minimise these unpleasant feelings it is best to start any flying training by emphasising looking ahead and to avoid drawing attention to the instruments. Later on instructors should make a particular point to emphasise the need to watch ahead during nose-down pitching manoeuvres, such as stall recoveries and recovering from a cable break during a winch launch.

Low g Sensitivity

Some people are more affected by sub-gravity sensations than others. They will tend to put their hands out and throw their head back at the slightest reduction in g.

I have noticed this response on first flights when they are trying out the elevator. As they move the stick forward a small amount causing only the slightest reduction in g, their response is almost always to move even further forward, making the sensation worse. This is totally irrational – the normal reaction would be to stop doing it or to move the control back in the other direction.

This response to a sensation of falling is a very natural and fundamental protective instinct. If we are falling our hands go out automatically to stop us hitting our face.

Our experience in gliders has made us aware of many aspects of low g sensitivity unnoticed in other types of aircraft. With the much lower stick forces and the higher rates of pitching possible, this instinctive movement of the hands can result in a sudden steep dive which can be disastrous near the ground. Accidents and incidents where a glider suddenly and inexplicably dives into the ground are still occurring all over the world – an indication that some people are flying solo quite unaware of their vulnerability.

It seems that there are two distinct causes of these accidents.

1. Mistaking the low g sensation for a stall.
2. Reacting instinctively to reduced g by moving the stick forward and being overcome by the increased sensation of the even lower g caused by moving the stick forward.

Stall Versus G

One survivor from a 'dive-in' accident confirmed he knew it was useless to try to pull out of the dive while he could 'feel' the glider was still stalled. This gave us the clue that some students were learning to think of the feeling of low g as an indication the glider was stalled. If they do this they may respond wrongly to any pitching or sharp descent. In making a normal stall recovery when the aircraft is not stalled, any movement forward will increase the pitching and produce a more vivid sensation, making these pilots think the aircraft isn't recovering or is more stalled. This is a sure recipe for panic and is fatal unless there is plenty of height.

I once had a student who responded with a stall recovery when the glider hit some turbulence on the final approach. The glider dived almost vertically and I was just in time to pull back on the stick so that we hit the ground in a level attitude, miraculously without damage.

Certainly several fatalities seem to have been caused in similar incidents, although this cannot be proven.

Since the instruction on stalls and recoveries has been modified to emphasise from the start that there is no sensation of stalling, only symptoms, it is also prudent
to teach the student to 'ease forward' or 'to relax the backward pressure' to
unstall the aircraft, rather than use the terms 'stick forward', 'push forward' or
'stick hard forward' which can result in a violent and uncontrolled movement
of the hand if a stall occurs unexpectedly.

During the early flights, any feeling of low g or even turbulence needs
explaining. Also when trying out the controls and lowering the nose the
instructor should draw attention to the sensation and explain it is caused whenever the nose is lowered.

After the first gentle straight stalls we should demonstrate that even a small
movement forward results in the reduced g feeling. We should take good care
to emphasise that this sensation, which sometimes occurs during a stall
recovery, is not a symptom of stalling and can occur when flying normally and, in
some cases when flying through turbulence. Only a very slight amount of
reduced g occurs during normal stalls and it only lasts a brief moment and
wouldn't be felt by anyone other than a beginner or the oversensitive. Any large
amount of reduced g sensation is caused by making far too much movement
forward during recovery.

Sensitive and Instinctive Reactions

A common sign of still being rather sensitive to reduced g is for the pilot to
repeatedly overdo the forward movement during stall recovery, in spite of
being reminded to ease forward gently. At a later stage he will often insist on
thermalling with excess speed and repeatedly poke the stick forward a little at
the slightest gust.

Apprehension about stalling is always a sign of under-training and usually a
lack of understanding of the causes of stalling and spinning and of the behaviour of the aircraft. The cure is better ground instruction and very careful
stall practice on every flight. Even if the rest of your flying is perfect, it isn't
safe to fly solo if you are still disturbed by stalls or low g.

Pilots who dislike stalling will seldom explore any new solo aircraft they are
flying. Then if an unintentional stall occurs their responses and recovery action
will be impaired and may lead to an accident.

Those Most at Risk

It is often the young, above-average student who is most at risk. They learn
very quickly and often make perfect stall recoveries from the very beginning
so they don't experience any significant reduction in g.

Pleased with their progress, the instructor is liable to move on quickly to
incipient and full spins which don't normally involve low g sensations. As a
result they have far less training and experience than the average beginner. They

may have learnt to associate stalling with the slight amount of reduced g they experience on recovery without this being obvious to the instructor.

Suddenly experiencing low g because of flying into turbulence on the base leg of a circuit, their response will be a stall recovery; but since the glider is flying normally any forward stick movement will reduce the g still further. This will make them think the aircraft isn't responding normally and they will move still further forward on the stick with disastrous results.

It is remarkably easy for someone affected by low g to slip through to solo without this fact being noticed. Some will manage to avoid stalling exercises by diverting the instructor's attention to other aspects of their flying and occasionally they have been known to make sure they get a poor winch launch when they have been briefed to do more stalling.

A persistent fear of stalling must be the result of being misinformed and of not understanding what an aircraft will and won't do if stalled. An intensive dislike of the sensation can only be overcome by a proper understanding of its cause, ie pitching not stalling, and by gradual acclimatisation and training. However it is difficult for the instructor to persist with stalling exercises when they are upsetting the student so much.

Super-sensitive People

Perhaps most interesting and most dangerous are a small minority who are chronically affected. Fortunately most of them dislike it so much they avoid flying again, but to a few overcoming their fear of flying becomes a challenge. In some forty years of full-time gliding instruction I have come across about a dozen students severely affected.

They look as though they are having an epileptic fit with the slightest lowering of the glider's nose or the most gentle stall. They become quite unconscious of what they are doing for a few seconds, and yet many still insist they want to learn to fly. If not spotted early in their training they become a menace to themselves and their instructors.

These are the students who really do freeze on the controls, and with the stick pushed and held firmly forward, the instructor has to be quick and strong to prevent an accident. With very gradual familiarisation training spread over many months some have been completely cured.

Negative G

It is very unusual to experience negative g in gliders except by flying upside down or by pitching violently nose down at high speeds. Even zero g where the dust leaves the cockpit floor is unusual except when making a violent nose-down recovery from a very steep attitude on a fast winch launch. Zero g is particularly unpleasant for almost every pilot and very alarming if it occurs for the first time when the pilot is solo. For this reason it should be demonstrated at least once towards the end of pre-solo training.

Prolonged and pronounced low g is a sure sign that the aircraft is not stalled. At very low speeds and when the aircraft is sinking, the accelerations are very small and do not continue for more than a few seconds. It is also important to realise that low g in any steep diving attitude indicates the aircraft is unstalled and can normally be levelled out of the dive by easing back.

There are often situations involving reduced g which can be incapacitating. Reports about light aircraft landing accidents often say the aircraft bounced or ballooned, pitched nose down then flew into the runway in a series of worsening crashes, smashing the nose gear and engine. Certainly a low g sensitive person is liable to become completely incapable of further thought once the aircraft pitches nose-down the first time and invariably shows the basic response of pushing forward on the stick and keeping it there.

The same kind of accident used to be common with gliders and the pilots could never remember anything after the first bounce. They have become less common since fully held-off landings have been taught. With these it is likely a student will experience ballooning a number of times in training and will have learnt how to avoid automatically moving forward on the stick. Those scared of ballooning will nearly always fly the aircraft on to the ground instead of making properly held-off landings.

Testing the Student Pilot

Gliding instructors must be aware of the problems and watch for them in their students. We should test every student before going solo to make quite sure they are not seriously affected by reduced g. This doesn't mean always pitching violently to get weightlessness or negative g but introducing small amounts of reduced g.

The student can be asked to pitch nose down gently from level flight and from diving and climbing attitudes. Those who are still sensitive are incapable of doing this exercise and their reactions are obvious. They should have more training until there are no bad reactions.

Then it is sensible to give them some experience in recovering from unusual attitudes to see if they remain unaffected. This must be done at a safe height, first explaining what will happen. A slow, steep, slipping turn, a very nose-high wing-down position so that a full stall is unavoidable, and a steep diving position are possible situations to try. They also have a confidence-raising effect because the student finds he can make safe recoveries from attitudes far steeper than he is likely to get into by error.

Perhaps this kind of test should be used for every pilot regardless of the aircraft they are learning in!

Summary

If you dislike stalling and the sensations of low g persist with your training, make sure your CFI understands your problem and get him to explain it.
Instructors should:

1. Explain to beginners the sensations involved in flying.
2. Avoid any pronounced pitching manoeuvres and particularly stalling on early flights while the student it still sensitive to these movements.
3. Emphasise visual clues on early flights. Introduce ASI later.
4. Explain low g on the same flight as stalling is introduced, emphasising that the low g sensation is not a symptom of a stall.
5. Avoid the terms 'stick forward' etc for recoveries from cable breaks and stalls. Teach them to lower the nose to a certain attitude instead.
6. Practise a few recoveries from unusual positions with every student.
7. If you have a student who is upset badly by low g or stalling, make sure he understands his problem and that your other instructors know about it too.

Chris Rollings, national coach, comments:

All the above is very good, however anyone reading it casually might be misled into thinking that if he experiences reduced g then he cannot be stalled, which is of course not the case. The hump-back-bridge sensation is familiar to all of us in a deep stall. What Derek is saying is that the reduced g sensation does not necessarily mean we are stalled. It can and does frequently have other causes. Anyone who doubts this should go and compare stalls and unstalled reduced g situations in a glider with an accelerometer."

I would add that nothing written about stalling or spinning should ever be read casually.

Charles Bremner: Fatal Nosedive of Flight 585 Baffles Experts

In 1991 a Boeing 737 unaccountably dived into the ground. This newspaper report from The Times, 4 March 1992 sets out the problem.

"When American airliners fall out of the sky, investigators usually take little time to find the probable cause, then apportion blame and advise on steps to avoid a repeat. Now, for once, the experts are stumped.
The disaster that has turned into one of the biggest mysteries of modern aviation happened a year ago yesterday. United Airlines Flight 585, a Boeing 737, was two minutes from landing at Colorado Springs when it suddenly pitched up, yawed to the right and rolled nose down into a park. For ten

seconds, Harold Green, the captain, and Patricia Eidson, the first officer, tried to regain control of the jet before breaking into their final screams and swearing. Only crumpled debris in a 10-foot hole remained of the jet and its twenty-five passengers and crew after its 1,000-foot plunge to the ground.

Four dozen people, including a control-tower operator and thirteen pilots, watched the crash from close range, some of them reporting the sight of horrified passengers staring out of the cabin windows. But despite the evidence of flight recorders, albeit not the most modern kind, reconstruction of the aircraft and expert witnesses, the National Transportation Safety Board says it has ruled out every conceivable cause.

Some experts are speculating that the aircraft ran into an extraordinarily powerful rotor, a violent rolling wave of air comparable to a horizontal tornado which is generated in the lee of mountains. Colorado Springs lies in the lee of the Rockies at 6,000 feet above sea level. The Safety Board says the Boeing 737, the world's most common airliner, should have withstood a rotor wave. 'None of us wants to leave an accident like this unsolved,' said John Lauber, who headed the enquiry. 'But we can't manufacture a cause out of thin air.'

The Boeing Company, United Airlines and the Safety Board have spent large sums reconstructing every vital system of the 737–200, attempting to replicate every theory, strutinising information on the weather that day and even calling in the Smithsonian Museum to identify a feather found at the site. It proved not to have come from any local bird, ruling out the possibility of a bird strike. Everything about Flight 585 was normal and the crew's performance, recorded by the cockpit and instrument recorder, was text-book.

'Nice-looking day. Hard to believe the skies are unfriendly,' said Mr Green as the airliner was moving from the gate at Denver before the twenty-minute flight. Along the way Ms Eidson commented about mountain rotors, 'They're dangerous, could tear a wing off.' Both pilots were veterans with good records.

Controllers warned the crew of possible wind shear on the approach to Colorado Springs, a common and potentially dangerous phenomenon. Crews are trained to respond rapidly to the airspeed fluctuations that denote wind shift. According to the data retrieved the airliner kept up adequate flying speed until the instant it lurched sideways and down.

The tower controller who watched the dive said: 'Nothing I've ever seen has fallen straight down like this. It never spun. It went straight in.'

For a while, the investigators thought a faulty rudder could have precipitated the yaw and dive. After rebuilding the tail assembly from the debris, the investigators confirmed reports from previous crews that the aircraft had suffered from a rudder malfunction, but said the condition could not have caused such a violent reaction.

The experts are revisiting the crash site again this week, exploring the possibility of a 'hydraulic jump', a strong updraft in the lee side of mountains similar to the effect in rivers when fast-moving water flows over a large rock. Supercomputers at the National Center for Atmospheric Research in Boulder, Colorado are being used to create a 'model airflow' at Colorado Springs in the hope of finding some freak condition. The NTSB does point out that the most modern type of flight recorder, not installed in the jet which crashed, would give a wealth of additional data to enable them to detect a cause.**

Newspaper reports are sometimes unreliable as a source of accurate information. Nevertheless, assuming that what Charles Bremner says is correct two facts emerge.

1. The aircraft was approaching to land in a perfectly normal way.
2. The aircraft then made a sudden change of direction and crashed.

It apparently stalled. It might have encountered a rotor or a lull in the wind. There might have been a mechanical failure, undetected. Did the flight recorder record the airspeed or only the reading on the airspeed indicator? It might have been inaccurate. Did the pilot have a sudden blood clot or go suddenly mad? Your guess is as good as mine or anybody elses.

I can only quote Sir Arthur Conan Doyle speaking as Sherlock Holmes: 'When all other contingencies fail, whatever remains, however improbable, must be the truth.' (The Adventure of the Bruce Partington Plans).

And I'm not sure I believe that either.

Lou Frank: To Spin or Not to Spin

In 1993, spinning was still being actively discussed, and the next two articles are typical. The first, by Lou Frank, appeared in the *Sailplane and Glider Year Book* for 1993.

**Not *another* article on spinning! Yes, another, because every year too many pilots, some experienced, others less so, are still being injured or paying the ultimate price for somehow failing to recognise or react to this life-threatening situation.

Why is it that despite our best training efforts, worldwide statistics continue to reflect an appalling record of spin-related accidents? We teach the dangers of low and slow flight, we supposedly learn the symptoms of an approaching stall and how to recover from it, so how can pilots get into this dangerous and often fatal situation?

The answer, I believe, lies in an understanding of some aspects of basic psychology; the role of the subconscious mind, stimulus and response, and the conditioned reflex. (Experts in this field will I hope forgive the writer grossly over-simplifying this complex subject; a little bit of knowledge is a dangerous thing, but then so is inadvertent spinning . . .)

Consider for a moment your reaction when driving a car on an icy road. The car starts to slide to the left as you negotiate a bend to the right. Most of us know that the only hope of checking the skid is to steer to the left − into the direction of the skid. Yet, despite this knowledge, most of us will find ourselves steering to the right! That is unless you are a professional driver engaged in sports such as rallying or motor racing. The difference is not a matter of knowledge but experience.

The professional driver has developed an alternative subconscious programme that issues a *different* set of commands in response to the particular symptoms received by his senses. This alternative or secondary programme (which in this case contradicts the primary programme) is kept accessible by constant practice, thereby reinforcing it. It is important to understand that knowledge alone will not provide an automatic response to a particular situation; only practice will provide the skill programme.

We all have 'survival programme' imprinted in our subconscious mind. Some are inborn (instinctive), others are learnt through experience – like ducking a fast-moving object heading our way. Ducking is not a considered conscious decision, but a learnt (conditioned) reflex to that particular stimulus. We have little control over such reflexes – try not blinking when someone claps their hands 2 inches from your face!

When you were learning to fly, you may have been well aware of the principles of controlled flight, but much practice was necessary for you to acquire the skill of co-ordinating the controls before becoming a proficient pilot – before your responses became automatic. As an experienced pilot you no longer need to focus your attention on using the controls to fly straight, turn, climb or dive. Your subconscious programme will look after that, freeing you to concentrate upon thermalling, navigation and other complex tasks that require judgement and decision-making.

Your subconscious programme will react automatically to perception 'nose dropping – pull back on stick' or 'right wing dropping – move stick to left' and so on. But as we all know, those are improper responses in semi-stalled flight, and we all know that should we be turning, such a response would be likely to induce an incipient spin . . . We know this because we have experienced it during our training – but did we really *learn* from this? Did we develop an alternative programme in our subconscious that commands *not* to pull back the stick when the nose starts to drop approaching full stall – not to attempt checking increasing bank with aileron when about to stall in a turn'? The answer all to often is 'no'.

The development of the alternative programme is dependent entirely on practice – particularly so in this case, as the commands of the alternative programme are opposite to the primary programme! Recovering automatically from a skid in your car is almost impossible without regular practice on a skid pan – ask any police driver! Similarly, regular practice in stall/spin exercises is essential if you are to keep the alternative programme alive and accessible the automatic response that requires little conscious effort.

Pilots rarely get themselves killed spinning in from over 1,000 feet. They either have time to get the brain in gear – to consciously analyse the situation and correct it – or the inherent stability of the aircraft saves them. Most spinning accidents occur from less than a few hundred feet above ground, usually when the work load of the conscious mind is high – or filled with overpowering apprehension. Without an alternative programme accessible, the primary programme will inevitably take over at the onset of a stall – with predictable, and sometimes fatal, results.

If you doubt the power of your primary programme when flying, there is a simple way to prove it; fly with an instructor in a two-seater and get him to put the aircraft into an incipient spin (stall off a flattish unco-ordinated turn) and ask you to recover. Despite your advance knowledge of what is going to happen, despite you knowing that you must not use aileron to check the dropping wing, just how much did you move the stick applying opposite aileron? Under such prepared circumstances you probably remembered to relax the backward pressure on the stick, which is all that is necessary. If so, a bit of opposite aileron is not going to make a great deal of difference to the recovery – but how would you respond facing a difficult field landing or similar high workload situation?

Prevention, they say, is a whole lot better than cure. So the best insurance you can have against being included among the stall/spin accident statistics is to first recognise the symptoms of an approaching stall – let me remind you.

Stimuli

1. Nose too high (in normal flight).
2. Airflow noise reduced or changed in pitch.
3. Aileron response less effective.
4. Indicated airspeed low.
5. An increased need to 'hold off bank' when turning.
6. Rate of sink often excessive.
7. Buffeting of tail surfaces.
8. Nose tending to drop despite increasing 'up' elevator.

Recognition of one or more of these symptoms should alert your alternative programme (if you have one) and prompt an automatic recovery procedure as follows.

Responses

Lower nose to improve angle of attack. Do not try to lift dropping wing with opposite aileron or opposite rudder.

If above actions are taken too late, and a full stall (straight) results, then recover from the dive with rudder neutral and wings level, using air-brakes as necessary to avoid exceeding VNE.

Should you fail to take corrective action in response to the symptoms when turning you may enter a full spin. Very few aircraft today will spin unless deliberately put into it and held there. Nevertheless it is vital that you know and practise full spin recovery.

1. Full opposite rudder (to direction of rotation).
2. Pause (to allow rudder to take effect).
3. Stick slowly forward until rotation stops.
4. Centralise rudder.
5. Recover from dive, wings level, taking care not to exceed placarded limits; use air-brakes as necessary.

Summary

Knowledge is not enough to prevent you making inappropriate responses in a high work-load situation. The development and subsequent reinforcement of a recognition and recovery stall/spin programme can only be brought about by regular practice. Just how well are you prepared . . . ? **"**

Comment

I would add to that, that on some occasions when I have been flying as a passenger, or a pupil, I have felt a little nervous when the pilot has seemed to me to be flying closer to the stall than I would myself in the same circumstances. Whether the pilot was flying closer to the limit because he was a better pilot than I or a worse one I could not always tell, but it did provide an incentive to probe a little further towards the limit myself, when the opportunity to do so safely arose.

Bill Scull: Teaching Stalling and Spinning

The next article, by Bill Scull, is also from the *Sailplane and Gliding Year Book* of 1993. Glider pilots seem to think about spinning more than the pilots of powered aircraft. I suppose that it is much more likely to happen to them by mistake, flying slowly as they do most of the time, and close to the stalling angle. With the ever-present possibility of mishandled turns close to the ground or a broken winch cable they have no doubts about the value of training in how to avoid and how to recover from a spin.

"Stalling and spinning accounts for a significant proportion of gliding accidents. The circumstances leading to the eventual spin may be a winch launch failure or cable break, running out of height in the circuit pattern, field landing or ridge soaring. All, or most, of the accidents are from an inadvertent spin starting at a height from which recovery is unlikely or impossible. Injuries are usually serious or fatal.

So the risks are real, but despite universal emphasis in training and additional exercises to heighten the awareness of the risk, the accidents continue. What then is the problem?

Most accidents in sporting and private aviation are due to pilot error. This may mean a lack of skill, a failure to manage the work load, a lack of awareness of the risk or simply lack of imagination. Once a pilot is past the stage of regular checks, maintaining an adequate standard is a matter of regular practice and a personal philosophy to 'do it right', that is within safe limits.

Maybe it's the philosophy that slips since a significant number of spinning accidents happen to pilots who are in practice and experienced. This may indicate that a combination of overconfidence and complacency are the root of the problem. Whatever the factors it seems that too many pilots do not appreciate the risks which need to be considered in both the context of dual training and solo flying.

Training Philosophy

In regard to stalling and spinning various views are put forward representing extremes of caution and risk-taking. This can best be appreciated by considering the height at which such exercises are carried out.

As a young (or new to the job!) national coach I well remember being asked to make a safety audit of a club with a poor record, particularly in stall/spin accidents. I flew with most of the instructors, none of whom would teach stalling, let alone spinning, below 1,500 feet! The obvious implication was that stalling and spinning are dangerous – but we all know that, don't we? Interestingly, although the demonstrations of stall recovery were satisfactory with good patter etc, they had little or no indication or emphasis that stalling and spinning are fraught, when it happens near the ground. The only emphasis was 'We don't do it below 1,500 feet.'

The other extreme is to carry out the training, some or all of it, at a height which really emphasises the message by frightening the student. Obviously this would incur significant risk and, let me stress, I am not advocating such practice. The necessary balance to be achieved must be based on what risks the instructor takes during training with the aim of minimising the overall risk.

Without getting into too much detail I believe the balance is achieved for each individual student by giving him, or her, a 'calibrated fright'. Let me qualify the point. A calibrated fright will have achieved its objective if at any time a pilot finds himself flying too slowly he recalls the fright; better never to fly too slowly. Generally the training exercise will involve a contrived inadvertent stall in circumstances which will alarm the student sufficiently, despite the fact that there are adequate safety margins.

Calibrated Frights

The circumstances may vary, the message should not. A good example might be soaring a ridge. 'Fly a bit slower,' you may say, and maybe the turbulence will do the rest. Obviously this only applies if you have enough height above the valley floor and may be more appropriate to hill-top sites. Whether the emphasis comes from the altimeter reading or the proximity of the ridge behind you is not important, so long as you get the message across.

Other circumstances are possible – flying slowly in turbulent conditions or thermalling (so long as there are no aircraft below!). In any case there may be a contrived element; afterwards you should point out that flying too slowly is not efficient.

Begging the Question

I have avoided the $64,000 question: what is the minimum height at which stalling and spinning should be completed? A difficult question because the answer depends on several factors: the philosophy of the instructor (in this context), his perception of his own ability (which may be flawed) and his skill and experience of stalling and spinning, the student's confidence or lack of it, the spin and recovery characteristics of the glider, the weather conditions and even the height available (consider a winch-only operation). Each of these factors warrants consideration even though they are to some extent inter-dependent.

The *glider's characteristics* are an important factor. How readily does it spin? What is the height loss per turn? Does it recover on command, that is with good authority? To what extent does an incorrect recovery (say less than full oppo-site rudder) delay recovery? Do the characteristics differ between forward and aft cg? The answers vary from type to type and each factor needs to be taken into account. More importantly, these are questions you must answer!

Obviously *minimum safety height* doesn't vary all that much but, based on height after pulling out from the dive, 700 or 800 feet for a K-13 but not less than 1,000 feet for a Puchacz. There, I've put numbers to it, but these will still be qualified by other factors!

The instructor's *personality profile* can be quite important. The implications of the macho image are obvious. 'Impulsiveness', a tendency to act without reflection, may be a compounding factor as may 'invulnerability' – 'accidents don't happen to me' 'Opposition to authority' may lead to flouting any height guidelines or limits. It is hoped that the selection and training of instructors goes some way to avoiding or modifying some of the least favourable traits. In principle letting pilots elect to become instructors is not good practice.

The instructor's philosophy should influence the conduct of the stall/spin exercises. His aim should be to convince the student that the risks are real and serious – like death! To achieve this metaphorical impact requires a good understanding of the hazards and a fine balance to give thorough training and bring the right degree of emphasis to the calibrated fright.

Confidence is relevant to both instructor and student. For the instructor his personality profile will interact with skill and experience. It is interesting to note that the break-off height goes up with age! A significant element in the training is to build up a student's confidence.

Confidence should be the determining factor when a particular exercise is taught; stalling and spinning too soon may destroy confidence which can be difficult to restore. In reality a pilot who continues to be nervous (for nervous read frightened) may never be safe in a spin-prone glider.

The weather conditions should also be considered. There may be adverse factors of turbulence, wind gradient and poor visibility which may affect the conduct of the exercise and even whether you carry it out at all.

The emphasis

Bringing the right degree of emphasis for each individual is obviously not easy and, as was said earlier, has to take the various factors above into account. If the height at which the spin recovery is made was the only factor then it might be relatively simple to give guidelines, such as the heights given earlier. However, spinning low down is clearly a relatively basic approach to bring the right degree of emphasis.

A key factor in determining the minimum height is the fact that the ground looks noticeably closer after the recovery than it did on entry. This is some-times known as the 'ground-rush effect'. Why is this important? Simply because it should make a student or any pilot aware of a serious risk in the inad-vertent spin, that is of pulling too sharply out of the spin recovery dive. Of course we all know the risk – a high-speed stall.

One final point. Continuous spins have a place in training insofar as they ensure that a pilot is not disorientated during the manoeuvre. A real test of ability and state of mind is to enter and stay in a spin counting the turns, monitoring the height loss, working out the height loss per turn and then recovering on a heading. [That is what Lindemann did – Ed] *There is no merit in combining this manoeuvre with the low-level recovery justified in the previous paragraph.*

Rules

Why not a rule no spinning below 'X feet'? In the circumstances who will decide X? Will it be a figure which precludes teaching spinning at winch-launch operation except on soaring flights? If there is a rule, would anyone comply? We all know rules which are more honoured in the breach than the observance don't we?

In the final analysis

Philosophies on spinning vary. Is this a counsel of perfection? I think not. The exercise was dropped from the PPL syllabus in the USA years ago and more recently in the UK. It is interesting to note the fresh emphasis on spinning in glider pilot training in the USA. One thing is for sure, despite recent trends towards gliders that seem to spin less readily, most of them will. Accidents still confirm this and no doubt will continue to do so. Your only insurance is good dual training and regular practice, both dual and solo. Or would you rather travel hopefully?**

I.K.A.C.Wilson: The CAAView

During the century which has elapsed since Otto Lilienthal first took wing, stalling and spinning have been ever-present hazards of flight. To obtain the latest views in 1994 I wrote to the Civil Aviation Authority to find out what they recommended. I received the following reply from Mr I.K.A.C. Wilson, Aviation Safety Adviser.

**In reply to your letter of 7 May 1994 asking for the Authority's views on spins and spinning, I have been advised by the Department of Flight Crew Licensing that the subject is, as you will appreciate only too well, rather large and cannot be reviewed in a few words.

I hope it will be of some assistance if I mention that mandatory spin training for PPL students was removed from the licensing requirements in the mid-1980s after consultation with industry. The statistics indicated that more accidents resulted form intentional rather than unintentional spinning. The 'recognised' PPL syllabus was amended to require 'stall/spin awareness training' to compensate for the removal of spin-recovery instruction. This element of training includes instruction in 'slow flight' to familiarise the students with the control of an aircraft in an approach configuration at a safe height. The spinning exercise remains within the recognised syllabus but is not mandatory.

The Authority continues to require spinning as an exercise within the flying instructor course syllabus and for renewal of the instructing privileges. The course syllabi for professional pilot licences CPL/BCPL include a requirement for spin recovery training.**

Is stall/spin awareness enough? Expert opinion is that it is. But would a pupil pilot with no experience of spinning, who was suddenly plunged into an unexpected and unintentional spin, (see letter from Harry W. Hawthorne, page 147), be able to cope? I suppose that if his name happened to be Wilfred Parke then perhaps he might.

C.C.Coton: The Ministry of Defence View

I then wrote to the Ministry of Defence to find out the current view on spin training for service pilots of the Royal Air Force. I received the following reply from Flight Lieutenant C.C.Coton, RAF.

"Stalling is covered fully before the first solo flight. The first solo sortie entails one circuit to land only. Subsequent sorties involve circuit consolidation work.

The next stage is aerobatics – spinning is also covered in this part of the syllabus but is done with an instructor. Before students are allowed to practise solo aerobatics, they must pass a spin and aerobatics test sortie . . .**"**

Fair enough, but nobody has yet been able to guarantee that a student pilot will only do one circuit on his first solo and will never get into a mess doing it.

R. Irving: The Cranwell View

I also made enquiries of the Royal Air Force Training College, Cranwell. Squadron Leader R.Irving sent me the following detailed reply.

"We have compiled the following unofficial comment on the subject of spinning and stalling.
1. Stalling is taught to students before spinning. There is always a danger that a student pilot, or any pilot for that matter, may inadvertently stall the aircraft in flight. Therefore, students have to demonstrate that they are able to recognise and recover from a clean stall and a stall in the approach configuration (gear and flap lowered) before flying solo. Stall-recovery technique is designed to achieve minimum height loss. Clearly, stalling for practice is conducted well away from the ground and not over populated areas. Eventually, students are cleared to fly stalling exercises solo. All staff pilots and students are required to practise stall recoveries monthly. Students are also taught how to recognise a stall during manoeuvre and how to unstall whilst continuing the manoeuvre.
2. The emphasis taught in stalling is prevention is better than cure. Therefore, students are taught to be speed- and angle-of-bank-aware when flying in the circuit to avoid getting anywhere near the stall. If this advice is not heeded, then the aircraft has several ways of warning the pilot of the approaching stall. These are: angle of attack gauge, audio stall warning, stick shaker and airframe buffet.
3. Spinning is taught after first solo and is only practised by students on dual

sorties; students do not practise spinning solo. During training, military pilots are required to fly their aircraft to the edge of the aircraft's flight envelope with confidence. Occasionally, they make excursions outside the flight envelope which can result in a 'departure' (auto-rotation or incipient spin). Therefore in the first instance, students are taught how to recognise 'departure' (ie a stall with undemanded roll/yaw) and then how to recover from the situation with minimum height loss. It is stressed that provided they take prompt recovery action, the aircraft will recover from an incipient spin. Incipient spin entries and recoveries are practised from straight and level flight and from manoeuvres. Should a student not take prompt recovery action at the incipient stage of a spin then a full spin would develop. Therefore, the next stage in spin training is for students to practise entry into and recovery from full erect and full inverted spins. Needless to say that spinning is practised well away from the ground.**

Eric 'Winkle' Brown: Non-stalling, Non-spinning Aircraft

Apart from rotary-wing aircraft, such as helicopters and autogyros, which cannot stall unless the rotary wing is allowed to slow too much, a number of aircraft have been designed which will not stall under normal conditions. One way of doing this is to limit the extent of the elevator travel so that the nose of the aircraft cannot be raised high enough for the wing to reach the stalling angle. But as aircraft are normally stalled onto the ground when landing, such aircraft may have difficulty being put down and may have to be 'flown' onto the ground, as was the old Bristol Boxkite. One such aircraft is the Boeing Stratocruiser which, although it could be stalled, had the wing set at such an angle that the aircraft always landed first on its nose wheel, a most unusual sight.

One aircraft which cannot normally be stalled in steady flight is the CFM Metalfix Streak Shadow. Another was the Erco Ercoupe, and there have been a number of others such as the Winter Zaunkönig over the years. This is an extract from Captain Eric 'Winkle' Brown's description of the Encoupe from *Wings of the Weird and Wonderful* Vol 1.

**This little aircraft, aimed at the pre-Second World War market, created a mild sensation when it arrived on the scene in 1940, largely because of its simplified control system which eliminated the rudder pedals. Production ceased on America's entry into the war, but restarted again in 1947.

As it arrived at RAE Farnborough in May 1948, it was a small low-wing, all-metal-cabin monoplane with side-by-side seating for two occupants. It had twin fins and rudders, a tricycle undercarriage with steerable nose wheel, and the ailerons, rudder and nose wheel were mechanically co-ordinated so that turning in the air or on the ground was accomplished by single wheel control . . .

The Ercoupe had obviously an induced root stall with the outer wing sections unable to reach stalling incidence due to loss of lift before the slow spread of the stall had extended to the aileron sector, and so lateral control was retained throughout.

With full backward elevator movement and engine throttled right back a very mild phugoid motion started at 45 mph and then the nose dropped without any stall warning. Application of power (1,500rpm) merely increased the amplitude of the phugoid until the nose dropped at 41 mph with control wheel fully back and again without any stall warning.

Various methods, orthodox and otherwise, were attempted to put the aircraft into a spin, but the eventual result was always the same – a spiral dive.

The normal approach speed was 60 mph with touch-down at 55 mph, but the undercarriage with its 12-inch travel on all main wheel shock absorbers could easily stand up to any touch-down speed between 50 and 80 mph. Since the aircraft ran out of nose-up elevator trim at 73 mph the approach at 60 mph required a very slight pull force. View ahead at this speed was pretty poor, becoming very bad at hold-off prior to touch-down.

It was the cross-wind landing technique that required some readjustment of conventional ideas. The makers recommended that the Ercoupe should be landed on a runway in a strong cross-wind with the nose crabbed upwind and the wings level and allowed to contact the ground in that manner, moving the control wheel well forward on impact to keep the nose firmly on the ground, and at the same time relaxing the lateral grip pressure to allow the nose wheel to castor freely. The strange thing is that this system worked.

Two things had to be borne in mind about landing with this control system – firstly the aircraft could not be side-slipped on the approach due to the absence of separate rudder control, and secondly, any touch-down in a cross-wind with the ailerons deflected from neutral meant the nose wheel was also deflected, with the inevitable consequences.

The Ercoupe certainly bid fair to the claim of being 'foolproof', although I had reservations about how far one could take the makers' recommended cross-wind landing technique without something busting. The single-wheel control system offered the weekend flyer a combination of simplicity and leg-room comfort, but I preferred the flexibility of the conventional system which allows greater finesse of control. Maybe that was because I was not a weekend flyer.**

However, should such an aircraft accidentally stray into a severe mountain rotor, and they can be fierce, or into the wake turbulence of a large aircraft, as was Harry W. Hawthorne (see page 147) or be carried up inadvertently into a thunderstorm, as once almost happened to me, there is no knowing what might happen. Assuming that the aircraft stayed intact, normal spin recovery would quite likely be successful, but without separate rudder pedals you never know. Wake turbulence can even be present close to the ground for some time after a large or powerful aircraft takes off. Air traffic controllers have strict instructions to separate aircraft taking off by several minutes, the time depending to some extent on the weather, to prevent an aircraft becoming out of control immediately after take-off.

Finally

Any aeroplane or glider will stall and can probably be made to spin, if not normally then in exceptional circumstances. Aircraft, however, are all different in this respect and although the standard recovery technique for a spin or a stall works for most there are exceptions, and sometimes the pilot will be unable to recover. There may be differences even between aircraft which are apparently identical. Slight differences in load or trim may determine the pilot's success or failure.

There is a risk involved in spin training. But there is a risk in any kind of flying whether as a pilot or as a passenger on a regular scheduled airline flight, and a pilot who is competent in spin recovery is best placed to combat this risk. If an aircraft stalls inadvertently, or spins, there may be very little time to decide what to do and to do it successfully. Unless the pilot gets it right there may be . . . only seconds to live.

Index